Conceptual PHYSICS

Third Edition

Teaching Guide

Paul G. Hewitt

Paul G. Hewitt

▲▲ Addison-Wesley Publishing Company
Menlo Park, California • Reading, Massachusetts • New York
Don Mills, Ontario • Wokingham, England • Amsterdam • Bonn
Paris • Milan • Madrid • Sydney • Singapore • Tokyo
Seoul • Taipei • Mexico City • San Juan

ACKNOWLEDGMENTS

Many people have helped me with the ideas that make up this teaching guide. I am most grateful to Charlie Spiegel, for providing insightful suggestions for every chapter of both the textbook and this teaching guide. I am also grateful to contributors Chase Ambler, Clarence Bakken, Bruce Eddman, Ken Ford, Marshall Ellenstein, Robert L. Hare, Tucker Hiatt, Paul Hickman, John Hubisz, Ronald E. Lindemann, Kathy Wong Nirei, Bruce Ratcliffe, Paul Robinson, Nate Unterman, Nancy Watson, and Helen Yan.

Cover photograph: Motor Press Agent/Superstock, Inc.

ISBN 0-201-46806-9

2 3 4 5 6 7 8 9 10-ML-00 99 98 97 96

Contents

Introduction

Conceptual Physics—The High School Program is a way of teaching physics that stimulates your students' higher-level cognitive skills. Unlike the traditional physics courses that were more math than physics, the credo of *Conceptual Physics* is CONCEPTS BEFORE COMPUTATION.

Conceptual Physics features the three-stage learning cycle with emphasis on LEARNING CONCEPTS. Only in the third stage are algebraic problems treated. Whereas physics courses that emphasize mathematical problem solving are often "watered down" in order to serve students who lack mathematical skills, nothing is watered down in *Conceptual Physics.* With its emphasis on concepts, this is the physics course that provides students a solid foundation — and a ramp to college physics.

The value of teaching physics conceptually is not in minimizing mathematics, but in maximizing the use of students' personal experience in the everyday world — in their everyday language (presumably English). Students need not see physics as a hodgepodge of mechanistic equations, or only as a class-room or laboratory activity, but need to see physics everywhere, part of everything they experience. People with a conceptual understanding of physics are more alive to their surroundings, just as a botanist taking a stroll through a wooded park is more alive to the trees and plants, and the life that teems in them. Richness of life is not only seeing the world with eyes wide open, but also knowing what to look for.

What many students enjoy about a course is not finding that it is easy, but finding that they can comprehend "non-easy" material. Students know the reputation of physics — that it is intellectually demanding. Because of this reputation, and because we are teaching comprehensible physics (i.e., enjoyable physics), we find ourselves highly valued by our students. Its nice to be rewarded with a greater-than-usual number of appreciative students and with the personal satisfaction that comes with being appreciated for the best of reasons — helping them to get the best from their own brains.

Because physics has always been an excellent way to teach mathematics, it has been used for that purpose. But physics can serve a higher purpose — to teach students how to THINK! There are very few courses that teach thinking. *Conceptual Physis* is one of them.

How to Use Conceptual Physics

The Three-Stage Learning Cycle

Conceptual Physics is a program that utilizes the three-stage learning cycle developed more than 25 years ago by Robert Karplus. Stage 1, *Exploration*, is done before students are introduced to material in the textbook. In this stage, students do an activity in the *Conceptual Physics Laboratory Manual* authored by Paul Robinson (student edition code 46800; teacher's edition code 46801). In Stage 2, *Concept Development*, the focus is on the textbook and the *Concept-Development Practice Book* (student edition code 46804; teacher's edition code 46805). In Stage, *Application*, focuses on experiments in the lab manual, follow-through questions and puzzles in the *Next-Time Questions Book* (code 46802), and optional algebraic problems in this *Teaching Guide*. This three-stage method of teaching optimizes learning.

Stage 1: Exploration. Before putting tires on your car you first jack the car up. Similarly with students; before putting ideas in their heads, you first jack them up. The activities in the lab manual are designed to spark an interest that will make your treatment of material more meaningful. Information is best learned if it answers questions — that is, if it is first needed. Activities set the stage for student's questions. Activities also ensure that students have common experience from which to develop concepts. Lab activities in the lab manual are distinguished from lab experiments by the gray tab at the edge of the page. Lab experiments (stage 3) have solid black tabs. It is very important that exploratory activities precede your presentation. Some activities may take only a few minutes, while some may take the better part of a class period.

Stage 2: Concept Development. Concept development may occur via reading assignments, lectures and demonstrations, practice-sheet assignments, lab work, and/or class discussions. Lectures and class discussions should relate closely to chapter material. They should not be "off-the-wall" presentations or discussions about obscure material, nor should they be a verbatim presentation of material in the textbook. Successful classroom presentations fall between these extremes. This Teaching Guide contains suggested lectures and demonstrations that make available selections of closely related ideas that are not in the textbook. They provide you with interesting ideas that supplement those in the textbook.

Lecturing skill is in the sequencing of ideas; the understanding that one idea leads to the next. Information is more valued if it answers questions. So include many CHECK QUESTIONS in your teaching. After discussing an idea, and before developing it further or advancing to a new idea, give your class a question to consider, by saying something like: "If you understand this — if you really do — then you can answer the following question." Then pose the question slowly and clearly, likely in multiple-choice form for a short answer, and ask the class to jot their response on paper. Then ask them to check their response with a neighbor. Such check questions -brings students into an active role. The check question procedure may also be used to *introduce* concepts. A discussion of the question, the answer(s), and some of the associated misconceptions gets more attention than the same concept presented as a statement of fact.

Equations are important in any physics course. In a conceptual physics course an equation is not a recipe for plugging in numerical values, but rather a GUIDE TO THINKING. The equation tells your students what variables must be considered. How much an object accelerates, for example, depends not only upon the net force on it, but also on its mass. Consideration of the equation $a = F/m$ reminds one of this. Does gravitation depend on an object's speed? Consideration of $F = GmM/d^2$ shows that it doesn't, and so forth. (Please do not dwell on "negligible-higher-order effects", such as decreasing force on a falling body due to decreasing distance, and mass depending on speed in special relativity. Nothing inhibits learning more than information overload! To cover every possible nuance may impress some of your colleagues and even a few of your brighter students, but the extra depth of your plow setting will probably dampen learning for most of your students. A hint of things to come is sufficient.)

We all acknowledge the value of DEMONSTRATIONS. But watching them and doing them are entirely different. Performing demonstrations is an art. It is one of those activities that looks easy from the sidelines but is demanding in practice. Perhaps that's why few teachers feature demonstrations in their teaching, although when new to the profession they strongly intend to bring life to their classes with wonderful demonstrations. Demonstrations are work! Not in performing them, which is fun, but in getting the necessary equipment in order. Consider enlisting some of your students to help set up demonstrations—they'll greatly benefit in doing so. Demonstrations that require simple equipment are listed in the suggested lectures. Please make the effort to include some demonstration props in every lecture. If you discuss falling objects, at least drop your chalk or an eraser on the table! Or have a student drop it for you. Remember the Chinese proverb, "I hear, and I forget — I see, and I remember — I do and I understand."

Practice-sheet duplication masters from the *Concept-Development Practice Book* are provided for every chapter to get your students *doing* physics (shown greatly reduced below). The practice sheets are very different from the traditional work sheets of other courses. Working through the practice sheets is an alternative to working through the algebraic problems that characterize the plug-and-chug type physics course. Practice sheets can generally be assigned right after your lecture and before homework is done and discussed. The practice sheets can be completed by student pairs (or trios), in which case the person doing the writing should sign it and other(s) check and initial it (as is done in R&D reports for industry). Your students should find them stimulating, interesting, and fun.

The suggested lectures in this book are as the name implies; *suggestions*. They suggest a sequence of ideas that has worked for me and others, and may work for you. They offer many interesting tidbits not found in the textbook that can make your presentation interesting. Some of the annotated suggestions in the margins of the textbook are included in these lectures, and some are not. Pick and choose the ideas that suit your style of teaching. What works for one teacher may or may not work for another. We all need to develop our own style of teaching. The suggested lectures, videotapes, and the videodisks provide a sample base for developing your own non-computational way of teaching.

Whatever your style, I strongly recommend you use a lesson plan or some form of lecture notes. I still bring a note sheet to every lecture (you'll see my green sheets on the lecture table in the videotapes). They are simply a check list that I glance at from time to time in my lecture to be sure that I cover the concepts intended. If I don't cover everything on the sheet, a mark or two will let me know next time what I missed or where I stopped. The sample of my lecture for Chapter 4 shown here is an abbreviation of the suggested lecture for that chapter in this guide.

Stage 3: Application. The follow-through to concept development is student *use* of concepts. You can instigate this by leading class discussion of worked-out answers to the Think and Explain and Think and Solve sections in the chapter-end material of the text.

Conclude class periods with the posing of more-involved questions to be thought about before the next class. These are the *Conceptual Physics Next Time Questions*, also available as part of your teacher resource materials. These provide a continuity device, an interesting way of picking up where you left off. Your next class can begin by discussing the answer. Post these on your physics bulletin board, or make transparencies of them for overhead projection.

Be sure to treat computational problem solving *after* students have demonstrated an understanding of the concept. Such problems are the Think and Solves in chapter backmatter, and additional problems are in this Teaching Guide. (When I was a student, every physics course I took started immediately with problem solving — stage 3 — from day 1. The primary difference between a conceptual and a computational course is the emphasis on the activity and concept-development stages *before* computational problem solving.) Then the problems build on concepts and reinforce them. Too many physics courses have been (and still are!) little more than applied mathematics, with concepts valued as gimmicks needed for the primary task of matching the answers given at the back of the book. Note here that the *Conceptual Physics* textbook supplies no answers for the student. Whether or not they are supplied answers is up to you. Only in the frontmatter of the Teacher's Edition of the book are there detailed answers to Think and Explains and problem solutions to Think and Solves.

Laboratory experiments (as noted by the black tab at the edge of the page in the lab manual) should comprise the strongest component of the application stage.

Laboratory Work

Lab work is a very important part of this program. In addition to reinforcing concepts, lab experiments familiarize your students with methods of taking, recording, and analyzing data.

Many labs in the *Conceptual Physics Laboratory Manual* call for use of a computer and instrument interfacing. Optional, these labs were designed to be compatible with the Apple II Series computer, because of the many quality programs for science education written for the Apple. There are ample lab experiments to choose from, both with and without the use of a computer. Lab information is in the front-matter of the Laboratory Manual.

Homework

You are the best judge of how much homework to assign, for only you know the level of your class. No homework at all leaves students dangling between classes, a little keeps them engaged, more keeps them busy, and too much blows them away. I recommend you devote a class period per chapter to guide student discussion of homework handed in.

Answering the REVIEW QUESTIONS should be an achievable task for even your less-than average students. Answers can be located in the text at the designated sections. This task ensures that the main points of the chapter have been covered. It is customary to assign about half or even all the Review Questions as homework. Answering the THINK AND EXPLAIN questions and solving the THINK AND SOLVE problems is more demanding, and some may stump your best students. Pick and choose among the offerings, and assign with discretion. Additional questions not in the text are offered with each suggested lecture. Practice sheets from the *Concept-Development Practice Book*, although primarily intended fomÁclassroom activity, may be used as homework assignments. In assigning homework, recall your own experience as a student with courses that demanded so much work that you couldn't see the forest for the trees — please do not overwhelm your students with excessive written assignments! You will have a handle on how much homework is right for your class from the feedback you get in the student discussion session. Homework done over until it's correct pays off.

In response to students who find physics difficult, be sure to remind them from time to time throughout the course that it *is* difficult, and not necessarily a sign of their own deficiencies. Remind them that they are coming to grips with concepts in a matter of days that took many great thinkers centuries to develop.

Over-Head Transparencies

For those who use overhead transparencies rather than the chalkboard, be sure to make use of the 100 over-head transparencies (OHTs, code 46699) that show central figures and tables from the textbook. With the OHTs is the OHT Teaching Guide, that details important information regarding the selected figures, and a teaching strategy for each. Their placement in your class is indicated in the lectures of this manual.

Videotapes and Videodisks

My classroom lectures were videotaped while I was a guest lecturer at the University of Hawaii at Manoa, in 1989 and 1990. They now comprise the 34 tape series, *Conceptual Physics Alive!*, marketed by Addison Wesley and by Arbor Scientific (1-800-367-6695). Excerpts from the tapes make up the two-hour videodisk, *The Best from Conceptual Physics Alive!*, marketed by Addison Wesley and by Pasco Scientific (916-786-3800). Only short segments from the lectures are on the videodisks, which are bar coded in the TE of the text, and in a separate booklet.

Usefulness of the tapes and videodisks is variable. They introduce your class to the author of their book (which may result in greater interest in studying the textbook). They bring into your class a guest lecturer. The tapes can be shown by substitutes whenever you can't make it to class. The tapes can also/instead be used in your learning resource center as supplementary material. Or you can treat them as part of this teacher guide and view privately the result of my 25 years of teaching physics conceptually, for tips in developing your own teaching style. Their best use, I have found, is loaning them to students for home viewing. They share them with family, and learning physics becomes a family affair!

Interactive Physics™ Simulations

This Macintosh® (code 84157) and Windows® (code 84167) software, developed by David Vasquez for Addison Wesley, is a player version of the Knowledge Revolution Interactive Physics™

software program. It is a set of 32 ready-to-run computer simulations that explore major physics concepts. Concepts are explored by running simulations, which require minipulation of variables, observing motion, interpreting graphs, and predicting and verifying outcomes. They can be used as exploration activities or concept development. Worksheets accompany the software.

Testing

The Addison-Wesley program has two testing options. Tests (code 46803) is a book of blackline master tests that contains one test for each chapter plus two semester tests. Questions in the test booklet are in multiple-choice, true-false, and essay form.

A second option is Addison-Wesley SelectTest™ Software (code 46810). It includes a test bank of over 1800 questions in multiple choice, true-false, and essay form. With SelectTest™ you can create tests using a simple point-and-click, drag-and-drop interface, and you can edit, add, or delete questions. You can also control page layout. The Test File Book provides a printed version of all questions and answers.

Selected References

Textbooks: I highly recommend the oldie but goodie, *Physics for the Inquiring Mind*, by Eric Rogers, published in 1960 by Princeton University Press. This book has been an inspiration to me both as a teacher and an author. (It is a very thick book, so much so that my department chairman forbade me to adopt it for my "Descriptive Physics" course. Had I been allowed to share it with my students I might never have written *Conceptual Physics*.)

At a deeper plow setting are the three volumes of *The Feynman Lectures*, edited transcriptions of lectures given to Caltech students in 1961. These volumes, published by Addison-Wesley, were also early inspirations that broadened my perspectives of physics, that I recommend to any physics teacher.

The reading I most highly recommend is not a textbook, but is the magazine of the American Association of Physics Teachers, *The Physics Teacher*. This monthly publication is a must for physics teachers, for it contains a wealth of information geared to high school physics teaching. AAPT, One Physics Ellipse, College Park, MD 20740-3845.

Audiotapes. "*Moments of Discovery*" by Arthur Eisenkraft, physics teacher at Fox Lane High School in Bedford, NY, is a valuable addition. Part I is a history of the discovery of fission using actual recordings of the physicists involved with this achievement including J.J. Thompson, Rutherford,

Bohr, Fermi, Einstein and others. Part II is a history of the discovery of the optical pulsar. This tape includes an inadvertent recording of Cocke and Disney on the night of their first observation of the pulsar. It is the only known live recording of a discovery as it is taking place. A teacher's guide with supporting material is included. The package was supported by the National Science Foundation, The Heideman Foundation, and The Friends of the Center for the History of Physics. Available from The Center For The History of Physics of the American Institute, One Physics Ellipse, College Park, MD 20740-3845.

Computer Software. The computer serves a variety of functions for classroom and laboratory use. Its optional role in the lab is described in the frontmatter of the *Conceptual Physics Laboratory Manual.*

Companion software to *Conceptual Physics* includes a Laboratory Interfacing Disk for Apple II series computers that enable the collection, recording, and graphing of data quickly and accurately. An interface box makes the game port easily accessible for the insertion of temperature probes (thermisters) and light probes (phototransistors). Another disk, *Conceptual Physics Laboratory Simulations I*, compliments some of the labs in the lab manual. Still another disk, *Good Stuff!*, are programs of ultra-fast machine language graphics animation of physics concepts by Professor Robert H. Good of California State University, Hayward. These materials are available from *Laserpoint*, 5629 Omni Drive, Sacramento, CA 95841. (916) 344 8824. Fax (916) 344 3233. E-mail LaserPablo@AOL.com.

Some of the best software for the Apple II, IBM-compatible and Macintosh computers described in the lab manual, has been developed by David Vernier, 8565 S.W. Beaverton-Hillsdale Hwy, Portland, OR 97225-2429. Phone (503) 297-5317, and fax (503) 297 1760. Internet: dvernier@vernier.com; WWW Home Page: http://www.teleport.com/~vernier.

For color IBM computers or compatibles, check out the *Physics Discovery Series*, developed by Roy Unruh of the University of Northern Iowa. These programs employ the same learning strategy used in the PRISMS material embraced in the lab manual. These programs are available from your local IBM software representative.

Videotapes and Videodisks. "*Teaching Conceptual Physics*" is a 60-minutes narrated tape by David Vasquez, that highlights 1984 footage of classroom lectures at City College (when my enrollments topped 1000 students per semester). Another tape from the same period is the 60-minute, "*Classroom Demonstrations in Conceptual Physics*," and "*Fusion Torch and Ripe Tomatoes*," 45 minutes. The first tape is narrated highlights of the course that is intended for teachers, the second is non-narrated highlights of demonstrations of the course, and the third is my opening lecture that is designed to elicit interest in the course. For more information, contact Media Solutions, 1128 Irving Street, San Francisco, CA 94122. (415) 665-1077.

Another set of physics videotapes are the set of 12 high school adaptations of *The Mechanical Universe*. The series was created initially for a college audience, and was produced at California Institute of Technology. These tapes feature a historical perspective, with outstanding graphics. They are available from the Southern California Consortium, 5400 Orange Avenue, Suite 109, Cypress, CA 90630.

Videodiscs. The complete college course of *The Mechanical Universe* is available on videodisk. Call 800 - LEARNER. *The Puzzle of the Tacoma Narrows Bridge Collapse*, by Robert Fuller, Dean Zollman, and Tom Campbell, and *Physics and Automobile Collisions*, by Zollman and Fuller, are published by John Wiley & Sons, Inc., 605 Third Ave., New York, NY 10158. Other attention grabbers by Fuller and Zollman are *Studies in Motion* (shows gymnastics, divers, and a dancer) and *Energy Transformations Featuring the Bicycle*. These along with Charles Eames' popular *Powers of Ten* and *Tops* are available from videodisk educational distributors such as Ztek Co., Inc. 1-800-247-1603, free catalog; The *Physics of Sports* (by Zollman) and *The Physics of Flight* are available from Videodiscovery, Inc., 1-800-548-3472, free catalog. The American Associa-

tion of Physics Teachers has produced a set of physics cinema classics discs that include PSSC and Project Physics films (1991). These discs and videotapes are available from Ztek, Inc.

Electronic Database: The Physics InfoMall CD-ROM is a complete physics text and graphics database for high school physics teachers. It includes many demonstrations, problems, and laboratory exercises in addition to the complete texts of 19 textbooks and about 3000 articles from physics teacher journals. It is available in Windows and Macintosh versions from The Learning Team 1-800-793-TEAM.

Filmstrips and Slides. Spectacular slides, most from Bob Greenler's *Rainbows, Halos, and Glories* (Cambridge University Press, 1980) are available from Blue Sky Associates, PO Box 429, Reading, MA 01867. Two sets of 5-lesson filmstrips with audio tape are *Gravitation*, by Lester Paldy; and *Optics* by Jacqueline Spears — available from Prentice Hall Media, Englewood Cliffs, NJ 07632. If you are interested in a wider selection of slides and filmstrips, write for the free AAPT Products Catalog from the American Association of Physics Teachers, One Physics Ellipse, College Park, MD 20740-3845.

Further Information

For further information on all components of the Conceptual Physics high school program, call Addison-Wesley's toll-free customer service number: 1-800-552-2259.

Course Planning

The *Conceptual Physics Program* is based on a 170 to 180-day teaching year, and assumes that most users will begin their course with Chapter 1 in the text, and more or less follow sequentially through the book toward Chapter 40. It would be unusual in one teaching year to cover everything in the book, given the distractions that usually occur. I take the view that the 40 chapters offer a wide selection for a 25 to 35-chapter course. All the units and chapters are important, which is why they are in the book, but when there isn't time to sufficiently cover them all, something has to give. It is up to the teacher to pick and choose course coverage.

The simplest way to limit course coverage is to simply omit an entire unit. I strongly recommend you not omit Unit I, Mechanics, because its physics is basic in the course. Omitting Units II or III, although excellent material, helps to trim content and allow for an unhurried coverage of the material you select. Unit IV is perhaps of highest initial interest to your students, and for that reason may not be a good candidate for omission. Unit V on Electricity poses a dilemma, for although it is more abstract and more difficult physics than other units, it is likely the only formal exposure that your nonscience students will ever have to this subject — even though every facet of their lives is touched by electrical phenomena. And for your science students, its conceptual nature as an introduction is very valuable. Unit VI, Atomic and Nuclear Physics, poses a similar dilemma. You will have to be the judge of your course content.

A strength of the book, I feel, is that most chapters can stand alone, so that omission of chapters within units allows an adequate flow of the remaining material. This allows you to touch all bases, with nipping and tucking of chapters within units, rather than omitting entire units. Suggestions for nipping and tucking, with possible consequences, are found in the discussions of chapters in this guide.

For omission I suggest the two on special relativity, Chapters 15 and 16. These can be omitted without consequence to the remaining chapters, even though the mass-energy relationship is again treated in Chapter 40. Other chapter candidates for skipping are Chapters 24-Thermodynamics, 30-Lenses, 31-Diffraction and Interference, and 38-The Atom and the Quantum.

If you try to cover 40 chapters in 36 weeks, it's easy to see you'll be covering 2 chapters a week

most of the time (who gets a full 36 weeks for course content?). That doesn't leave much time for exploratory activities, experiments, and application activities — not to mention testing. So you might consider assigning some chapters as outside reading, (without lecture, homework, and testing) and spend more class time on selected chapters. Unless you have a very good class and excellent teaching conditions, I suggest you not try to completely cover every chapter in the book.

Suppose, for example, that for the first half year you cover Units I and II, and assign the relativity chapters as outside reading with no homework or testing. This gives you 18 weeks to cover 18 chapters (a bit more considering that Chapter 1 should take at most 2 or 3 days). One chapter per week may allow you ample time for activities (which often require less than a full class period), lecture, workbook exercises (again often less than a class period), homework discussion time, and an experiment. Chapters such as 4, 6, 10, and 14, take less time than the others, which gives you some time for testing. If you want quizzes and exams to be a positive reinforcement tool, then give small quizzes often rather than only large comprehensive exams. Entry level students have difficulty with long-range retention of physics concepts.

This plan would leave you the second 18 weeks to cover 20 chapters. Again, you might consider assigning some chapters as outside reading, perhaps Chapters 24, 30, 33, and 38. This leaves you with a chapter per week and two weeks for spring fever. In this way, you may cover the entire book.

The following breakdown is suggested for lecture time for all the chapters of the book. The word *lecture* is more appropriate in college than in high school, and perhaps I should call these *instructional periods*. My personal experience has been with 50-minute lectures to large groups, so the material that I have been used to covering in one lecture may be very different than what you will cover in one class period. When you have compared the time you take on material to what I consider one or two lectures, you can translate my coverage time to your own. My pace is fairly brisk, for I treat the course as an overview of serious physics, and I don't get caught up in having my students master all the details we encounter.

The lecture time per chapter breakdown that follows does not take into account class time for activities, experiments, workbook exercises, homework discussions, and testing. It is an estimate of relative lecture times for various chapters that may help you to select the combination of lessons that best meets your class needs.

Unit I: Mechanics

Time for Chapter 2 can be long or short, depending on how much you expect and how deep you wish to set your plow. I suggest you cover its rudiments in two lectures, one on the distinction between speed, velocity, and acceleration, and the other on the physics of falling bodies; then move on to Chapter 3 where these concepts are reinforced. The conceptual treatment of vectors in Chapters 3 is extended in Chapter 4 and is a useful foundation that goes beyond mechanics. Considerable emphasis is given to vectors in the Practice Book. Resist spending more than a week or so on projectile motion, and then move to the meat — to Newton's laws in Chapters 4, 5, and 6. Many teachers become so enamored with the physics toys available for kinematics that they get bogged down for weeks on end with projectile motion. Although the measuring and plotting is useful to the few students who will be science majors, the excess time developing the concepts of velocity and acceleration is, in my opinion, not worth it. These concepts are further developed throughout mechanics. So I advise resisting the toys and the computer plotting and instead cover physics concepts. A course that has to rush through electricity and never gets to rainbows is not the course you would have wanted in your own student days. Momentum, Chapter 7, can be covered in two lectures, whereas three lectures may be required to cover all of energy in Chapter 8. Chapter 10 on center of gravity is a "shorty," can be covered in one lecture. Gravitation is divided into two chapters, Chapters 12 and 13, and together can be covered in two or three lectures. Chapters 9 and 14, on circular motion and satellite motion can each be covered in one lecture. Rotational Mechanics, Chapter 11, will need at least two lectures. Chapters 15 and 16, on special relativity, together require at least 3 lectures. To shorten Unit I these two chapters are the best candidates for omission. One reason is their abstractness and remoteness from the students' everyday experience, and another is their high level of difficulty.

Unit II: Properties of Matter

Even the briefest treatment of this unit should include Chapter 17 on atoms, which is background for much of the rest of the book. So Chapter 17 is a "must." It can be covered in one and a half lectures. Chapters 18, 19, and 20 can each be covered in two

lectures and are not prerequisites for the chapters that follow. Unit II, with the exception of some mention of kinetic energy in Section 20.7 in Chapter 20, may be taught before, or without, Unit I. With minor difficulties, Unit II can stand alone without Unit I. Many teachers omit Unit II when their students have covered this material in a chemistry or other science course.

Unit III: Heat

Knowledge of kinetic and potential energy, and the conservation of energy is a prerequisite for this unit. Chapters 21 and 22 can be covered in one or one and a half lectures each, and Chapter 23 (change of phase) and Chapter 24 (thermodynamics) will each require two lectures. If time is tight the best chapter to skim or omit is Chapter 24, thermodynamics. The concepts of Chapter 21 (heat and thermal equilibrium) make a useful background to similar concepts in electricity, Chapters 32 through 35, and radiation in Chapter 23, and again in Chapter 27 (electromagnetic waves). Although some of this material makes good background for some of the material to follow, it is not a prerequisite for following chapters.

Unit IV: Sound and Light

Each of these chapters is packed with information and each requires at least two lectures for adequate coverage. Units I, II, and III are not prerequisite for this unit, so consider using it to begin your course. A brief treatment of this unit can omit Chapters 30 and 31. Chapter 30 is background for laboratory work, and without lab work should be minimized or omitted. Section 28.11 on atomic spectra is useful background for the quantum physics in Chapter 38.

Unit V: Electricity and Magnetism

Much of Unit I, and Chapter 25 of Unit IV are a prerequisite for this unit, the most conceptually demanding in the book. Chapter 32 requires one and a half lectures, Chapter 33 one lecture, 2 lectures each for Chapters 34 and 35, one lecture for Chapter 36, and two for Chapter 37. Because of the abstractness of the material, more time should be spent on supporting activities than with other units. This unit is too demanding to be taught during the first half of your school year. For a light treatment of physics it can be entirely omitted. But the cost of omission is rather high, considering the importance of electricity in the modern world, and the low likelihood of students encountering a serious study of it elsewhere.

Unit VI: Atomic and Nuclear Physics

Chapter 17 on atoms is a prerequisite for this unit. If you are not covering Unit II, consider doing Chapter 17 immediately before this unit. Then Unit VI can stand on its own. Chapter 38 can be covered in one lecture, and the following two chapters need two lectures each. For a short treatment, Chapter 38 can be assigned as reading, or omitted entirely.

Appendices

Graphical analysis is the topic of Appendix B. This may supplement motion analysis in Chapter 2 and projectile motion in Chapter 3, or much of the Lab Manual. More about vectors is in Appendix C, which can follow Chapter 3 for those who wish a full treatment of vectors. Exponential growth and doubling time, which doesn't fit well in any of the chapters of the book, is treated in Appendix E. It's not hard-core physics, but is important enough for inclusion. If you have a stray period in your schedule, it's great lecture and /or discussion material.

A teacher's influence knows no bounds — our immortality begins with our students.

1 About Science

Objectives

- Explain why physics is the basic science.
- Outline five steps of the scientific method.
- Distinguish between an observation and a fact.
- Distinguish between a fact and a hypothesis.
- Distinguish between a hypothesis and a law or principle.
- Describe the circumstances under which a hypothesis or law must be changed or abandoned.
- Distinguish between the everyday meaning and the scientific meaning of *theory*.
- Explain why the refinement of theories is a strength in science.
- Distinguish between a hypothesis that is scientific and one that is not.
- Distinguish between science and technology.

Possible Misconceptions to Correct

- Physics is the most difficult of the sciences.
- Physics is applied mathematics.
- Facts are unchangeable.
- A theory is a scientific word for guess.
- It is bad science to change your mind.
- Science and technology are the same.
- Religion and science are opposites, and educated people must choose between them.

I suggest you spend only one class period lecturing on Chapter 1. Although this material is important groundwork for science in general, it should not be considered material to *study*, like the following chapters. It is enough for your students to be familiar with the objectives above, think about them, and save deeper digging for later on. Then your course can start with hard-core physics without undue pressure.

One Practice Page accompanies this chapter in the Concept-Development Practice Book, one activity in the lab manual, and there is one Next-Time Question. The activity *Trial and Error* in the lab manual is a good way to kick off the lab potion of your course. If you do *Making Hypotheses*, consider NOT telling them how the device works, or waiting till the end of the course — long-term suspense!

The "Two-Word Game"

Here is a game you can play with your class: the "Two-Word Game." It illustrates physics as an activity to search for laws to explain, simplify, and predict. Tell your class you will say two words that have a particular relationship between them. Continue with other pairs of words that have the same relationship. (The relationship is the same for all pairs of words.) The students are to figure out the relationship, just as scientists try to discover relationships in nature. When the students think they have figured it out, they then "predict" by giving two new examples WITHOUT SAYING THE RULE. To make sure that they just didn't stumble on examples that are correct, have them give additional examples. They are never to say the rule, just examples that use the rule.

When they understand the rules of the game, start. It's *off* but not *on*. It's *cool* but not *cold*. It's *kitten* but not *cat*. It's *wall* but not *ceiling*. It's *Milwaukee* but not *Chicago*. It's *Illinois* but not *Wisconsin*. It's *nineteen* but not *twenty*. It's *three* but not *two*. It's *pepper* but not *salt*. It's *book* but not *text*. It's *tall* but not *short*. It's *knee* but not *elbow*.

The rule has to do with the spelling of the words, rather than any meaning they might convey. That is, a double letter appears in the first word and not in the second. If a student guesses, for example, it's *calf* but not *cow*, say it's neither *calf* nor *cow*. If the student should guess, its *sixteen* but not *seventeen*, say that it is both *sixteen* and *seventeen*. Soon some students should figure out the rule, especially if they make a list of words. When some have, stop, and ask how those who don't understand the game feel — confused? frustrated? stupid? That is the way humankind felt before scientists finally figured out some of nature's rules or laws.

Point out the parallel between this game and learning physics. If the student knows the rules, he or she doesn't have to memorize scores of meaningless data and examples. If the student knows the rules when called upon in class or a test, he or she could come up with examples that are new and original.

As is stated in the "To the Student" page of the textbook, learning the rules of the physical world is what physics is about. To know the rules allows one to see the world with meaning, and with more interest. A person with a knowledge of music better appreciates music, a person trained in art better appreciates art, and a person acquainted with the rules of nature better appreciates nature and is more alive to the beauty of the surrounding world. Do you agree that for every case where ignorance is bliss, there are far more cases where knowledge is even more blissful? There is more beauty in the eye of the beholder who knows what to look for.

Photo Scrapbook

Consider this course-long assignment. Each student takes one or more original photographs of things that illustrate physics. Each photo should be an example of physics in everyday life, and have a title and a short paragraph explaining the photo. One example might be of a book lying on a table, with the title, "Sum of the forces = 0" and a short explanation that the force of gravity on the book is balanced by the equal force of the table pushing up on the book.

Another example, one that is omnipresent, is of the student who takes a picture of him/herself in the mirror. The photo might be titled "Reflection," with a short paragraph on the law of reflection or on virtual images. As photographs are submitted they can be displayed in a photo scrapbook or on a bulletin board. Students who initially find difficulty in choosing photo subjects finally come to the realization that a photograph of anything at all involves physics. The realization (not to be stated at the outset!) is the value of this activity. Physics is truly all around us!

The double-letter game and assignment of the photo scrapbook on the first day of class should be a good start. If you choose not to do these, discussion of them is still of some value.
(Both the Two-Word Game and the Photo Scrapbook were suggested to me by Marshall Ellenstein. With the popularity of video cameras these days, you might consider doing as Marshall now does and give your students the option of doing a short video in place of the photograph.)

Teaching Suggestions

This section describes some points not in the book but related to particular sections of Chapter 1.

Section 1.1: Considering physics, chemistry, and biology, which is the simplest? Which is the most complex? Does the most complex science necessarily make for the most difficult course of study? Is it the "depth of the plow" or the field of study that makes for course difficulty? In terms of science courses in school, physics has traditionally been more demanding of students than "easier" chemistry and biology courses. Why? Because more understanding of the subject is expected in physics than in the more complex chemistry and biology courses? Because physics is now taught conceptually, science students can logically begin with the study of physics, then take chemistry, and then progress to a serious course in biology. Con-

ceptual physics, without the mathematical "roadblock," is interesting to nonscience students also.

Section 1.2: Although mathematics is a language of physics, it is not the focus of this course. The principal language of conceptual physics is *everyday English*, and the focus will be on seeing physics visually. This course stresses comprehension, and except for elementary computations in the practice sheets and lab part of the course, emphasis on computation is left for those who have time and interest, or those who take a follow-up course. With a base of conceptual comprehension first, computation later will be more meaningful. It's nice to compute what you know something about!

Section 1.3: Point out that the scientific method, although revolutionary four centuries ago, is a guide to good science practice. Most discoveries happen otherwise.

Section 1.4: Distinguish between *hypothesis, theory, fact,* and *concept*. Point out that theory and hypothesis are not the same. A **theory** applies to a synthesis of a large body of information. The criterion of a theory is not whether it is true or untrue, but rather whether it is useful or non useful. It is useful even though the ultimate causes of the phenomena it encompasses are unknown. For example, we accept the theory of gravitation as a useful synthesis of available knowledge that relates to the mutual attraction of bodies. The theory can be refined, or with new information it can take on a new direction. It is important to acknowledge the common misunderstanding of what a scientific theory is, as revealed by those who say, "But it is not a fact; it is *only* a theory." Many people have the mistaken notion that a theory is tentative or speculative, while a fact is absolute.

Impress upon your class that a fact is not immutable and absolute, but is generally a close agreement by competent observers of a series of observations of the same phenomena. The observations must be testable. Since the activity of science is the determination of the most probable, there are no absolutes. Facts that were held to be absolute in the past are seen altogether differently in the light of present-day knowledge.

By **concept**, we mean the intellectual framework that is part of a theory. We speak of the concept of time, the concept of energy, or the concept of a force field. Time is related to motion in space and is the substance of the Theory of Special Relativity. We find that energy exists in tiny grains, or quanta, which is a central concept in the Quantum Theory. An important concept in Newton's Theory of Universal Gravitation is the idea of a force field that surrounds a material body. A concept envelops the overriding idea that underlies various phenomena. Thus, when we think "conceptually" we envelop a generalized way of looking at things.

Prediction in science is different from prediction in other areas. In the everyday sense, one speaks of predicting what has not yet occurred, like whether or not it will rain on next Saturday. In science, however, prediction is not so much about what *will* happen, but of what *is* happening and is not yet noticed, like what the angular momentum is for a particular elementary particle — or newfound star. A scientist predicts what can and cannot happen, rather than what will or will not happen.

It is important that a scientist be openminded *and* skeptical. It is not enough to be skeptical, and it is not enough to be openminded. Strive to be both.

Section 1.5: You may consider elaborating on the idea about the possible *wrongness versus rightness* of ideas; a practice that characterizes science. This is generally misunderstood, for it is not generally a criterion in other disciplines. State that it is the prerogative of science, in contrast to the speculative procedures of philosophy and metaphysics, to embrace only ideas that can be tested and to disregard the rest. Ideas that can't be tested are not necessarily wrong — they are simply useless insofar as advancement in scientific knowledge is concerned. Ideas must be verifiable by other scientists. In this way science tends to be self-correcting.

Section 1.6: Science is finding things out; technology is doing them. Both science and technology in themselves are neither good nor bad. What people or governments choose to do with them can be good or bad. It is the responsibility of all of us to see that science and technology are wisely used to promote the general well-being. Responsibility and authority should go together. Do they?

In discussions of science and technology and their side effects, a useful statement is: *You can never do just one thing.* Doing *this* affects *that*. This is similar to "there is never just one force" in discussions of Newton's third law.

Section 1.7: One of the important objectives of this course is to help students think critically, which begins by making distinctions between concepts and between words used to communicate those concepts. When distinctions such as those between science and technology, hypothesis and theory, and force and pressure are understood, clearer thinking can follow. The very important distinction between science and religion is missed by many people, particularly teenagers who have the notion that science and religion are opposites, and that they must choose between them. This is often a very disturbing choice to make. But it is a choice that is needless when one understands that the domains and purposes of science and religion are different from each other. Knowledge of this distinction clears one from having to choose between the two. Either or both can be embraced without contradiction. Difficulty usually occurs, however, when religion is used to explain science or visa versa.

Chapter 1 End-matter: I have no suggested additions to Chapter 1 endmatter, and urge that you move quickly to Chapter 2.

2 Motion

Objectives

- Explain the idea that motion is relative.
- Define speed and give examples of units for speed.
- Distinguish between instantaneous speed and average speed.
- Distinguish between speed and velocity.
- Describe how to tell whether a velocity is changing.
- Define acceleration and give examples of units for acceleration.
- Describe the motion of an object in free fall from rest.
- Describe the motion of an object thrown straight up until it hits the ground, when air resistance is negligible.
- Determine the speed and the distance fallen at any time after an object is dropped from rest, when air resistance is negligible.
- Describe how air resistance affects the motion of falling objects.
- Explain why acceleration is *a rate of a rate*.

Possible Misconceptions to Correct

- Speed and velocity are the same.
- Acceleration is simply a change in velocity.
- How fast something goes when moving is how far it goes.

Demonstration Equipment

- [2-1] Textbook and two regular half-sheets of paper.

Introduction

Wisdom is knowing what to overlook; good teaching is knowing what to omit. By all means, avoid the temptation to get into the classic motion problems that involve 90% math and 10% physics. DO NOT SPEND TOO MUCH TIME ON THIS CHAPTER! Time spent on kinematics is time not spend on why satellites don't fall to earth when they fall, why high temperatures and high voltages can be safe to touch (for similar reasons), why rainbows are round, and how nuclear reactions deep the earth's interior molten. When I cover kinematics, I spend no more than 2 class lectures on it.

I have had mixed feelings about beginning the course with mechanics, and in particular, motion. This is because the study of motion can be quite demanding and calls for our students' highest cognitive skills. But since motion is basic to the other areas of physics, rather than beat around the bush and begin with less demanding material, we jump into the foundations of mechanics right away. As stated earlier, the demand a course places on students has more to do with how deep the plow is set than the field being plowed. Therefore Chapter 2 covers the essentials of kinematics using only simple examples. Only motion in a straight line is treated. Only uniform acceleration is discussed, with emphasis on falling objects. More complex motion analysis can be counterproductive, so we make the distinction between velocity and acceleration, understanding that freely falling objects fall in a predictable way, and then move on to Newton's laws of Motion.

Take care that you aren't seduced by the wonderful tools of graphical analysis. Like the astronomer whose love is more for telescopes than stars, many teachers are more enamored with ticker timers, sonic rangers, and computers, than the concepts they illustrate. Hence kinematics gets overtime. We teachers love graphical analysis. But I think students, given a choice between learning to plot motion graphs and learning to analyze rainbows, would prefer rainbows. So I recommend going light on graphical analysis, that you resist the temptation of extended initial time on kinematics. The concepts of kinematics are further developed in the other chapters on mechanics. I think that if there is time left at the end of the course, after "rainbows," then the ticker timers and computers graphing tools can be used. Let's not get bogged down with kinematics. Most of the fascination of physics lies beyond.

An exploratory activity should precede each chapter in the course. Whether or not each student does the activity, or you do it as a group demonstration, will depend on equipment and time considerations. Chapter 2 Practice-Book material should be passed out to your class toward the end of your lecture, or on the day following your lecture. Having your students do practice sheets in class, either singly, in pairs, or in trios, enables mutual feedback. You can identify trouble areas on the spot.

In the following suggested lectures, keep in mind the old Chinese proverb, "I HEAR, AND I FORGET; I SEE, AND I REMEMBER; I DO, AND I UNDERSTAND." So when discussing a falling object, let your students see you actually drop something — even an eraser or only a piece of chalk. Or do as Cliff Swartz does and toss a baseball from hand to hand when discussing speed, and secretly substitute a tennis ball when winding up and pitch it to the class. Try to show your students *something* while you talk. Also, consider this strongly: your students will remember what *they themselves* are prompted to talk about, more than what *you* talk about, so let's use the "check-your-neighbor routine" discussed in the introduction. Get them "talking physics." And very importantly, get them "doing physics," via exploratory activities, practice-book exercises, and lab experiments. These ancillaries should be a strong part of the course.

Throughout the course remind your students that physics for the most part is common sense — with structure. Physics is structured common sense.

Some tidbits from Peter J. Brancazio, physics prof and sports buff from Brooklyn College in New York (*Just a Second*, March 91, Discover):

• Carl Lewis has run 100 m in 9.92 s. At this speed Carl covers 10.1 m per second. But because he starts from rest and accelerates up to speed, his top speed is more than this — about 10% over his average speed.

• Downhill skiers attain speeds of 70 to 80 mph on winding runs inclined about 10 - 15°. A speed of 70 mph is 102.7 ft/s, which means a skier covers 10.3 ft in 0.1 s. Even quicker are speed skiers, who ski slopes inclined up to 50° at speeds up to 139 mph or 204 ft/s. At this speed a skier could cover the length of a football field in 1.5 s. (This is faster than a skydiver falls in spread-eagle position.)

• Baseball pitchers such as Roger Clemens and Nolan Ryan can throw a baseball nearly 100 mph. Since the pitcher's mound is 60.5 feet from home plate, the ball takes less than 1/2 second to get to the batter. Due to the pitcher's reach, actual distance is about 55 feet. Because of air drag, a 95 mph ball slows to about 87 mph, giving a travel time of 0.41 s. On average it takes 0.2 s for a batter to get his bat from its cocked position up to speed in the hitting zone, so he must react to the pitcher's motion in a quarter-second or less, beginning his swing when the ball is only a little more than half the distance to the plate. These abilities and reflexes are rarities!

• Michael Jordan's hang time at the peak of his basketball career was less than 0.9 s (discussed in the box *Hang Time* in the text). Height jumped is less than 4 feet (those who insist a hang time of 2 s are way off, for 1 s up is 16 feet — clearly, no way!). A neat rule of thumb is that height jumped in feet is equal to four times hang time squared (d = g/2 (T/2)^2 = g/2 T^2/4 = g/8 T^2 = 4 T^2).

Have your students do the Activity 2, *The Physics 500*, before your lecture, then follow your lecture and discussion of chapter material with either Activity 3, *The Domino Effect*, or Experiment 4, *Merrily We Roll Along*. Lab 5, *Conceptual Graphing* utilizes an ultra sonic range finder as found in automatic focus cameras, and is the most powerful introduction to graphing that I have ever seen. If you have a computer, Lab 6 is the place to use the *Racetrack* program.

Four pages from the Concept-Development Practice Book can be treated anywhere in this chapter.

Suggested Lectures

Starting with Motion: Assuming you start your course sequence with this chapter, you might acknowledge that a sensible way to begin the course is with simple concepts and then gradually build to more complicated concepts as the course progresses — however, you're *not* going to do it that way. Instead you're going to begin with a description of motion that will be more quantitative than later material — serious stuff. This idea that the course does not become progressively more difficult should lessen anxiety for students who have read Chapter 2 and found it intimidating. Although kinematics can be a difficult field to cover, your plow setting will not go too deep. Rather than bear down at the beginning of the course and end up racing over material at semester's end, you're going to do it the other way around and race through Chapter 2 to have time for more interesting physics later!

Your first question: What means of motion has done more to change the way cities are built than any other? [The elevator!]

Neglecting Air Resistance: If Aristotle had neglected air resistance in his descriptions of motion, the history of physics would likely be very different. Although air resistance, buoyancy, spin, and the shape of a moving object are important considerations in the study of motion, we ignore them for the time being and instead look for the simple relationships beneath them. These *relationships* are what Chapter 2 and your lecture are about. Neglecting the effects of air resistance not only exposes the simple relationships, but is a reasonable assumption for heavy and compact (dense) objects traveling at moderate speeds; i.e., one would notice no difference between the rates of fall of a heavy rock dropped from the class-room ceiling to the floor below, when falling through either air or a complete vacuum. For a feather and heavy objects moving at high speeds, air resistance does become important, and will be treated in Chapter 5. Resistance is more pronounced for objects dropping in water.

DEMONSTRATION [2-1]: Here's a simple and nice one: First drop a sheet of paper and watch it flutter to the floor. Then crumple the paper and watch it fall faster to the floor. Drop the two side by side. The effect of air resistance is obvious. Then drop a sheet of paper and a book, side by side. Of course the book falls faster, due to its greater weight compared to air resistance. (Interestingly the air resistance is greater for the faster-falling book because it falls faster and plows more air out of its path than the piece of paper — an idea you'll return to in Chapter 5.) Now place the paper against the lower surface of the raised horizontally held book and when you drop them, nobody is surprised to see them fall together. The book has pushed the paper with it. Now repeat with the paper on *top* of the book and ask for predictions and neighbor discussion. Then surprise most of your class by showing that the paper falls as fast as the book! (Or you may choose to tease your class and *not* show what happens — ask them to try it on their own after class.) The book will "plow through the air" leaving an air-resistance free path for the paper to follow! Now with your class sufficiently impressed you continue!

Speed: Define *speed*, writing (speed = distance/time) on the board while giving examples — automobile speedometers, etc. Consider using the delta symbol Δ from the beginning, so speed = Δdistance/Δtime, even though the textbook waits until later. Stress that the slash in your notation is a division sign that means "per" — as in so many kilometers *per* so many hours. Then walk across the floor with 1-meter strides once per second and explain that you cover a distance of 1 meter per second; hence your speed is 1 m/s.

CHECK QUESTIONS: If you ride a bike a distance of 5 m in 1 s, what is your speed? For 10 m in 2 s? For 100 m in 20 s? [Each answer is 5 m/s.] (Very important point: As Mary Budd Roe suggests, you'll appreciably improve your instruction if you allow some thinking time (say 3 s) after you ask a question. Not doing so is the folly of too many instructors.) If no one answers in 5 seconds, perhaps your class needs an easier question first.

Velocity: Similarly define *velocity*, (speed with direction). Tell your students that the distinction between speed and velocity, although not critical in this chapter because cases are along a straight-line path, will be covered later when vectors are treated in Chapter 3. Point out the more important distinction between average speed or velocity and instantaneous speed or velocity. It is the average speed for a particular trip that is usually calculated. The speed-

ometer of a car reads the speed at any instant. These distinctions need not be belabored, for they will make more sense when their need arises in particular cases. The concepts that are important to distinguish are *velocity* and *acceleration*.

CHECK QUESTIONS: If an airplane travels 500 km due north in 1 h, what is its velocity? 250 km due north in 1/2 h? 125 km north in 1/4 h? [Each answer is the same 500 km/h north.]

Acceleration: Write the equation for *acceleration* (acceleration = CHANGE in velocity/change in time), and emphasize the word *change*. Cite how it is the change in motion that one feels in a vehicle when accelerating. We lurch in a vehicle when it undergoes changes in speed or direction. State there are three controls in an automobile that make the auto accelerate. Ask for them (accelerator, brakes, and steering wheel). State that we accelerate on a curve even though the speed may not change. The direction changes, so we see that the definition of velocity includes direction in order to make the definition of acceleration all-encompassing.

Numerical Examples: Give numerical examples of acceleration in units of kilometers/hour per second to establish the idea of acceleration. Be sure that your students are working on the examples with you. For example, ask them to find the acceleration of a car that goes from rest to 100 km/hr in 10 seconds. It is important that you not use examples involving seconds twice until they taste success with the easier kilometers/hour per second examples. Have them check their work with their neighbors as you go along. Only after they get the hang of it, introduce examples involving meters/second/second to develop a sense for customary units m/s^2. There are no square seconds.

CHECK QUESTIONS: What is the acceleration of a car that goes from 0 to 100 km/h in 10 s? [(10 km/h)/s.] What is the acceleration of a mechanical part that moves from 0 to 10 m/s in a time of 1 s? [10 (m/s)/s, or 10 m/s^2.]

10 m/s^2: Although the acceleration of free fall at the earth's surface is about 9.8 m/s^2, we round this off to 10 m/s^2 to more easily establish the velocity and distance relationships. When making measurements in lab, then the more precise 9.8 m/s^2 can be used.

Free Fall — Speed and Acceleration: Drop an object from your outstretched hand and ask if it accelerated. Ask how much it accelerated, and then ask what it means to say it accelerated 10 m/s^2. Nurture neighbor discussion. In words — in every second of fall the object's speed increases 10 m/s.

This is made clearer if you suppose the falling object is equipped with a speedometer (as per the practice sheet for this chapter!). Even without a knowledge of physics, most people instinctively know that the speed of a falling object increases with time. (That's why one wouldn't hesitate to catch a baseball dropped for a height of 1 meter, but would be quite reluctant to catch the same baseball dropped from a tall building.) Now your students presumably understand that a freely falling object somehow equipped with a speedometer, has speed reading increases of 10 m/s each successive second of fall.

CHECK QUESTION: If an object is dropped from rest from the top of a cliff, how *fast* will it be going at the end of 1 second? (You might add, "Write the answer on your note paper." And then, "Look at your neighbor's paper — if your neighbor doesn't have a good answer, reach over and help — talk about it." And then with some discretion, "If your neighbor isn't cooperative, sit somewhere else next time!" Peer pressure, properly used, can change a passive class to an active class.)

(You may distinguish between the acceleration of free fall and the deceleration the ball undergoes when it strikes the floor. Deceleration upon impact is considerably more than 10 m/s^2 because the velocity change occurs in a much briefer time. Deceleration is simply negative acceleration.)

Table 2-2: After explaining the answer to the above check question and when class discussion dies down, repeat the process and ask for the speed at the end of 2 seconds, and then for 10 seconds. This leads you into stating the relation $\Delta v = g\Delta t$, which by now you can express in shorthand notation. You have three ways to assess Table 2.2: In Practice Book 2-1b, where the data is visualized via the falling speedometer, the table itself, and a graph of the table, Figure 2.9.

[**Transparencies 1 and 2**, showing Figure 2.6, then Table 2.2 and Figure 2.9 should be shown here.]

Summary: This should be enough information for a class period. After any questions, discussion, and examples, state that you are going to pose a different question in the next class period — asking not how *fast*, but how *far* — that you'll discuss how far a freely-falling object falls in 1 second.

NEXT-TIME QUESTION: Consider leaving your class with the "bikes and bee" question shown here, which highlights the relation $d = vt$. Show via overhead transparency or post in an appropriate area for viewing (a glass case outside the classroom where other students can catch the flavor of conceptual

physics!) Shown here are reduced versions of 8-1/2 x 11 sheets of paper that you can photocopy from the Next-Time Questions book. At least one of these Next-Time Questions each with a separate answer sheet is available for every chapter in the text. Because of space limitations, Next-Time Questions for other chapters are not shown in this guide

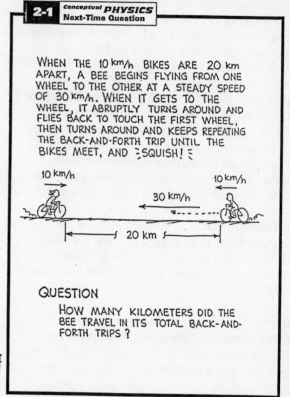

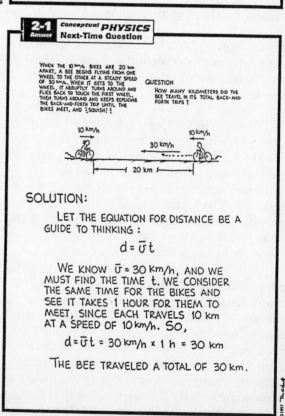

"Bikes and Bee" Solution: State the usefulness of the equation $d = vt$ in solving the "Bikes and the Bee" problem. Note it is simpler when time is considered. Whether or not one thinks about time should not be a matter of cleverness or good insight, but a matter of letting the equation dictate the variables to consider. The v is given, but the time t is not. The formula instructs one to consider time. The key is that the time for the bee's trip is the same time for the bikes' (and we neglect the short time of the bee's turn-arounds). Equations are important in guiding our thinking about things.

Free-Fall Distance: Ask how *fast* an object is falling 1 second after release from rest; after 2 seconds; after 10 seconds. Now pose the very different question "How *far* does an object fall in 1 second?" How far it falls is entirely different than the free-fall case. Ask for a written response and then ask if the students could explain to their neighbors *why* the distance is only 5 m rather than 10 m. [In free fall, the object does not maintain a speed of 10 m/s throughout the second of fall. Its average speed during this time is only 5 m/s, where $v_{ave} = (v_f + v_i)/2$.] Point out that the relation $d = vt$ only holds when v is the *average* speed or velocity.

[**Transparency 3**, showing Table 2.3 and Figure 2.10 should be shown here.]

Table 2-3: Treat the check questions and answers, pages 19 and 20 of the text. Then direct attention to Table 2.3 on page 20. Be sure your students see the difference between this table (which is about distance of free fall) and Table 2.2 (which is about speed of free fall). You may or may not deem it profitable to derive on the board $d = 1/2\ gt^2$, as is done in the footnote on page 20. (I usually do so, and say that the derivation is a sidelight to the course — something that would be the crux of a follow-up physics course. In any event, the derivation is not something that I expect of them, but is to show that $d = 1/2\ gt^2$ is a reasoned statement that doesn't just pop up from nowhere.)

CHECK QUESTION: How far will a freely falling object that is released from rest, fall in 2 seconds? In 10 seconds? (When your class is comfortable with this, then ask how far in 1/2 second.) [20 m, 500 m, 5/4 m.]

To avoid information overload, I restrict all numerical examples of free fall to cases that begin at rest. Why? Because it's simpler that way. (I prefer my students understand simple physics than be confused about not-so-simple physics!) If you wish to go further, then consider nonzero initial speed.

CHECK QUESTION: Consider a rifle fired straight downward from a high-altitude balloon. If the muzzle velocity is 100 m/s and air resistance can be neglected, what is the *acceleration* of the bullet after one second? [If most of your class say that its g, you're on!]

(What I do *not* do is ask for the time of fall for a freely-falling object, given the distance. Why? Unless the distance given is the familiar 5 meters, algebraic manipulation is called for. If one of my teaching objectives were to teach algebra, this would be a nice place to do it. But I don't have time for presenting this stumbling block and then teaching how to overcome it. I'd rather put my energy *and theirs* into straight physics!)

Nonzero Initial Speed:

CHECK QUESTION: Consider a rifle fired straight downward from a high-altitude balloon. If the muzzle velocity is 100 m/s and air resistance can be neglected, what is the *velocity* of the bullet after one second? [110 m/s]

The three activities at the end of the chapter, page 23 and 24, about measuring speed, and measuring reaction time, are interesting and worthwhile classroom activities. Encourage students to do these either in or out of class.

Again, resist spending too much time on Chapter 2 material. Don't get bogged down here. If most of your class have made the distinction between velocity and acceleration, move on to Newton's laws of motion and the tasty physics that follows.

Hang Time: The box on Hang Time should be fascinating information, especially for your sports-minded students. A widely held misconception is that the great jumpers stay airborne for considerably more than a second. Note that a 2-second hangtime means 1 second up and another 1 second down. How far does an object fall in 1 second? A long 5 meters, or 16 feet! That's quite a jump! Have students calculate their own hang times from measurements of their own personal vertical jumps.

More Think-and-Explain Questions

1. Distinguish between running and walking in terms of contact time on the ground.
   Answer: When walking, one foot is always on the ground. When running, between each bound the feet are off the ground.

2. What is the acceleration of a vehicle that travels at a steady speed of 100 km/hr for 10 seconds?

Explain your answer.
Answer: The acceleration is zero, because no change in motion occurs. (It cannot be overemphasized that many mistakes are made in not carefully reading the question that is asked!)

3. Suppose you stood at the edge of a cliff as in Figure 2.6 and threw a ball straight up with a certain speed. Suppose that you also threw another ball straight down with the same speed. Neglecting air resistance, which ball would have the greater speed in striking the ground below?
Answer: Although the upward-thrown ball will be airborne for a longer time, both balls will strike the ground below with the same speed. When the upward-moving ball returns to its starting point it will have the same downward speed as the ball that is thrown down.

4. If you drop an object in the absence of air resistance, its acceleration toward the ground is 10 m/s^2. If instead you throw it down, will its acceleration immediately after the throw be greater, the same, or less than 10 m/s^2? Explain.
Answer: Although its instantaneous speed is greater at any time by the amount of its initial speed, the acceleration it experiences (a pickup of 10 m/s each second) is the same. (Speed and acceleration are entirely different concepts!)

5. Give an example of an object that has a non-zero velocity and a zero acceleration. Can you give an example of an object that has zero velocity but non-zero acceleration?
Answer: Any object that moves at constant velocity, such as a bowling ball rolling along an alley, has zero acceleration. Any object that moves first in one direction, and then the other, goes through an instant of zero velocity while it is accelerating. A ball thrown upward, for example, comes to a momentary stop, but its state of motion is undergoing a change as it passes through the zero-velocity point. So its velocity is zero and its acceleration is g (this idea will be explained further in Chapter 4).

6. Suppose you are watering a garden, and hold the hose vertically so that the water stream rises 5 meters above the nozzle before falling back. What is the speed of the water as it leaves the nozzle?
Answer: 10 m/s. (The water will fall back a distance of 5 m, which from Table 2-2 is seen to take 1 second. Movement up and movement down are symmetrical (Figure 2.6), so 1 second is required for the water to go from the hose to the 5-m elevation. So the average speed of the water is 5 m/s. This means its initial speed is twice the average, or 10 m/s).

7. Why does a stream of water get narrower as it falls from a faucet?
Answer: The stream picks up speed as it falls, so it "stretches". The volume of water that passes any point per second is the same, so as the water gains speed, the length of the column lengthens and is correspondingly thinner. It soon get so thin that the water breaks up into drops!

8. Two balls are released simultaneously from rest at the left end of the tracks A and B as shown. Which ball reaches the end of its track first?

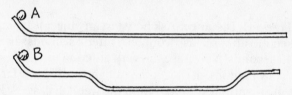

Answer: The ball on B finishes first, for its average speed along the lower part as well as the down and up slopes is greater than the average speed of the ball along track A.

9. What is the impact speed when a car moving at 100 km/h bumps into the rear of another car traveling in the same direction at 98 km/h?
Answer: 2 km/h.

10. It takes about 3 hours for the sun to cross the United States, about 3000 miles. With this information, plus the fact there are 24 hours in a day, how could you estimate the earth's circumference?
Answer: Knowing the "speed" of the sun, and the time it takes to make a complete trip around the world, we multiply speed by time for distance. The sun moves 1000 miles per hour. In 24 hours it moves 24 000 miles, nearly the 25 000-mile circumference of the earth.

More Think and Solves

1. How far will a freely falling object released from rest fall in 1 second? In 2 seconds? In 10 seconds? In 1/2 second? In 1/10 second?
Answer: 5 m, 20 m, 500 m, 1.25 m, 0.05 m (by substitution into $d = 1/2 \ gt^2 = 5t^2$; no answer is complete without units).

2. What will be the speed of a car that accelerates at 2 m/s^2 for 10 seconds from a position of rest?
Answer: 20 m/s (speed = acceleration x time = $[2 \text{ m/s}^2][10 \text{ s}] = 20 \text{ m/s}$).

3. A ball rolls from rest down an inclined plane tilted at 30° to the horizontal and accelerates at 5 m/s^2 to the bottom in 2 seconds. How long is the inclined plane?
Answer: 10 m ($d = 1/2 \ at^2 = 1/2 \ [5 \text{ m/s}^2][2^2] = 10 \text{ m}$)

4. If you throw a ball straight upward at a speed of 10 m/s, how long will it take to reach zero speed? How long will it take to return to its starting point? How fast will it be going when it returns to its starting point?
Answers: 1s; 2s; 10 m/s (Since it loses speed at a rate of 10 m/s each second, it takes 1 second to reach zero speed. The time it takes going up will be equal to the time it takes coming down. And the speed it loses going up will be equal to the speed it gains coming down.)

5. How fast must a ball be thrown straight upward in order that it remain in flight for 10 seconds?
Answer: 50 m/s (Time up = time down, so one way takes 5 seconds. So $v = gt = [10 \text{ m/s}^2][5 \text{ s}] = 50$ m/s. [or, 49 m/s for $g = 9.8 \text{ m/s}^2$]).

6. What is the speed of an apple that falls from a tree to the ground 5 meters below?
Answer: 10 m/s (To fall 5 meters takes 1 second. Then $v = gt = 10 \text{ m/s}^2][1 \text{ s}] = 10$ m/s. [or 9.8 m/s for $g = 9.8 \text{ m/s}^2$]).

7. A dragster going at 15 m/s north increases its velocity to 25 m/s north in 4 seconds. What is its acceleration during this time interval?
Answer: 2.5 m/s^2 (acceleration = [change in velocity]/[time change] = [25 - 15 m/s]/4s = 2.5 m/s^2).

8. A car going at 30 m/s undergoes an acceleration of 2 m/s^2 for 4 seconds. What is its final speed? How far did it travel while it was accelerating?
Answer: Final speed is its initial speed v_0 plus that gained by accelerating. i.e., $v = v_0 + at = 30$ m/s + $[2 \text{ m/s}^2][4 \text{ s}] = [30 + 8]$m/s = 38 m/s. Distance traveled is distance it would have gone in 4 s without accelerating, plus the additional distance $(1/2\ at^2)$ it travels by accelerating. i.e.,
$d = v_0 t + 1/2\ at^2 = [30 \text{ m/s}][4 \text{ s}] + 1/2\ [2 \text{ m/s}^2][4^2]$
= 120 m + 16 m = 136 m.

9. We drive for 1 hour at 20 km/h. Then we drive for 1 hour at 30 km/h. What is our average speed?
Answer: 25 km/h (average speed = distance traveled/time = [20 km + 30 km]/2h = 50 km/2h = 25 km/h).

10. We drive a distance of 1 kilometer at 20 km/h. Then we drive an additional distance of 1 kilometer at 30 km/h. What is our average speed?
Answer: 24 km/h (Note that the time taken to travel the first kilometer is 1/20 hour, and the time to travel the second kilometer is 1/30 hour. So average speed = distance traveled/time = [1 km + 1 km]/[1/20 h + 1/30 h] = 2 km/[(3/60 + 2/60)h] = 2 km/[5/60 h] = 24 km/h. Be careful that you don't simply average numbers when finding average speeds. The key is being sure to consider the time involved!).

3 Projectile Motion

Objectives

- Distinguish between a vector quantity and a scalar quantity, and give examples of each.
- Draw vector diagrams for velocities.
- Use the parallelogram method to find the resultant of two vectors that have different directions.
- Given a vector, resolve it into horizontal and vertical components.
- For a projectile, describe the changes in the horizontal and vertical components of its velocity, when air resistance is negligible.
- Explain why a projectile moves equal distances horizontally in equal time intervals, when air resistance is negligible.

Possible Misconceptions to Correct

- 1 + 1 = 2, always.
- The curved motion of a projectile is very complicated.
- An object at rest will drop to the ground faster than the same object moving horizontally at high speed.
- At the top of its trajectory, the velocity of a projectile is always momentarily zero.

Demonstration Equipment

- [3-1] Sailcart and fan.
- [3-2] Spring gun apparatus to simultaneously project a ball horizontally while dropping another from rest.
- [3-3] Monkey-and-hunter apparatus.

Introduction

Students are introduced to vectors. They are restricted to velocities, and in following chapters they will be applied to forces. A full treatment of vectors is often a formidable stumbling block for students. This chapter does not present vectors in full bloom, but samples only some simple and interesting vector applications. We want students to learn to combine pairs of vectors with the parallelogram rule, and to learn to resolve vectors into components graphically, as featured in Practice Book page 3-1. This way your students should not see the material in this chapter as a stumbling block. Vectors are combined and resolved by the parallelogram rule and no trigonometry is needed. Only the Pythagorean Theorem is used (footnote on page 30, and Practice Book 3-2).

If vector analysis is formidable to your class, consider spending a class period discussing only vector combination, and a different class period discussing vector resolution. A sailboat sailing into the wind demonstration is a fascinating application of vector force resolution (See Appendix C and in Chapter 5, Practice Book page 5-5). Save this for later and concentrate only on velocity vectors at this stage.

The interesting fact that projectiles launched at a particular angle have the same range if launched at the complementary angle is stated without proof in Figure 3.14 on page 37. This fact is a consequence of the range formula, $R = (2v^2\sin\theta\cos\theta)/g$, which is symmetrical for sine and cosine. Since the sine of an angle is the cosine of the complement of that angle, replacing the angle with its complement will give the same range. So the range is the same whether aiming at θ or at $(90° - \theta)$. Maximum range occurs at a projection angle of 45°, where sine and cosine are equal.

For your personal information and at the risk of contributing to "information overload" with your students, there is a simple rule for estimating how much less than 45° to project when the landing spot is below the launching elevation, like downhill. Simply subtract *half* the angle of the "incline" from 45°. For example, if the landing spot is 10° below the launch point, project at (45° - 5°) 40° for maximum horizontal displacement. If the landing spot is above the launching point, say uphill, then add half the angle of "incline" above the launch point to 45°. So if your projectile is to land uphill by 10°, launch it at 50°. This rule holds for maximum horizontal distance from launch point to landing point when air resistance is not important. This and other interesting tidbits about the projectile motion of baseballs, footballs, and Frisbees, can be found in the delightful book, *Sport Science*, by Peter J. Brancazio (Simon & Schuster, 1984).

Bull's Eye is a very-well liked lab experiment and can be done here. However, consider doing it after you've covered Newton's laws.

Suggested Lectures

Begin by calling attention to the fact that on a windy day one can run faster when running with the wind rather than against the wind. Similarly, a plane is often late or early in arriving at its destination due to wind conditions. Flying with the wind results in an increase in ground speed. Represent speed with arrow. Since you are representing magnitude by the length of the arrow, and direction by the arrowhead, you are now talking about velocity — a vector quantity. Discuss Figure 3.2 and variations of wind conditions that are only with or against the motion of the aircraft. Parallel this with a similar treatment of boats sailing with and against the stream.

> CHECK QUESTION: How fast would an airplane move over the ground if it had an airspeed of 100 km/h when flying headwind into a strong gale of 100 km/h? [It would have a ground speed of zero (like birds are often seen to have when facing into a strong wind).]

[**Transparency 4**, Figures 3.2 and 3.3 here]

[**Next-Time Question 3-2** here]

Vectors at an Angle: Continue with the airplane and wind, and consider a wind at right-angles to the nose of the plane, as shown in Figure 3.3. Ask if a crosswind will speed up an airplane, slow it down, or have no effect. (This is Next-Time Question 3-2.) Don't be surprised when many in your class say "no effect." Logic leads to this wrong answer. Here is where vectors are NEEDED. At this point introduce the parallelogram rule. Only consider 90 degree cases, and invoke the Pythagorean Theorem — like 3-4-5 triangles for a start. After discussing the geometry of the square in Figure 3.5, follow up with a boat sailing across a stream, and ask:

> CHECK QUESTION: How fast will a boat that normally travels 10 km/h in still water be moving with respect to land if it sails directly across a stream that flows at 10 km/h? [14.14 km/h.]

Non-Right-Angled Vectors: Consider an airplane flying sideways to a wind that does not meet it at 90 degrees. The Pythagorean Theorem cannot be used for non-right angle situations — at least not directly. More analysis is called for. Introduce the technique of parallelogram construction, first for rectangles as in Figure 3.4, and then for vectors like those of Practice Book 3-2, page 9. Check their work before going further.

Physics of Sports — Surfing: This feature on page 32 can be further explained as follows. Hold a meter stick at an angle of about 30° or so above your table. Slowly lower the stick, maintaining its angle, so that it misses the table's edge. Ask your class to note the point of "contact" of the stick with the table — the point that moves horizontally across the surface as the stick is lowered. Ask for a comparison of the speed of the stick and the speed of the point. They should see the point moves about twice as fast. Tip the stick to about 10° with the horizontal and repeat. The point moves faster. Similarly for the surfer who angles across the crest of a moving wave!

(This is a good break point.)

Projectile Motion: Discuss the idea of the "downwardness" of gravity, and how there is no "sidewaysness" to it. Consider a bowling ball rolling along a bowling alley: gravity pulls it downward, completely perpendicular to the alley with no horizontal component of force, even if it rolls off the edge of the alley like a ball rolling off a tabletop. Pose the situation of the horizontally-held gun and the shooter who drops a bullet at the same time he pulls the trigger, and ask which bullet hits the ground first. [Neglecting the earth's curvature, both hit the ground at the same time.]

> DEMONSTRATION [3-2]: Show the independence of horizontal and vertical motions with a spring-gun apparatus that will shoot a ball horizontally while at the same time dropping another that falls vertically. If you don't have such an apparatus, place a coin at the edge of a table and slide another coin across the tabletop to knock it off. The struck coin should fly across the room while the other coin more or less falls straight downward. Students will see that they hit the floor at the same time. Then announce, "Gravity does not take a holiday on moving objects."

Independence of Horizontal and Vertical Motion: Ask for an explanation of how the photograph in Figure 3.14 was taken. [A strobelight was flashed in rapid bursts in a dark room while the device dropped one ball while projecting the other horizontally. The photo was taken by a camera with its shutter held open during this time.] Compare the downward motions of each ball, and note they are the same. Investigate the sideways motion of the projected ball and see that it moves equal horizontal distances in equal times. Here we see the law of inertia at play, and we have not gotten that far at this point. Simply state that objects moving in the absence of a force in the direction of motion, keep moving in that direction, and this will be treated in detail in the next chapter.

CHECK QUESTION: How is the horizontal component of motion affected by the vertical component of motion? [It isn't! The horizontal and vertical components of motion are independent of each other.]

Point to some target at the far side of your classroom and ask your class to imagine you are going to project a rock to the target via a slingshot. Ask if you should aim directly at the target, above it, or below it. Easy stuff. Then ask your class to suppose it takes 1 second for the rock to reach the target. If you aim directly at the target, it will fall beneath and miss. How far beneath, if the floor weren't in the way? Do a neighbor check on this question. When the class agrees it is 5 meters, ask how far above should you aim to hit the target. [The same 5 m.] After another neighbor check you're ready to discuss Figure 3.10 on page 35.

[**Transparency 5**, Figure 3.10 here]

Upwardly-Moving Projectiles: Investigate Figure 3.10 on page 35. Call attention to the vertical distances fallen and Table 2.3 back on page 20 (the same physics of free fall, only "stretched out horizontally").

DEMONSTRATION [3-3]: Perform the famous "Monkey and Hunter Demonstration" if available. An alternative is showing the same sequence with a crossbow from the old PSSC film, *Projectile Motion.*

[**Next-Time Question 3-1** is a version of the "monkey and hunter" demo]

CHECK QUESTION: If the cannon were aimed downward instead of upward in Figure 3.10, how would the distances below the new "dashed line" compare? [The projectile displacements below the dashed line would be no different; 5 m at the end of the 1st second, 20 m at the end of the 2nd second, and so on.

[**Practice Book 3-1** develops the concept shown in Figure 3.10]

[**Transparency 6**, Figure 3.10 here]

Investigate the relative vectors in Figure 3.11. Note how the horizontal component doesn't change (because no horizontal force acts). Note how the vertical component does change (going

upward against gravity, then downward with gravity). Note the same is true of the steeper angle of Figure 3.12.

CHECK QUESTIONS: True or False? The velocity of projectile at its highest point is zero. [False, the vertical component of velocity is zero at the highest point, not the velocity itself (unless it is projected straight upward).] What can be said of the velocity of the projectile at its highest point? [At its highest point and neglecting air resistance, the velocity of a projectile will be the same as its horizontal component of velocity at any other point.]

Projectile Ranges: The equal ranges for projectiles launched at complementary angles is quite interesting. Leave it at that for now. The explanation has to do with sine and cosine trig functions, so let that wait until a future physics course (save and direct your students' banks of gray matter to more fertile ground).

CHECK QUESTION: To direct water to flowers that are farthest away, at what angle should a water hose be held? [Ideally $45°$, and somewhat less if you're holding it high off the ground.]

[**Next-Time Question 3-3** is a range problem]

Air Resistance: Acknowledge the large effect that air resistance (air drag) has on the foregoing analysis, particularly for fast-moving objects such as bullets and cannonballs. A batted baseball, for example, travels only about 60 percent as far in air as it would in a vacuum. It's curved path is no longer a parabola, as Figure 3.15 indicates.

Hang Time Again: Ask if one could jump higher if on a moving skateboard. Or in a moving bus. It should be clear that the answer is no. But one can usually jump higher from a running jump. It is a mistake to assume that the horizontal motion is responsible for the higher jump and longer hang time. The action of running likely enables a greater force between the foot and floor, which gives a greater vertical lift off component of velocity. This greater bound against the floor, and not any holiday by gravity on a horizontally moving body, is the explanation. Stress that the vertical component of velocity alone determines vertical height and hang time.

Satellite Motion: When the earth's curvature is taken into account, and the launch speed is great enough, a projectile can become an earth satellite. Time permitting, you can end your lecture by acknowledging this fact. The physics is summed up in the comic strip, "Satellite Physics," ahead on page 39. Done properly you can delightfully tease your class with the interesting physics that is yet to come!

More Think-and-Explain Questions

1. Suppose you jump straight upward while in a train traveling 200 km/hr on straight track. Where will you land—at the same place, in front, or in back of your jumping place?
Answer: Same place, for your horizontal motion is the same as that of the train—whether you're on the floor or jumping above it. We'll see in the next chapter that this idea is encapsulated in the law of inertia.

2. Why does vertically falling rain make slanted streaks on the side windows of a moving automobile? If the streaks make an angle of 45°, what does this tell you about the relative speeds of the car and falling rain?
Answer: The rain has a horizontal component of motion *relative to the moving car*, which when combined with their vertical motion produces the slanted streaks. 45° means the speeds of the rain and car are the same.

3. A newspaper boy walks a series of 100-m city blocks. His route takes him 5 blocks east, then 3 blocks north, then 4 blocks west, and finally 2 blocks south. How far away is he from his starting point?
Answer: 141.4 m (his total east-west distance is 5 - 4 = 1 block east. His total north-south distance is 3 - 2 = 1 block north. This puts him one diagonal block north-east from his starting point, 141.4 m. We say his *displacement* is 141.4 m, quite different than his total walking distance of 1400 m).

4. Harry Hotshot can paddle a canoe in still water at 8 km/h. How successful will he be at canoing upstream in a river that flows at 8 km/h?
Answer: Harry will be unsuccessful because his speed relative to the bank will be zero.

More Think and Solves

1. Harry Hacker is playing shuffleboard on an ocean liner that travels due north at 3 m/s on the blue Caribbean. He makes a starboard shot (toward the east), relative to the deck, of 4 m/s. What is the velocity of the puck relative to the stationary stars?
Answer: 5 m/s in a north-easterly direction (37 degrees east of north, to be exact. The path of the puck makes the hypotenuse of a 3,4,5 right triangle).

2. John and Tracy look from their 80-m high-rise balcony to a swimming pool below — not directly below, but 20 m from the bottom of their building. They wonder how fast they would have to jump horizontally to succeed in reaching the pool. What is the answer?
Answer: At least 5 m/s, because they have 4 seconds to fall while they are moving horizontally. [An 80-m drop requires 4 s. We see this from the equation for falling distance, $80 = 1/2 \, gt^2$, $t = \sqrt{2(80)/g} = \sqrt{160/10} = 4$ s.] Then horizontal speed = (horizontal distance)/time = 20 m/4 s = 5 m/s. This would put them at the pool's close edge, so slightly more than 5 m/s is needed for success.

3. If the pool in the above question is 20 m long, estimate John's and Tracy's upper limit of initial horizontal velocity for success?
Answer: About 9 m/s. If they jumped twice as fast, 10 m/s, they would go twice as far in the same time and land 40 m from the building, at the far edge of the pool. Ouch! Even a meter from the edge would put them in trouble, 2 m may work, and 4 m would be more sensible. This puts the horizontal distance at 36-m. Then initial horizontal speed = 36 m/4 s = 9 m/s. (Likelihood of overshooting the pool is small compared to whether they can muster the 5+ m/s to reach the near-side of the pool. Better to do this high jump in safer territory!)

4. A cannonball shot with an initial velocity of 141 m/s at an angle of 45° follows a parabolic path and hits a balloon at the top of its trajectory. Neglecting air resistance, how fast is it going when it hits the balloon? What is the acceleration of the cannonball just before it hits the balloon?
Answer: 100 m/s; g. At the top of its trajectory, the vertical component of velocity is zero, leaving only the horizontal component. The horizontal component at the top or anywhere along the path is the same as the initial horizontal component, 100 m/s [the side of a square where the diagonal is 141]. The acceleration at the top or at any other point along the path is that due to gravity, g.

In your teaching, it's better to be a guide on the side than a sage on the stage!

4 Newton's First Law of Motion—Inertia

Objectives

- Describe Aristotle's concepts of natural motion and violent motion.
- Describe Copernicus' idea about the earth's motion.
- Describe Galileo's contribution to the science of motion.
- Define inertia.
- State Newton's first law of motion.
- Distinguish among mass, volume, and weight.
- Distinguish between the kilogram and the newton as units of measurement.
- Explain how something that is not connected to the ground is able to keep up with the moving earth.
- Explain why a clothesline or wire that can easily support an object when strung vertically may break when strung horizontally and supporting the same object.
- For an object on a slope, resolve its weight into a component that causes acceleration along the slope and a component that presses it against the slope.

Possible Misconceptions to Correct

- Constant motion requires a force.
- Even if no force acts on a moving object, it will eventually stop.
- Inertia is a force.
- Weight and mass are two names for the same thing.
- Mass and volume are two names for the same thing.
- The tension in a string that supports a load is generally equal to the weight of the load.

Demonstration Equipment

- [4-1] Coathanger and clay blobs (pictured on next page).
- [4-2] Wooden block stapled to piece of cloth.
- [4-3] Tablecloth (without a hem) and set of cheap dishes.
- [4-4] Massive ball with hooks for strings above and below.
- [4-5] Hammer and massive wooden block.
- [4-6] Hammer and same wooden block.
- [4-7] Wooden dowel that snugly fits in wooden block (see sketch).
- [4-.8] Metal hoop and jar (see sketch).
- [4-9] A pair of scales, string, and a mass of 1 kg or so.
- [4-10] A heavy chain, several meters long.

Introduction

A historical perspective is used to introduce the concept of inertia in this chapter. Historical figures are Aristotle, Copernicus, Galileo, and Newton. If you're a science-history buff you should consider amplifying the small amount of history in this text.

The videotape, *Inertia*, of the *Conceptual Physics Alive!* series goes with this chapter. The basic ideas of the chapter are covered, with some demonstrations that are not so easily done in class — such as banging on large blocks of wood and iron, and showing the inertia of a massive anvil on your stomach that is hit with a sledgehammer. You may show this tape as your lecture of the chapter, for it covers the material enough to allow devoting more of your time and effort to discussion, and to lab preparation.

Practice Book page 4-3 distinguishes between force and velocity vectors.

Before you treat Section 4.8 have your class do the activity *24-Hour Towing Service*. If you want to cover vectors extensively, continue to Appendix C and if you didn't do so for the previous chapter, demonstrate a sailboat sailing into the wind. This is a fascinating and powerful demonstration of vector resolution. Do this with a sailcart, preferably on an air track (as in the lab *Riding With the Wind*).

Suggested Lecture

The Old Idea That Constant Motion Needs a Force: Begin by pointing to an object in the room and stating that if it started moving, one would reasonably look for a cause for its motion. We would say that a force, a push or a pull of some kind, was responsible. It doesn't seem that things move of themselves. Only living things do that. A cannonball remains at rest in the cannon until a force is applied, and the force of expanding gases drives the ball out of the barrel when the cannon is fired. But what keeps the ball moving when the expanding gases no longer act on it? This leads to a discussion of inertia. In the everyday sense, inertia refers to a habit or a rut. In physics it's another word for laziness, or the resistance to change as far as the state of motion of an object is concerned. Roll the ball along the lecture table to show its tendency to keep rolling. Inertia was first introduced by Galileo's with his inclined plane experiments.

Aristotle and Galileo: Contrast Aristotle's and Galileo's way of looking at motion — Aristotle's classification of natural and violent motion, and Galileo's idea of inertia — that objects once set in motion *do* continue moving without added effort. This is easy to understand when air resistance and other factors are not part of the situation, as happens in outer space. It's easier to visualize the unchanging motion of a ball thrown in outer space than at the earth's surface (it may curve in outer space also, due to gravity, but there is no air resistance to affect its motion).

Law of Inertia: Do the following demonstration before stating the law of inertia :

DEMONSTRATION [4-1] : Do as Jim Szeszol does and fashion a wire coat hanger into an m shape as shown. Two globs of clay (or any massive material) are stuck to each end. Balance it on your head, with one glob in front of your face. State you wish to view the other glob and ask how you can do so without touching the apparatus. Then simply turn around and there it is! It's like the bowl of soup you turn only to find the soup stays put. Inertia in action!

State the law of inertia for objects in the rest case, and then do the following demonstrations:

DEMONSTRATION [4-2]: Place a wooden block on a piece of cloth and ask what will happen to the block if you pull suddenly on the cloth (the old table-cloth-and-dishes trick). But for humor have the cloth stapled to the block beforehand. Then you're illustrating Newton's "zeroeth" law: Be skeptical!

DEMONSTRATION [4-3]: The classic tablecloth demo complete with dishes. It is important to pull slightly downward when you whip the table cloth from beneath the dishes. This insures that the cloth moves horizontally. Even the slightest upward component produces disaster. Even though your students may know what to expect, it is nevertheless well worth your while to do this. Seeing it live, and by you, is a delight!

(Of course when we show a demonstration to illustrate a particular concept, there is almost always more than one concept involved. The tablecloth demo is no exception, which also illustrates impulse and momentum (Chapter 7 stuff). The plates experience two impulses; one that first involves the friction between the cloth and dishes, which moves them slightly toward you. It is brief and very little momentum builds up. Once the dishes are no longer on the cloth, a second impulse occurs due to friction between the dishes and table, which acts in a direction away from you and prevents the dishes from sliding toward you. This brief impulse brings the dishes to rest. Done quickly, the brief displacement of the dishes is hardly noticed. Is inertia really at work here? Yes, for if there were no friction in the demo, the dishes would strictly remain at rest.

Mass vs. Volume: Distinguish also between mass and volume. Cite an automobile battery and a fluffy king-size pillow as examples. Mass is not volume, as Figure 4.8 in the text illustrates.

Mass vs. Weight: Distinguish between mass and weight. Mass is more fundamental, meaning that it has only to do with matter and not on any external gravity. Weight is the force due to earth gravity on an object and depends on both. In a region where there is negligible gravity, there is negligible weight. But objects there still have mass. A useful way to impart the distinction between the two is to place two objects of about equal mass in the hands of a student. Ask the student to judge which is heavier. If the student responds by shaking the objects back and forth, one in each hand, point out that the student is unconsciously comparing their *inertias*, and is making use of the intuitive notion that mass and weight are directly proportional. In the same part of the earth's gravitational field, twice the mass also has twice the weight. But this does not mean that mass is weight. (Twice as much sugar has twice the sweetening power, but this does not mean that sugar *is* sweetening power. Sugar *has* sweetening power, just as mass *has* weight in a gravitational field.)

DEMONSTRATION [4-4]: Perform the activity described in Think-and-Explain #6 on page 57 of the text, and shown in the sketch. Ask for predictions and then show that the bottom string breaks when it is jerked, and the top string breaks when the bottom string is gradually pulled harder. Ask for the explanation, and use the "neighbor check" routine. [The answer is that the slow pull demonstrates the role of weight, for there is tension in the top string even before the added pull of your hand. This tension is increased as you pull down and is greater than the tension in the bottom string. By how much? By the weight of the ball. The quick jerk, on the other hand, demonstrates inertia, for the ball resists the sudden downward acceleration asked for by the lower string.]

DEMONSTRATION [4-5]: Place a massive block on your hand and strike it with a hammer blow. You are not hurt, because of the mass of the block. Or do as I do in the videotape — place an anvil on your stomach and invite a skillful person to whap it with a sledgehammer. In any event, be sure to show the relationship of this demo to the previous demonstration of the suspended ball and strings.

Emphasize the motion part of Newton's first law; that moving things continue at constant velocity in the absence of a force.

DEMONSTRATION [4-6]: Show how you tighten the hammerhead of a hammer (Figure B of Think-and-Explain #7 on page 58 of the text) — not by banging the head against a solid surface, but by banging the handle, as shown in the sketch. Why? Because the massive head remains in motion, nestling it tighter on the handle.

Shorter at Night: Relate the idea of tightening the hammer head with the bones of the human spine, and as a result of jostling throughout the day, we are a bit shorter at night. The bones of the spine settle closer together, enough to be noticeable! Ask your students to find a place in their homes that is just out of reach with upstretched hands before they retire for the night. Then tell them to try again when they arise the next morning. They can't help but appreciate physics when they find that they can touch the place that was out of reach the night before! (Astronauts returning from orbit are more than an inch taller, for the same reason — the absence of a force compressing an otherwise upright back. Short people trying to qualify for a minimum

height have been known to stay in bed for days before having their height measured.)

DEMONSTRATION [4.7]: Follow the hammer bit with a broom handle or wooden dowel that fits rather snugly in a hole through a few-kilogram wooden block. When held as shown, they stay together due to friction. Strike the top of the dowel with a hammer and viola, the block climbs the handle! The block tends to stay put while the handle suddenly moves downward. More inertia in action.

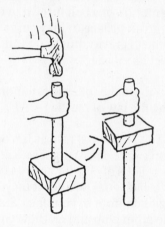

DEMONSTRATION [4.8]: Do as Marshall Ellenstein does and place a metal hoop atop a narrow jar. On top of the hoop balance a piece of chalk. Then whisk the hoop away and the chalk falls neatly into 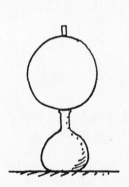 the narrow opening. The key here is grabbing the hoop on the inside, on the side farthest from your sweep. This elongates the hoop horizontally and the part that supports the chalk drops from beneath the chalk. (If you grab the hoop on the near side, the elongation will be vertical and pop the chalk up into the air!)

[**Next-Time Questions** 3-1 and 3-2 treat motion in a straight line]

Motion Without Force: Ask what the motion would be of a ball tossed in empty space, practically away from gravity and other forces? [straight-line path at constant speed] Ask what two words say the same thing as "straight-line path at constant speed?" [constant velocity] Consider a rock swinging in a circle at the end of a string; what is the path of the rock when the string breaks? [A straight line, except for the influence of gravity. Note that before the string breaks, the rock swings at constant *speed*, not constant *velocity*. It is accelerating nonetheless for it is changing the direction part of velocity. We'll return to this idea in Chapter 9.]

[**Transparencies 7 and 8**, Figure 4.10 on net forces here, followed by Figures 4.13 and 4.14]

Net Force and Equilibrium: Introduce the idea of net force by placing an object on your table and pushing it. Neglecting friction, if you push it to the right with 10 N, state that the net force is 10 N. Ask what the net force would be if a student simultaneously pushed it to the left with 10 N. [0]. With 4 N? [6 N to the right]. State that the block would accelerate no differently if pushed with the two forces that produce a 6-N net force, and a single applied 6-N force. The two are equivalent.

[**Practice Book 4-3b** on page 16 nicely treats net force, extending it to forces at right angles.]

[**Next-Time Question 3-3** treats friction]

DEMONSTRATION [4-9]: Set up a pair of scales that support a heavy weight (a 1-kg mass is fine) as shown (refers to Figure 4.13 on page 53). Show that as the supporting angle increases, the tension also increases.

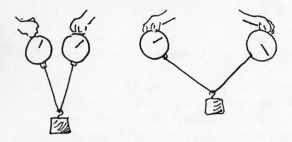

Figure 4.14 Explanation: Explain why the tension increases with increasing angle; that the resultant of tensions in each strand must combine to a vector equal and opposite the weight vector. Carefully explain Figure 4.13.

DEMONSTRATION [4-10]: Have two students hold the ends of a heavy chain. Ask them to pull it horizontally to make it as straight as possible. Then ask what happens if a bird comes along and sits in the middle (as you place a 1-kg hook mass on the middle of the chain!) What happens if another bird comes to join the first (as you hang another 1-kg mass). Ask the students to keep the chain level. Now what happens if a flock of birds join the others (as you hang additional masses). This works well! (Note that this parallels the lab *24-Hour Towing Service*.)

Relate this to the Questions on page 54, and why there is always a sag, however slight, in a horizontally stretched rope or wire. Why? Because the

weight of the rope or wire must be matched by upward components of the tension along the rope or wire. The rope or wire must be directed slightly upward to provide the needed vertical component to offset the weight. This is reinforced in Practice Page 4-2b.

Vectors: Practice Book 4-3, page 13, makes the important distinction between force and velocity vectors for the same situation — a ball tossed into the air. Net force and resultant vectors are on Practice Book 4-3b, page 14.

Moving Earth: Stand next to a wall on the west-side of your classroom. State that relative to the sun, the wall and the whole room is traveling at about 30 km/s, toward the east. Aristotle's followers would say that you move at 30 km/s also because you are standing on the moving floor. Now jump up. Ask why the wall didn't slam into you. After all, you can say, when you are no longer "attached" to the moving floor — there is no force making you travel along with the moving floor. Let your class discuss this before you point out that this is simply the bird and worm example discussed and answered in Section 4.8 in the chapter. Interestingly enough, Johannes Kepler didn't accept the notion that the earth turns on a daily axis. He reasoned that if it did, cannonballs shot east and west would have different ranges. Pose this to your class for discussion.

More Think-and-Explain Questions

1. Johannes Kepler, famous astronomer of the early 17th Century, did not believe the earth spins on its axis and cited the argument that if the earth did spin, then cannonballs shot eastward would travel farther than cannonballs shot westward. Discuss this argument.
   Answer: Kepler was not aware of the law of inertia, or at least didn't apply it to this situation. The cannonball at rest in the cannon has the same speed as the earth's surface at that point. Its firing speed is relative to the moving earth, so there would be practically no difference in range whether the cannonball were fired east, west, north or south. (For longer-range cannons after Kepler's time, some effect does occur — the Coriolis Effect.)

2. If you're playing catch with a friend in the aisle of a fast-moving airplane that travels at constant velocity, in which (if any) direction does the ball gain more speed due to the plane's motion?
   Answer: The speed of the ball is relative to the frame of reference of the throwers, who are in the frame of reference of the moving craft. The speed of the ball relative to the throwers has nothing to

do with the speed of the craft. Tossing the ball on an airplane that moves at constant velocity is no different than tossing the ball while the plane is at rest. Newton's first law: a body in motion remains in motion in the absence of an outside force. The only outside force that acts is gravity, which is the same whether the plane moves or not.

3. Your empty hand is not harmed if it bangs lightly against a wall, but is harmed if your are carrying a heavy load. Why so?
Answer: A heavy load has a lot of mass, that once in motion has a lot of tendency to remain in motion. More force is required to stop more mass so your unfortunate hand is squashed.

4. Does a person diet to lose *mass* or to lose *weight*?
Answer: A person diets to lose mass. One loses weight whenever gravity is reduced, like being on the surface of the moon. Even with less weight on the moon, an obese person is still obese.

5. When and where can a 1-kg mass weight more than a 2-kg mass?
Answer: Where gravity is suffcently less, like on the moon.

6. How does a car headrest help to guard against whiplash in a rear-end collision?
Answer: In a rear end collision your head tends to stay put while you body is pushed forward by the seat. Relative to your body, your head "whips" back. The headrest extends the seat up to your head and keeps your head and body together.

7. Can the force of gravity on a 1-kilogram mass ever be more than on a 2-kilogram mass? Defend your answer.
Answer: Yes, for example, the force of gravity on a 1-kg mass on the surface of the earth is considerably more than on a 2-kg mass on the surface of the moon (actually three times as much).

8. A car at a junk yard is compressed until its volume is less than 1 cubic meter. Has its mass changed? Has its weight changed? Explain.
Answer: Neither its mass nor its weight changes when it has been compressed, because the same quantity of matter is present. Only its volume is less.

9. If you jump up in bus that is moving at constant velocity, will you land farther back? Explain.
Answer: No, you will land as you would if the bus were at rest. The explanation is that you are moving with the bus before, during, and after your jump. In accord with Newton's lst law, a body in motion remains in motion unless acted upon by a force. There is no horizontal force on you during your jump, so you simply continue moving with the bus. (If the bus accelerates while you are in the air, you land in a different place.)

10. If the first law is really a description of nature, why do moving things in our environment eventually slow down?
Answer: Moving objects slow down because of forces, usually friction.

More Think and Solves

1. An average apple weighs about 1 newton. What is its mass?
Answer: [1/10] kg (1 kg weighs about 10 newtons, so we find: 1 kg/10N = x/1N; where x = 1 kg 1N/ 10N = [1/10] kg. At sea level on the earth's surface, 1 kg more precisely weighs 9.8 N. In the next chapter we will see that Weight = mg.)

2. Find your weight on a bathroom scale and compute your mass in kilograms. If the scale reads pounds, compute your weight in newtons.
Answer: Each kg weighs about 2.2 lb, or 10 N. So divide your weight in pounds by 2.2 and you have the number of kilograms. Multiply the number of kilograms by 10 (or 9.8) and you have your weight in newtons. (This simple but very good activity helps to distinguish between mass and weight).

3. A firefighter who weighs 300 N slides down a pole at constant velocity. What is the friction force that acts on her?
Answer: She slides at constant velocity, because net force on her is zero, which means the force of friction exactly balances her weight — 300 N.

4. A refrigerator is pushed at constant velocity across the kitchen floor with a force of 200 N. What is the force of friction acting on the frig?
Answer: 200 N, to give a net force of zero.

5 Newton's Second Law— Force and Acceleration

Objectives

- Define and explain net force.
- State the relation between acceleration and net force.
- State the relation between acceleration and mass.
- Distinguish between the concepts of *directly proportional* and *inversely proportional.*
- State and explain Newton's second law of motion.
- Describe the effect of friction on a stationary and on a moving object.
- Distinguish between force and pressure.
- Apply Newton's second law to explain why the acceleration of an object in free fall does not depend upon the mass of the object.
- Describe what happens to the acceleration and the speed of a falling object when there is air resistance.

Possible Misconceptions to Correct

- If an object has zero acceleration, it must be at rest.
- Pressure and force are the same.
- Heavy objects always fall faster than light objects.
- Objects have no weight in a vacuum.

Demonstration Equipment

- [5-1] Spool and string.
- [5-2] Cart pull [same apparatus of the lab experiment *Constant Force and Changing Mass* .

Introduction

Acceleration and inertia, as introduced in previous chapters, are further developed and are related to force in this chapter. Falling objects, introduced in Chapter 2, are given in more detail in this chapter.

Avoid placing too much emphasis on unit analysis. Don't get bogged down with the unit relationships N = kg m/s^2 and m/s^2 = N/kg. Belaboring these can be counterproductive, and is best emphasized later — after concepts are understood and problem solving is needed. Present effort is better placed on building a savy of Newton's 2nd law with interesting examples.

Magnitudes can be presented on a chalkboard by exaggerating the sizes of mathematical symbols rather than plugging in numerical quantities. This is shown on pages 66 and 88, and in other chapters. Rather than writing "change in," for equations on the board, introduce the symbol Δ, if you have not already done so. This is done in the footnote of page 59.

For your information, the terminal speed for a skydiver is about 60 m/s (215 km/h or 134 mi/h), for a baseball about 42 m/s (150 km/h or 95 mi/h), and for a Ping-Pong ball about 9 m/s (32 km/h or 21 mi/h). Students can drop Ping-Pong balls from small to large elevations and observe the height of rebound after bouncing on the floor. Beyond a certain elevation the balls bounce no higher, indicating they have reached their terminal speed!

Friction is treated briefly. An extended discussion is in *Slip and Stick* in the Laboratory manual.

Precede your lecture with *Getting Pushy*, and follow up with both *Constant Force* and *Changing Mass and Constant Mass and Changing Force,* which are a two-part sequence. *Impact Speed* is the most advanced experiment in the manual and is meant for your very best students. If you are into computers, this special topic can be pursued with the LaserPoint computer program *Impact Speed,* which introduces the idea of area under the curve and sets the stage for integral calculus. Do not use *Impact Speed,* either lab experiment or computer program, with students who are finding physics difficult. It will further overwhelm them. Your whiz kids will eat it up.

Suggested Lecture

Review Acceleration: Begin by reviewing examples of acceleration and its definition. Ask how one produces the acceleration of an object. Write the idea that acceleration is imposed by an impressed force; $a \sim F$, and give examples of doubling and tripling the impressed force and the subsequent doubling and tripling of acceleration.

Review Net Force: Push your book across the table with just enough force so that it slides at constant velocity. Ask for the net force in this case? [0 N]. Then state that if you pushed with 5 N, what would be the friction force? [5 N in the opposite direction] It is the net force that accelerates things.

[**Practice Book 5-1** develops friction, and the concept of the normal force.]

[**Practice Book pages 5-3, 5-4, and 5-5** treat vectors. Note that coordinate systems are minimized, and the parallelogram rule used. One important concept they emphasize is that acceleration is always in the direction of the net (resultant) force.]

DEMONSTRATION [4-1]: Place a spool of string or thread on your table, with the string wrapped over the top of the spindle. Pull the string horizontally toward you and nobody is surprised to see that it rolls toward you. You state that Newton said that the net force and acceleration would always be in the same direction. Then place the spool so the string comes from the bottom (as shown). Ask in which direction will the spool roll. [The spool will roll toward you (providing your pull is horizontal) whether the string is wrapped over the top or under the bottom of the spindle. You can either show this also on your chalkboard by the sequence of sketches shown — or resist the temptation to show your class, and ask them to try it at home — for extra credit!]

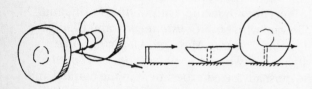

Sign-Painter Skit: Draw the sketch shown on the board. It shows two painters on a painting rig suspended by two cables. Step 1: If both painters have the same weight, and each stands next to each cable, the tension forces in the cables will be equal. Ask what the tension in each cable will be in ths case.

[The weight of one man plus half the weight of the rig. Why? Because like the girl in Figure 4.12, the total support force upward must equal the total weight downward.] Step 2: Suppose one painter walks toward the other as shown in the second sketch, which you draw on your chalkboard (or overhead projector). Will the tension in the left cable increase?

[Yes, because the left cable is sharing a greater portion of the total weight.] Will the tension in the right cable decrease? [Yes, because the left cable is doing most of the supporting.] Grand question: Will the tension in the left cable increase exactly as much

as the tension in the right cable decreases? [Yes, the increase in the tension in one cable exactly matches the decrease in the other. This is in accord with Newton's laws; 1st and 2nd. By the 1st, the system at rest means no net force acts on it. Or by the 2nd law of motion, $a = F/m$. Since there is no acceleration of the supported system of rig and painters, the net force acting on the system must be zero. That means the upward support forces balance the downward forces of gravity. So a decrease in the tension of one cable is met with a corresponding increase in the tension of the other, to produce a net force on the system of zero.] (This example is dear to my heart. When I was a signpainter and before I had any training in physics, signpainter Burl Grey posed this question to me. He didn't know the answer, nor did I. That was because neither he nor I had a model for analyzing the problem. We didn't know about Newton's laws, and therefore didn't think in terms of zero acceleration and therefore a corresponding zero net force. How different one's thinking is when one has or does not have a model to guide it. If my friend and I were into pseudo science, we might have been more concerned with the notion of how each cable "knows" about the condition of the other. This is the approach that intrigues many people with a non-scientific view of the world.)

Nonaccelerated Motion: Pull a block across your lecture table with a spring balance so everyone can see how much force you are applying. Pull the block so it slides at constant velocity. Ask for the acceleration? [Zero, as there is no change in its velocity once it is moving steadily.] Ask what the applied force is. [Answer: That showing on the scale.] Ask for the value of the net force acting on the block. [Zero, as evidenced by its nonchanging velocity.] Ask how the net force can be zero. [It is zero because of the friction between the block and the surface of the table.] Ask how much friction force acts on the block. [Equal to the scale reading but oppositely directed.] You are demonstrating the idea of a zero net force on a moving system. Stress the idea that zero acceleration applies both to the state of rest and the state of constant velocity. In both cases, there is no change in the state of motion. This is because in both cases the forces that act on the object balance to zero. Zero net force means zero acceleration. Zero acceleration is evidence of zero net force.

CHECK QUESTION: (as in Question 2 on page 43) Suppose in a high-flying airplane the captain announces over the public address system that the plane is flying at a constant 900 km/h and the thrust of the engines is a constant 80,000 newtons. What is the acceleration of the airplane? [Zero, because velocity is constant.] What is the combined force of air resistance that acts all over the plane's outside surface? [80,000 N, to produce a zero net force. If resistance were less, the plane would speed up; if it were more, the plane would slow down.]

Draw a free-body diagram on the board to illustrate the foregoing.

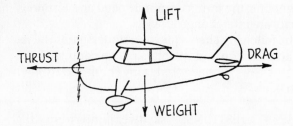

Pressure: Return to the block that you pulled across the table with the spring balance. Drag it with its wide side down, then with its narrow side down, and show that the force required to pull it uniformly across the table is independent of which surface is against the table. Lead to the idea that in both cases the weight of the block against the table is the same, but the *distribution of weight* is different. Define pressure. Conclude this part of your lecture with examples (sharp points versus blunt surfaces, being stuck with a boxing glove versus a bare fist, taking too many courses and too many social activities at one time).

(The lab experiment "Inflation" scheduled for Chapter 12 in the lab manual can be moved here if you wish to go further with pressure. It involves computing the weight of a car by measuring the area of contact of its tires on the pavement. This idea with regard to a person's weight is discussed in this chapter on page 65.)

See the bed of nails demo with Paul Robinson in the opening titles of the *Conceptual Physics Alive!* video series, or on Videodisk I of the 2 disk set. In a recent repeat of that demo we've done together for many years, I had to swing harder than before to break the block. Why? Because the blocks are of more sturdy construction following the California earthquakes of the past decade. It is important that the block break, for otherwise Robinson gets more of the hammer's kinetic energy!

Mass: How much acceleration depends on force, which till now has been emphasized. But it also depends on mass.

DEMONSTRATION [4-2]: Compare the accelerations of a large mass and a small mass when impressed upon by equal forces, and bring inertia into the discussion, completing Newton's 2nd law. You might do this with the apparatus for the lab experiments *Constant Force and Changing Mass* and *Constant Mass and Changing Force*.

[**Practice Book 5-2** goes nicely here.]

[**Next-Time Question 5-1** also]

Falling Objects: Drop a book and a sheet of paper to show the different falling rates. Then crumple the piece of paper and show that it and the book accelerate about equally when dropped. State that air resistance for the low speeds involved does not reveal itself in your demonstration. State also that you are not going to talk about the effects of air resistance until you have first investigated the physics that occurs in the absence of air resistance. A too-early preoccupation with air resistance can hide some very basic physics. [Here is where your self discipline may be challenged by an overanxious student who asks questions about air drag anyway. Defer such questions until the simplest case is understood by your class.] State that Galileo, who is reputed to be the first to publicly show equal accelerations for unequal masses, could not adequately explain why. He lacked the model offerred by Newton, namely Newton's 2nd law.

LECTURE SKIT: Parallel the comic strip on page 67 by pretending you are experimenting with two bright youngsters. Hold a kilogram weight and a piece of chalk above your head and ask the class which will hit the ground first if you release them at the same time. [Your class should answer, "the same."] Ask your class to pretend you are asking this question to a youngster who has not been exposed to this idea before. Then carefully articulate a good argument for the heavy weight falling first (as Charles Schultz might have his little characters in "Peanuts" do).[The kilogram is pulled more by gravity than the chalk.] Then go through the motions of asking the same of another child, who responds with a good argument for the chalk hitting first. [The kilogram has more inertia then the chalk, and will take more time to get moving than the chalk.] Summarize the first child's argument by writing on the board, a ~ F, and the second child's argument with, a ~ 1/m. State that the beauty of science is that such speculations can be determined by experiment. Drop the weight and the chalk to show that however sound each child's argument seemed to be, the results do not support either. Then bring both arguments together with a = F/m, Newton's 2nd law. Relate this to the case of the falling cannonball and stone in Figure 5.10.

[**Transparency 9** of Figure 5.10 here]

Falling and Air Resistance: Thus far you have avoided the effects of air resistance in your discussion (if you've been successful in fending off this consideration until after you have discussed the simpler case first — that of free fall). Newton's 2nd law will still be the model for investigating falling in the presence of air resistance. The only difference will be that the net force is not the weight, but the weight minus air resistance (see the TE anno at the top of page 69).

[**Next-Time Questions 5-3, 5-5,** and **5-6** about air drag here]

The "Principle of Exaggeration:" In discussing the effects of air resistance on falling objects, it is useful to exaggerate the circumstance so that the effects are more clearly visualized. For example, in comparing the falls of a heavy and a light skydiver, ask your students to substitute the falling of a feather for the light person, and the falling of a heavy rock for the heavy person. It is easy to see that the air resistance plays a more significant role for the falling feather than for the falling rock. Similarly, but not as much, for the falls of the two skydivers.

Terminal Speed: Discuss Figures 5.11 and 5.12 (the skydivers and the flying squirrel). State that the air resistance that a falling body encounters depends on two things: (1) how big it is, or how big the path of plowed air, like the difference between the air resistance that acts on a flying squirrel and a regular squirrel; and (2) how fast it's going. Ask if anyone has ever put their head out the window of a fast-moving car and noticed that the faster the car, the greater the "wind"? Add that if the speed is great enough the wind will clean the dandruff from one's hair! Air resistance depends on both size and speed. As an object falls faster and faster, there may be a point where the force of air resistance is equal to the weight of the falling body.

CHECK QUESTIONS: When the force of air resistance on a falling object is equal to the object's weight, what will be the net force on the object? [Zero.] What will the acceleration then be? [Zero] Does this mean the falling object comes to an abrupt halt; i.e., that zero acceleration means zero velocity? [No, zero acceleration does not mean zero velocity, but zero CHANGE in velocity.]

Non-Free Fall: Thus far you have dissussed two cases of falling; falling with no air resistance with acceleration g, and falling at a terminal velocity with acceleration zero. Analyzing accelerations between g and zero for falling objects requires more thought. Gauge your class for how far you wish to explore this, the subject matter of the last page of the chapter, page 70. You can either share the anno at the top of page 69 with your class, and direct discussion to this equation, or describe how the net force on a falling object will decrease as air resistance builds up to decrease the accelerating effect of the object's weight. If a skydiver steps from a high-altitude balloon (at rest to reduce the variables involved), she

will initially accelerate downward at g. When she reaches terminal speed, her acceleration will be zero. What happens between the time she first jumps and reaches terminal speed? The answer is, her acceleration must have diminished as she gained speed (and therefore air resistance). (So long as motion is in a straight line, the terms terminal speed and terminal velocity are interchangeable.)

The following check question underscores the fact that acceleration and velocity are two completely different rates. It is adapted from Think and Explain #8 on page 73.

CHECK QUESTIONS: A skydiver jumps from a high-altitude balloon. As she falls faster and faster through the air, does air resistance increase, decrease, or remain the same? [Increase.] Does the net force on her increase, decrease, or remain the same?

[Decrease, because the net force on her is her weight minus air resistance. As air resistance increases, net force decreases.] As she falls faster and faster, does her acceleration increase, decrease, or remain the same? [Acceleration decreases because net force decreases. When she falls fast enough her acceleration will reach zero and she will have reached terminal velocity.

CHECK QUESTION: Which would be more advantageous in a soap-box derby race (where only a component of gravity supplies the acceleration force) — a heavy cart or a light cart? [The heavy cart is more effective in countering air drag. Which would hit ground first if dropped from a high-flying balloon? Similarly for the inclined plane!]

I strongly recommend coverage of the vector treatment of forces that is developed in **Practice Book 5-3 - 5-5**. A fuller treatment of force vectors in Appendix C, which should be read before attempting the sailboat physics of **Practice Book 5-5**.

More Think-and-Explain Questions

1. If it takes 1 N to push horizontally on your book to make it slide at constant velocity, how much is the force of friction on the book?
   Answer: 1 N in the opposite direction to the applied 1-N push.

2. Can we accurately say that if something moves at constant velocity that there no forces acting on it? Explain.
Answer: No, we can only say that the net force is zero. There may be other applied forces equal and opposite to friction, for example.

3. Consider an object that doesn't accelerate when acted on by a force. What inference can be made?
Answer: Another force such as friction must be counteracting the first force.

4. When a car moves along the highway at constant velocity, the net force on it is zero. Why then, does the engine continue to burn fuel?

Answer: The engine burns fuel to supply the force to overcome air resistance and other friction forces that combine to produce the zero net force.

5. What is the net force on an apple that weighs 1 N when it is held at rest above your head? What is the net force on it when released?
Answer: Net force is zero when it is at rest; net force equals 1 N, its weight, when it is in free fall.

6. As you stand on the floor, does the floor exert an upward force against your feet? If so, why are you not moved upward by this force?
Answer: Yes, the floor exerts the upward force on you that prevents you from falling. You are not moved upward by this force because it is balanced by the downward force, your weight.

7. How does the added tension of a 1-kg bird on a horizontally stretched wire compare to the bird's weight?

Answer: If the angle to the horizontal is more than 30°, the tension in the wire is greater than the bird's weight. The smaller the angle, the greater the tension.

8. The monkey is supported by the rope as it pulls horizontally on the chain link fence. Is the rope tension greater to, or less than, or equal to the monkey's weight?

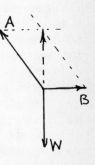

Answer: Rope tension is greater. Three forces act on the monkey, as shown in the vector diagram; rope tension A, fence pull B, and weight W. The resultant of A and B has to have the same magnitude as W for equilibrium. Note in the diagram that A is larger than W.

8. Why is a soft couch more comfortable to sit on?
Answer: Compared to a hard surface, there is more area of contact when sitting on a soft couch. The greater area results in less pressure and more comfort.

9. Why will a heavy tractor sink less deeply in mud than a horse's hoof or people's feet?
Answer: The large tire area of the tires results in less pressure than hoofs or feet.

10. Why is it safer to crawl rather than walk over thin ice on a frozen pond? [10 - 12 cm is thick enough]
Answer: Crawling reduces pressure by increasing area of contact. Less pressure, less chance of breaking through the ice.

11. Why is there no sound of moving air in a high-flying balloon?
Answer: The balloon moves with the air. The sound of wind occurs when there is motion between air and an object.

12. A balloon is carried due west. In which direction will flags on it fly?
Answer: Flags will be limp, because the balloon travels with the wind, with no relative wind for its occupants.

13. How does the weight of a falling object compare to air resistance just before it reaches terminal velocity? How does it compare after it has reached terminal velocity?

Answers: Just before reaching terminal velocity, weight is slightly greater than air resistance, so it is still accelerating. After reaching terminal velocity, air resistance has built up to equal weight, so acceleration becomes zero (terminates).

14. In the absence of air resistance, if a ball is thrown vertically upward with a certain initial speed, on returning to its original level it will have the same speed. Why?
    Answer: It will have the same speed because the "deceleration" while ascending is the same as the acceleration while falling. The speed it loses going upward, is the same as it gains coming down.

15. In the preceding question, if air resistance is a factor, will the speed of the ball reaching the ground be greater than, less than, or the same speed without air resistance?
    Answer: The speed of the ball will be less, because air resistance opposes its motion. This is easy to see with the "principle of exaggeration:" Suppose the ball is a feather cast upward into the air. Its speed is quickly diminished because of air resistance, and it flutters slowly to the ground with much less speed than it began with.

16. In the preceding question, would you expect the time ascending to be greater, less, or the same as the time descending in the presence of air drag.
    Answer: The ball will ascend in less time than it falls. Like the preceding question and answer, this is best seen by the principle of exaggeration. The time for the feather to fall from maximum altitude is clearly longer than the time it took to attain that altitude. The same is true for the not-so-obvious case of the ball.

17. What physics principles are violated in the cartoon below?
    Answer: To begin with, Newton's first law is ignored. Note that the fellow is at rest while the force of gravity is unopposed. It also appears he then suddenly moves downward at great speed, perhaps the speed he has when he meets the ground. Actually speed picks up gradually. But these humorous violations are the province of cartoonists!

More Think and Solves

1. If a 1-N net force accelerates a 1-kg mass at 1 m/s², what is the acceleration of a net force of 2 N on 2 kg?
   Answer: The same; $a = F/m = 2\text{ N}/2\text{ kg} = 1\text{ N}/1\text{ kg} = 1\text{ m/s}^2$.

2. What is the acceleration of a 747 jumbo jet, mass 30,000 kg, in takeoff when the thrust for each of its four engines is 30,000 N?
   Answer: $a = F/m = (4 \times 30,000\text{ N})/30,000\text{ kg} = 4\text{ m/s}^2$.

3. A certain force applied to a 2 kg mass accelerates it at 3 m/s². How much acceleration will the same force produce on a 4-kg mass?
   Answer: The acceleration will be half as much, 1.5 m/s², because the same force acts on twice the mass. $F = ma = (2\text{ kg})(3\text{ m/s}^2) = 6\text{ kg m/s}^2 = 6\text{ N}$. So $a = F/m = 6\text{ N}/4\text{ kg} = 1.5\text{ N/kg} = 1.5\text{ m/s}^2$. [Note that the units check: kg is mass, m/s² is acceleration, and mass x acceleration = force, N. So $(\text{kg m/s}^2) = \text{N}$]

4. An occupant of a car has a chance of surviving a crash if the deceleration is not more than 30 g's. Calculate the force on a 70-kg person at this rate.
   Answer: $F = ma = (70\text{ kg})(30 \times 9.8\text{ m/s}^2) = 20,580\text{ N}$. (This is about 4,620 pounds.)

5. What will be the acceleration of a skydiver when air resistance is half the weight of the skydiver?
   Answer: $g/2$, because the net force $(W - R)$ is half that of free fall. $[a = F/m = (W - R)/m = (W - W/2)/m = W/m - W/2m$. Since $W/m = g$, we see that $a = g - g/2 = g/2$.]

6 Newton's Third Law— Action and Reaction

Objectives

- Define force in terms of interaction.
- Explain why at least two objects are involved whenever a force acts.
- State Newton's third law of motion.
- Given an action force, identify the reaction force.
- Explain why the accelerations caused by an action force and by a reaction force do not have to be equal.
- Explain why an action force is not cancelled by the reaction force.

Possible Misconceptions to Correct

- Pushes and pulls are applied only by living things.
- Things such as high-speed bullets contain force.
- Reaction forces occur slightly after the action force is applied.
- Action and reaction forces are equal and opposite only under certain conditions.

Demonstration Equipment

[none]

Introduction

Many people think of "reaction" as the response to a given force; that, for example, if someone gives you a shove, you in turn respond by shoving back. Or that when the earth pulls on the moon, the moon in turn responds by then pulling back with the same magnitude of force. But that's not what Newton's 3rd law is about. Strictly speaking, bodies don't respond or "react" to pushes and pulls. The pushes and pulls are *simultaneous interactions* between the bodies concerned.

You can offer an A in the course to whatever pair of students succeed in the following task: In tug-of-war style, pull two ends of a rope with one scale close to one end, and another scale close to the other. Pull them so one scale reads 10 N and the other reads 0 N. Tricks aside, they'll be no A grades earned this way!

Newton's 3rd law leads nicely into momentum conservation. All the examples that illustrate action and reaction also serve to illustrate the conservation of momentum. For example, we say that the kick of a fired gun is the reaction to the force on the bullet, but we could as well say that the momentum

of the kicking gun matches the momentum of the bullet. If one started with momentum conservation, one could as nicely lead into Newton's 3rd law. Either may be considered fundamental.

Do the both the exploratory activity *Tension* and the experiment *Tug-of-War* before you lecture on this chapter. *Balloon Rockets* can be done with this chapter or just before the following chapter on momentum.

Suggested Lecture

Begin by reaching out to your class and stating, "I can't touch you without you touching me in return — I can't nudge this chair without the chair nudging me — I can't exert a force on a body without that body exerting a force on me. In all these cases of contact there is a twoness — contact requires two bodies." Then state Newton's 3rd law and support it with examples.

Examples of Newton's Third Law: Extend your hand and show your class that you can bend your fingers only very little. Show that if you push with your other hand, and thereby apply a force to them, they will bend appreciably more. Then walk over to the wall and show that the inanimate wall does the same (as you push against the wall). State that everybody will acknowledge that you are pushing on the wall, but only physics types realize that the wall is simultaneously pushing on you also — as evidenced by your bent fingers. State that this is just one of the fundamental physical laws that completely escape the notice of most people, even though its staring them right in the face. We look without seeing. State that much of physics is pointing out the obvious that is all around us.

In walking you interact with the floor; that is, you push back on the floor and the floor pushes forward on you. In swimming you interact with the water; that is, you push backward on the water and the water pushes forward on you. A balloon pushes escaping air backward and the escaping air in turn pushes the balloon forward, just as a jetplane does the same. A car pushes backward on the road, and the road pushes forward on the car (so it is the road that pushes a car along!)

CHECK QUESTIONS: Suppose two bowling balls A and B are separated and connected by a stretched spring. Is A pulling on B, or is B pulling on A, or are both pulling on each other? [They are part of the same interaction and pull on each other.] The earth and the moon are "connected" to each other by a gravitational force. Is the earth pulling on the moon, or is the moon pulling on the earth, or are both pulling on each other? [same as previous answer.]

Identifying Action and Reaction: Call attention to the examples of Figure 6.5 on page76 of the text, and relate these to the interaction rule:

Object A exerts a force on object B.
Object B exerts a force on object A.

CHECK QUESTION: Identify the action and reaction pair of forces for the case of a bat interacting with a ball.

[**Transparency 10** is Figure 6.5]

[**Practice Book 6-1** is a rather simple exercise for most students, while 6-1b about Nellie Newton is somewhat more challenging. It treats the concept featured in the Next-Time Question, **6-6.**]

Most people say that the moon is attracted to the earth by gravity. Ask most people if the earth is also attracted to the moon, and if so, which pulls harder, the earth or the moon? You'll get mixed answers. Physicists think differently than most people on this topic: rather than saying the moon is attracted to the earth by gravity, a physicist would say there is an attractive force between the earth and the moon. There is an important difference here.

Asking if the moon pulls as hard on the earth as the earth pulls on the moon is similar to asking if the distance between New York and Los Angeles is the same as the distance between Los Angeles and New York. Rather than thinking in terms of two distances, we think of a single distance *between* New York and Los Angeles. Likewise there is a single gravitational interaction between the earth and the moon.

Discuss the action and reaction pairs of forces when a bullet is fired from a rifle. Use the exaggerated symbol technique of page 77 to show how equal forces produce unequal accelerations when different masses are involved. I cite the imagined case of a person who is found guilty of rational thinking in a totaliarian society and is about to be shot by a firing

squad, and is given one last wish. Because his punishment should be harsher than being struck by a tiny bullet, his last wish is that the mass of the bullet be much more massive than the gun from which it is fired — and that his antagonist pull the trigger!

Tug-of-War: Ask your students to pretend a tug-of-war is taking place, and one team pulls their end of the rope with 1000 newtons of force, and the other team similarly pulls their end of the rope with 1000 newtons. Ask what the tension will be in the rope, as would be read by a spring balance in the middle. Put the options in multiple choice form: (1) 2000 N; (2) 1000 N; or (3) 0 N. After several seconds of class discussion and without giving the answer, dismiss the answer of zero newtons. Do this by reminding your class that if a person were to take the place of the rope and two teams pulled equally on each arm, the tension would be appreciably more than zero! The rope really is being stretched. Ask the class to pretend one team gets tired, so you call a halt to the tug-of-war. Then you tie their end of the rope to the wall, out of view of the other team. Pretend you drape a curtain between the groups. Then when the game resumes, will the pulling team be able to tell that the other team has been replaced by a wall? They may attribute a great "steadyness" to the other team, but when they pull as before, everything will seem the same. Ask now what the scale reading will be? It should be clear that it will read 1000 N, and not 2000 N as many will presume. So the rope pulls just as a team does. When you pull on the wall, the wall really does pull back on you!

Points about a tug-of-war: The team to win is not the team to pull hardest on the rope, but the team to push hardest against the ground. To win in a tug-of-war, you can (1) maintain your stance until your opponent tires and lessens his push against the ground; (2) push harder against the ground than your opponent and maintain rope tension; or (3) push harder against the ground than your opponent and increase rope tension.

CHECK QUESTION: Apply Newton's 3rd law to the tug-of-war. If action is you pulling on the rope, is the reaction force the ground pushing back on you or your opponent pulling back on the rope? [Neither, reaction is the rope pulling back on you — A on B; B on A!]

[**Next-Time Questions 6-4** and **6-5** treat the tug of war.]

Why Action and Reaction Forces Don't Cancel: Call attention to Figure 6.10 on page 79, of the apple and orange pulling on each other. Action and reaction are like apples and oranges, in that they act on different objects. You can't cancel a force on an orange with a force on an apple. This is the essence of the horse-and-cart problem.

Horse-Cart Problem: Discuss action and reaction in terms of the horse and cart situation described on page 80 and the comic strip, "Horse Sense" on facing page 81. Point out that the action force on the cart is not cancelled by the reaction because the reaction acts on the horse. This is the apple and orange example of Figure 6.10; you can't cancel a force on the cart by a force on something else.

Difficulties that occur with action-and-reaction situations usually stem from failing to clearly identify the *system* in question. [Skip ahead to page 40 in this manual for more about defining systems.] Basically, if you want to know the effect of a force or forces on something, call that something your system. Define your system by a real or imaginary dotted line around that something. Restrict your attention only to the external forces that originate outside the dotted line and act on the system, and not to the forces that the system may exert on things external to the dotted line. We distinguish between forces ON a system, and forces BY the system on other objects. In the horse-cart problem, if the system is the cart, then the only horizontal force that acts on the cart is the pull of the horse — period! So there is a net force on the cart and acceleration occurs. If the system is the horse, draw a dotted line around the horse. Two horizontal external forces act on this system: the reaction by the cart, and the reaction by the ground (friction) due to the horse's push against the ground. If the ground push is greater than the cart's pull, the horse accelerates (just as much as the joined cart!). If the system is both the horse and the cart, then only one horizontal external force acts on this system: the same push of the ground. Divide this push by the mass of the horse and cart, and you have the acceleration of both (the same as before). Interestingly, we can't say that action and reaction forces *never* cancel, for they do if they are *within* the system being considered. All the intermolecular forces within a pencil on your desk, for example, are pairs of action and reaction forces. And since they are within the pencil, they do cancel. Only external forces change the motion of things.

Paper Punch: Drop a sheet of paper and then punch it in midair. State that the heavy-weight boxing champion of the world couldn't hit the paper with a force of 50 pounds. No way! That's because the paper is not capable of "hitting back" with the same amount of force. A 50-pound interaction between his fist and the paper isn't possible.

There is a moral parallel to all this: Whenever you interact with something, be it a friend, your family, or the world — the way you touch or push is the way you are touched or pushed.

More Think-and-Explain Questions

1. Your weight is the result of the gravitational force of the earth on your body. What is the corresponding reaction force?
   Answer: If action is the earth pulling on your body, reaction is your body pulling on the earth.

2. Why can you exert greater force on the pedals of a bicycle if you pull up on the handlebars?
   Answer: When you pull up on the handlebars, the handlebars push down on you with the same amount of force, which is transmitted to the pedals. [See the answer to T&E 5.]

3. Consider the two forces acting on the person who stands still, namely, the downward pull of gravity and the upward support of the floor. Are these forces equal and opposite? Do they comprise an action-reaction pair? Why or why not?

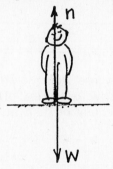

Answer: The forces are equal and opposite because they are the only forces acting on the person, who obviously is not accelerating. They cancel to produce the zero net force that non-acceleration requires. Note that they do not comprise an action-reaction pair, however, for they are not the parts of a single interaction. There are two interactions in question here; the interaction between (1) person and earth, and (2) floor and the person. Interaction (1) is the weight; earth pulls down on person (action) and person pulls up on earth (reaction). Note action and reaction are co-parts of a single interaction that acts on different bodies. Interaction (2) is upward support by floor on person (action) and downward push by person on floor (reaction). Again, action and reaction act on different bodies in a single interaction. But the equal and opposite forces cited in the question act on the same body. They therefore do not constitute an action-reaction pair. Action-reaction pairs follow the rule, A on B, B on A. In this case we have A on B, and C on A.

4. You exert 200 N on your refrigerator and push it across the kitchen floor at constant velocity. What friction force acts between the refrigerator and the floor? Is the friction force equal and opposite to your 200 N push? Does the friction force make up the reaction force to your push?

Answer: Constant velocity means zero acceleration which means zero net force. Therefore the friction force must be equal and opposite to your 200-N push. But it does not make up the reaction to your push. The reaction to your push against the refrigerator is the refrigerator pushing back on you. You and the frig make up one interaction, and the floor and the frig make up another. Even though the magnitudes of all forces are the same, there are two interactions with two sets of action-reaction pairs of forces.

5. Your teacher challenges you and your best friend to each pull on a pair of scales attached to the ends of a horizontal rope, in tug-of-war fashion, so that the readings on the scales will differ. Why can you or can't you do this?

Answer: No way Jose! Doing so would violate Newton's third law, for one end of the rope would be under greater tension than the other end.

6. When you get up from a sitting position, do your feet push against the floor with a force equal to, more than, or less than your weight?
Answer: More than your weight, because you accelerate upward and push against the floor to do so.

7. When a weightlifter jerks a barbell over her head, is the force exerted on the barbell more than, less than, or equal to the barbell's weight? Explain.
Answer: More than, because the barbell is accelerated upward.

8. A balloon floats motionless in the air. An occupant begins climbing up the supporting cable. In which direction does the balloon move as the occupant climbs?
Answer: To climb upward means pulling the rope downward, which moves the balloon downward as the person climbs.

9. Why cannot the heavyweight champion of the world punch a piece of tissue paper in midair with a 100-N force?
Answer: Because the tissue paper is not capable of "puching back" with 100 N! A 100-N interaction between a fist and tissue paper isn't possible.

7 Momentum

Objectives

- Define momentum.
- Define impulse, and relate it to momentum.
- Give examples of how both the size of the force and the length of the time interval affect the change in momentum.
- Explain why impulses are greater when an object bounces than when the same object simply comes to a complete stop.
- State the law of conservation of momentum.
- Distinguish between an elastic collision and an inelastic collision.
- Give an example of how the vector nature of momentum affects the law of conservation of momentum.

Possible Misconceptions to Correct

- Impulse equals momentum (rather than change in momentum).
- Momentum is conserved only when collisions are perfectly elastic.
- Impact and impulse are the same.

Demonstration Equipment

- [7-1] Sheet to hang and eggs to throw in it.
- [7-2] Go-Cart apparatus if your students don't do the activity *Go Cart*.
- [7-3] Air track and carts of equal and unequal masses.

Introduction

It is interesting to note that Newton expressed his 2nd law in terms of momentum ($F = \Delta P/\Delta t$) rather than the familiar $F = ma$ (P, the usual symbol for momentum, is not used in this text until Chapter 16). Many interactions that are explainable by Newton's 3rd law are as well explained by momentum conservation. So Newton's laws flow nicely into momentum and its conservation. If it weren't for the need to treat vectors, this chapter would directly follow the chapters on Newton's laws. It is interesting to note that either Newton's 3rd law or momentum conservation can be considered fundamental. That is, momentum conservation can be a consequence of Newton's 3rd law, or equally, Newton's 3rd law can be a consequence of momentum conservation.

We emphasize the impulse-momentum relation-

ship with applications selected to catch student interest. In presenting your own, the exaggerated symbol technique shown in Figures 7.3, 7.4, and 7.5 is suggested.

Angular momentum is not treated until Chapter 11.

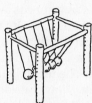

The popular swinging balls apparatus shown in the sketch provides an excellent illustration of momentum conservation. Students can easily see that when the balls on one side are lifted and released so they make contact with the others, the momentum of balls is the same before and after the collision — the same number of balls emerge at the same speed on the other side. So momentum before collision is seen to be equal to the momentum after collision. But the question is often raised, "Why cannot two balls be raised and allowed to swing into the array, and one ball emerge with twice the speed?" Be careful here. Momentum would indeed be conserved if this were the case. But the case with different numbers of balls emerging never happens. Why? Because energy would not be conserved. For the two-balls-one-ball case, the KE after would be twice as much as the KE before impact. KE is proportional to the square of the speed, and the conservation of both momentum and KE cannot occur unless the numbers of balls for collision and ejection are the same. So if you include this demonstration, treat it in the next chapter instead of here.

On bouncing: How great impact force is when bouncing occurs depends on impact time. For example, if bouncing from a circus net where time is appreciably extended, then impact force is relatively small. But when bouncing is not accompanied by extended time, like when a falling plantpot bounces from your head, then impact force can be relatively large. For an elastic collision where momentum is reversed, and Δmv is twice that of merely halting, impulse is twice. Compared with a moving object coming to a stop, a full bounce in twice the time yeilds the same impact force as in stopping; less than twice the time, more impact force; more than twice the time, less impact force. So although impulse is greater for bouncing, impact may or may not be depending on time.

Applications of momentum conservation often results in confusion if the idea of a *system* and the *isolation* of that system are not clear. The momentum of a system is conserved when no external forces act on the system. Defining and isolating that system is therefore important. Consider a cue ball that makes a head-on collison with an 8-ball at rest. If the system is taken to be only the 8 ball at rest, then we isolate it with a dotted border around it, sketch I. So long as no outside force acts on it, there will be no impulse on it and no change in its momentum. But when the cue ball strikes it, there is and outside force and an impulse on it. Its momentum changes as it speeds away with the speed of the incident cue ball. Or take the system to be the cue ball, sketch II. Initially it has momentum mv. Then it strikes the 8-ball and its momentum undergoes a change. The reaction force by the 8-ball brings it to a halt. Now consider the system of both balls, sketch III. Before collision the momentum is that of the moving cue ball. When the balls strike, no outside force acts, for the interaction is between the balls, both parts of the same system. So no impulse acts on the system and no change in momentum of the system occurs. In this case momentum is converved. It is the same before and after the collision. Again, the momentum of a system is conserved only when no external impulse is exerted on the system. Forces that are internal to a system do not change the momentum of the system.

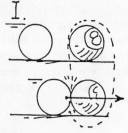

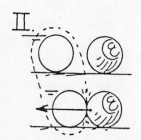

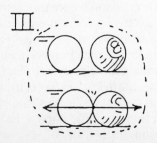

A system is not only isolated in space, but in time also. When we say that momentum is conserved when one pool ball strikes the other, we mean that momentum is conserved during the brief duration of interaction when outside forces can be neglected. After the interaction, friction quite soon brings both balls to a halt. So when we isolate a system for purposes of analysis, we isolate both in space and in time.

You may want to assign an "Egg Drop" experiment. Students design and construct a case to hold an egg that will be dropped from a three-or-four story building without breaking. The design cannot include means to increase air resistance, so all cases should strike the ground with about the same speed. By requiring the masses of all cases to be the same, the impulses of all will be the same upon impact. The force of impact, of course, should be minimized by maximizing the time of impact. This project is one that stirs considerable interest, both for your students and others who are not (yet?) taking your class. Interesting sidelight similar to the sheet and egg: Loose heavy blankets are effective in slowing bullets and shrapnel when hung in the windows of buildings in bullet and shrapnel-strewn areas.

Begin this chapter with the pre-lecture activity Go Cart, which simply and clearly demonstrates that the impulse imparted by a colliding object is greater when it bounces than when it doesn't. Do this activity after you've discussed the impulse-momentum relationship and just before you treat bouncing. Then as a follow-up, have your class do the experiment *Tailgated by a Dart*.

Suggested Lecture

Momentum: Begin by stating that there is something different between a Mack truck and a roller skate — they have different mass. And that there is still something different about a moving Mack truck and a moving roller skate — each has a different *momentum*. Define and discuss momentum as moving mass — inertia in motion.

CHECK QUESTION: After stating that a Mack truck has more mass than a roller skate, ask if the Mack truck will always have more momentum than the roller skate? [No, if a Mack truck is at rest it has no momentum. If a roller skate moves, it has momentum, and therefore more momentum than a Mack truck at rest.] Then ask if a Mack truck and a roller skate could have the same nonzero momentum? How? [A Mack truck moving very slowly and a roller skate moving very fast could have the same momentum. When this occurs, the product of mass x speed for both will be equal.]

Cite the case of huge oil-carrying supertankers that normally cut off their power when they are 25 or

so kilometers from port. Because of their huge momentum (due mostly to their huge mass), about 25 kilometers with water resistance are needed to bring them to a halt.

Impulse and Momentum Derive the impulse-momentum relationship. In Chapter 2 you defined acceleration as $a = \Delta v/t$ (really Δt, but you likely used t as the "time interval"). Then later in Chapter 5 you defined acceleration in terms of the force needed, $a = F/m$. Now simply equate; $a = a$, or $F/m = \Delta v/t$, with simple rearrangement you have, $Ft = \Delta mv$. (as in the footnote, page 87.)

   Then choose your examples in careful sequence: First, those where the object is to increase momentum — pulling a sling shot or arrow in a bow all the way back, the effect of a long cannon for maximum range, driving a golf ball. Second, those examples where small forces are the object when decreasing momentum — pulling your hand backward when catching a ball, driving into a haystack versus a concrete wall, falling on a surface with give versus a rigid surface. Then lastly, those examples where the object is to obtain large forces when decreasing momentum — karate.

   Point of confusion: In boxing, one "follows through" whereas in karate one "pulls back". But this is not so — a karate expert does not pull back upon striking his target. He strikes in such a way that his hand is made to bounce back, yielding up to twice the impulse to his target (just as a ball bouncing off a wall delivers nearly twice the impulse to the wall than if it stuck to the wall).

CHECK QUESTION: Why is falling on a wooden floor in a roller rink less dangerous than falling on the concrete pavement? [Superficial answer: Because the wooden floor has more "give." Emphasize that this is the beginning of a fuller answer—one that is prompted if the question is reworded as follows:] Why is falling on a floor with more give less dangerous than falling on a floor with less give? [Answer: Because the floor with more give allows a greater time for the impulse that reduces the momentum of fall to zero. A greater time for Δ momentum means less force.]

DEMONSTRATION [7-1]: Throw an egg in a sagging sheet as stated in Think and Explain Question #3.

[**Transparency 11**, Figures 7.3 and 7.4 here]

Railroad Cars: The loose coupling between railroad cars provides a very good example of the impulse-momentum relationship. The loose slack in the coupling of railroad cars is evident when a locomotive either brings a long train from rest into motion, or when it brings a moving train to rest. In both cases a cascade of clanks is heard as each car in turn is engaged. This can be annoying at night if you're trying to get some sleep near a switching yard (where I got this idea in the first place.) Why the loose coupling? Without it, a locomotive might simply sit still and spin its wheels. The friction force between the wheels and the track is simply inadequate to set the entire mass of the train in motion. But there is enough friction to set one car in motion, so the slack allows the locomotive to get one car going. Then, when the coupling is tight, the next car is set in motion. Then when the coupling for two cars is tight, the third car is set in motion, and so on until the whole train is given momentum. So the slack allows the required impulse to be broken into a series of smaller impulses, or in effect, an extension of time so that the friction between the locomotive wheels and the track can do the job. (Anology: Just as a locomotive that pulls too great a load may sit still and spin its wheels, a student who takes on too many courses or activities in school may similarly sit still and spin his or her wheels!)

Karate: Confusion point: In boxing, for maximum impact one "follows through" whereas in karate it is commonly thought that one "pulls back." But this is not so — a karate expert may pull back for the purpose of repositioning and manuevering, but not for imparting a maximum blow. Maximum impact force occurs when the target is struck in such a way that the hand bounces back (not pulled back). This yeilds up to twice the impulse to the target (just as a ball bouncing off a rigid wall delivers nearly twice the impulse to the wall than if it stuck to the wall).

Bouncing: Discuss, as the text does, how Lester Pelton made a fortune by applying some simple physics to the old paddle wheels. Wind bouncing off a sail similarly provides additional impulse to sailcraft. If you are not going to have your student do the activity *Bouncing Dart*, show it as a classroom demonstration [7-2].

DEMONSTRATION: This one by Rich Langer of Beaumont High School in St. Louis, MO, who uses a toy dartgun and computer-disc box. Tape some toothpicks to one side the box, so the

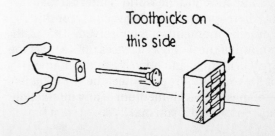

Toothpicks on this side

suction-cup dart shot against it won't stick to it. First fire the dart against the smooth side of the box. The dart sticks and the box slides an observed distance across the table. Then repeat, but with the box turned around so the dart hits the toothpick side. When the dart hits, it bounces. Note the appreciably greater distance the box slides!]

(This is a good break place.)

Conservation of Momentum: Distinguish between external forces and internal forces — like the difference between sitting inside a car and pushing on the dashboard and standing outside and pushing against the outside of the car. Only an external force will produce a change in the momentum of the car. No change in momentum can occur in the absence of an external net force. That is, when $F = 0$, $\Delta mv = 0$ also.

Isolating Systems: Discuss the idea of isolating a system when applying the conservation of momentum. We isolate a system in space by imagining a dotted boundary line around the perimeter of the system, and we isolate a system in time by considering only the duration of the interaction. Show that where momentum may be conserved for a particular system, it may not be conserved for part of the system (for example, the pool balls previously illustrated).

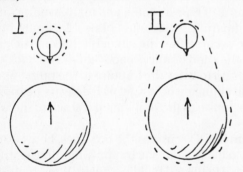

For another example, consider a dropped rock in free fall. If the system is taken to be the rock, sketch I, then momentum is not conserved as it falls because an external force acts on the system (its vector is seen to penetrate the dotted border of the system). This external force, gravity, produces an impulse on the rock that changes its momentum. If the system is instead considered to be the rock + the entire world, sketch II, then the interaction between the rock and the world is internal to the system (there is no penetrating vector). For this larger system, momentum *is* conserved. That is, the momentum of the world as it "races up" to meet the falling rock, is equal and opposite to the momentum of the rock as it drops to meet the world (at its center of mass). The momentum of any interaction is always conserved if you make your system big

enough. As far as we can tell, the momentum of the universe is without change.

Collisions: When no external forces act on a system, no change in the momentum of that system occurs. This is best seen in collision. Distinguish between elastic (bouncy) and inelastic (sticky) collisions.

> DEMONSTRATION [7-3]: Show examples of momentum conservation in both elastic and inelastic collisions with carts on an air track. If you represent the collisions on the board, it will be sufficient to use the exaggerated symbol technique (big m, little v, and vice versa).

[**Transparency 12**, Figures 7.9 and 7.10 here]

For the case of equal-mass carts in an inelastic collision (Figure 7.10 on page 95 in the text), go over the equation in the middle of page 95 in detail. Write the similar equations for collisions you demonstrate on the air track so students will relate the equations to visual examples. Have your students write the equations for other examples you show. In writing the equations for head-on collisions, be careful to show velocities in one direction as positive and oppositely-directed velocities as negative. For example, the equation for Figure 7.9b is; [mv + m(-v)] before = [m(-v) + mv] after. In both the before and after cases, the net momentum is zero.

Momentum Vectors: Illustrate the vector nature of momentum by discussing Figures 7.12, 7.13, and 7.14 in the text. Resist making a big deal out of this section unless you have ample time on your hands and your class is anxious for you to set your academic plow deeper. I think it is enough for students to be exposed to the general idea here and then move on.

More Think and Explain Questions

1. A fully-dressed person is at rest in the middle of a pond on perfectly smooth ice and must get to shore. How can this be accomplished?
   Answer: An article of clothing can be thrown in a direction opposite to the direction the person wishes to slide. The momentum given to the clothing will be offset by an equal and opposite momentum of the person. Another technique is to blow air like a jet. (When breathing in again, be careful to tilt the head downward or upward so that sliding is not slowed by inhaling!).
2. Your friend says that momentum conservation is violated when a ball rolls down a hill and gains speed. What do you say?
   Answer: The ball gains momentum because of the impulse that the force of gravity provides. It is in

the *absence* of an external force that momentum doesn't change. If the whole earth and the ball are taken together as a system, then the gravitational interaction between the ball and the earth is internal and no external force acts. The momentum of the ball is accompanied by an equal and opposite momentum of the earth that results in no net change in momentum.

3. If a huge truck and a motorcycle have a head on collision, which vehicle will experience the greater force of impact? The greater impulse? The greater change in momentum? The greater acceleration, and hence the greater damage?
Answer: The magnitude of force, impulse, and change in momentum will be the same for each. The motorcycle undergoes the greater deceleration because its mass is less. The motorcyclist is in more trouble than the truck driver: "Its not the fall that hurts you; its the sudden stop!" [Note that the value of this question is in understanding the meanings of the terms *force, impulse, momentum,* and *acceleration.*]

4. A 1000-kg car moving at 20 m/s slams into a stone wall and comes to a halt. Here are two questions to consider: (a) What impulse acts on the car? (b) What is the force of impact on the car? Which of these questions has a direct answer, and which cannot be directly answered? Explain.

Answer: Question (a) has a direct answer, namely 20,000 Ns (because impulse = ^momentum). Question (b) cannot be answered without the *time* of impulse, in which case the average force could be calculated. (In the next chapter we will see that having the *distance* traveled during impact would also allow solution of average force.)

5. A lunar vehicle on earth moves a 10 km/h. When it travels as fast on the moon, is its momentum more, less, or the same?
Answer: Its momentum is the same (its weight might change, but not its mass).

6. Why the extra thickness of floor mats used by gymnasts?
Answer: The extra thickness extends the time during which momentum changes and reduces impact force.

7. Bronco dives from a high flyhing plane and finds his momentum increasing. Does this violate the conservation of momentum? Explain.
Answer: If we consider Bronco to be the system, then a net force acts and momentum changes. In

the system of Bronco, momentu;m is not conserved. If, however we consider the system to be Bronco and the world, then each has equal and opposite momentum, which cancels to zero. In this larger system, momentum is conserved. Momentum is conserved only in systems not subject to external forces.

More Think and Solves

1. A car of mass 1100 kg moves at 24 m/s. What braking force is needed to bring the car to a halt in 20 s?
Answer: From $Ft = \Delta mv$, $F = \Delta mv/t = $ [1100 kg x 24 m/s]/20 s = 1320 N. (Here the change in momentum is simply the momentum 1100 x 24 kg m/s the car has before braking.)

2. What average force is exerted on a 25 gram egg by a bedsheet if the egg hits the sheet at 4 m/s and takes 0.2 seconds to stop? (Remember to work in kilograms!)
Answer: To begin with, 25 gram = 0.025 kg. Then from $Ft = \Delta mv$, $F = \Delta mv/t = $ 0.025 x 4/0.2 = 0.5 N.

3. A 100-kg quarter back is traveling 5 m/s and is stopped by a tackler in 1 s. Calculate (a) the initial momentum of the quarter back, (b) the impulse imparted by the tackler, and (c) the average force exerted by the tackler.
Answers: (a) $mv = $ (100 kg)(5 m/s) = 500 kg m/s. (b) Impulse $Ft = \Delta mv$ so impulse = 500 Ns. (c) $F = \Delta mv/t = $ 500 Ns/1s = 500 N.

4. A 40 kg football player going through the air at 4 m/s tackles a 60 kg player who is heading toward him at 3 m/s, in the air. What is the speed and direction of the tangled mess?
Answer: Before they make an inellastic collision the combined momentum is -20 units. Likewise after, with 100 kg $v = $ -20. $v = $ 1/5 m/s in the direction of the 60 kg player's initial motion.

5. A jet engine gets its thrust by taking in air, heating and compressing it, and then ejecting it at a high speed. If a particular engine takes in 20 kg of air per second at 100 m/s, and ejects it at 500 m/s, calculate the thrust of the engine?
Answer: Thrust (applied force) = 8000 N. From $Ft = \Delta mv$, $F = \Delta mv/t = $ [(20 kg x 500 m/s - 20 kg x 100 m/s)] /1 s = [20 kg (500 - 100) m/s]/1 s = [20 kg (400 m/s)]/1 s = 8000 N.

6. A 40 kg projectile leaves a 2000 kg launcher with a speed of 400 m/s. What is the recoil speed of the launcher?
Answer: The launcher will have to have a recoil momentum that is equal and opposite to that of the projectile. The momentum of the projec-

tile is 40 kg x 400 m/s = 16000 kg m/s. For the launcher, 2000 kg x v = 16000 kg m/s, where v = 16000/2000 = 8 m/s.

7. A car of mass 700 kg travels at 20 m/s and collides with a stationary truck of mass 1400 kg. The two vehicles interlock as a result of the collision and slide along the icy road. What is the velocity of the car-truck system?

Answer: Momentum before is all in the car; 700 kg x 20 m/s = 14000 kg m/s. Momentum after is the same, but consists of the mass of both vehicles, 2100 kg. So 2100 kg x v = 14000 kg m/s, where v = 14000/2100 = 6.6 m/s.

8. A 1-kg dart moving horizontally at 10 m/s makes impact and sticks to a wood block of mass 9 kg, which slides across a friction-free level surface (similar to the lab experiment, *Go Cart*). What is the speed of the wood and dart after collision?

Answer: 1 m/s. 1 kg x 10 m/s + 0 = (9 + 1) kg x V; where V = 10/10 = 1 m/s.

9. A 10,000-kg vehicle moving at 10 m/s collides with a 2000-kg car moving at 30 m/s in the opposite direction. If they stick together after impact, how fast and in what direction will they be moving?

Answer: 3.33 m/s in the same direction as the 10,000-kg vehicle. Momentum before collision = (10,000 kg x 10 m/s) + (2000 kg x [-30 m/s]) = 100,000 kg m/s - 60,000 kg m/s = 40,000 kg m/s in the direction of the more massive vehicle. This is also the momentum after collision, which = (10,000 + 2000) kg m/s x V, the combined mass moving at velocity V. Solving we find, V = 40,000/ 12,000 = 3.33 m/s.

10. In a fireworks display a 3-kg body moving at 4 km/h due North explodes into 3 equal pieces: A, at 4 km/h East; B, at 5 km/h 37° South of West; and C, at 15 km/h due North. After the explosion, what is the total momentum of all the pieces?

Answer: The same as before explosion, 3 x 4 = 12 units of momentum! If you wish to do this the long way, the momentum of piece A is cancelled by the east-west component of B, which is also 4 units (note that B makes a 3-4-5 right triangle, and the east-west 4 side opposes A). This leaves a 3-unit-due-South component of momentum for B, which opposes the 15 units due North of A. So the total momentum is 15 - 3 = 12 units due North, exactly the momentum the system had to begin with! (Here's a case where knowing the concepts saves a lot of work.)

8 Energy

Objectives

- Determine the amount of work done, given the force and the distance moved.
- Determine the amount of power required, given the work and the time .
- Define work in terms of energy.
- Distinguish among mechanical energy, potential energy, and kinetic energy.
- Give examples of situations in which (a) the gravitational potential energy changes and (b) it does not even though something is moved.
- Describe how the kinetic energy of an object depends upon the speed of the object.
- State the law of conservation of energy.
- Describe the function of a lever.
- Give examples of situations in which the mechanical advantage of a machine is (a) greater than 1 and (b) less than 1.
- Explain why no machine can have an efficiency of 100%.

Possible Misconceptions to Correct

- Momentum and kinetic energy are much the same concept.
- Energy is conserved only under certain conditions.
- It is possible to get more energy out of a machine than is put in.

Demonstration Equipment

- [8-1] Simple pendulum, say a small weight at the end of a 1-m length of string.
- [8-2] Hand cranked generator that lights a light bulb.
- [8-3] Spring balance and model pulleys, as in Figure 8.12.

Introduction

This is an important chapter. The concept of energy is central to physics and is discussed in various forms throughout the text. The concept of mechanical energy is elusive because it becomes evident only when it changes from one form to another, or when there is motion. Also it is relative: that is, it depends on the location we choose for our reference frame. A 1-newton apple held 1 meter above the floor has 1 joule potential energy, but when held out the window 10 meters above the ground it has 10 joules. Or the same apple held in your lap has zero kinetic energy,

but if your lap is on the seat of a high-flying jet plane, it has many joules of kinetic energy relative to the ground below. Potential and kinetic energies are relative to a specified or an implied frame of reference.

According to my friend Dave Wall who worked for a couple of years in the patent office in Washington D.C., the greatest shortcoming of would-be inventors was their lack of understanding of the law of energy conservation. The patent office has long been besieged with schemes that promise to circumvent energy conservation. This point is addressed in the question about fuel economy on page 111, and is well worth discussing. There are still charlatans who pretend to have invented energy-producing machines, and sell shares to people who are misinformed about the conservation of energy. Your students should not be among this group.

The young archer in Figure 8.4 is my former student and teaching assistant, Tenny Lim, who is now a design engineer at Jet Propulsion Labs in Pasadena.

Levers and pulleys are treated briefly. If there weren't so much other good physics to cover, you could spend several lectures on simple machines. I recommend you give it one lecture period at most.

The last section of the chapter, *Energy for Life*, can be expanded in your lecture.

In lab, *Wrap Your Energy in a Bow* nicely follows *Impact Speed*, both of which involve finding the area under a curve. There are many energy labs to choose from. For power, have them do *Muscle Up!* and your class will have a better idea of just how much 100 watts is.

An interesting lecture presentation is found at the beginning of Chapter 4 in the first volume of *The Feynman Lectures on Physics* (Addison-Wesley, 1963). Feynman compares the idea of energy conservation with a child's misplaced blocks. The analogy is good resource material for class discussions.

Suggested Lectures:

Fashion a long pendulum that extends to the ceiling two or three meters from a wall. Then begin by standing on a chair against the wall with the extended heavy pendulum bob held at the tip of your nose, or against your teeth. Say nothing. Release the bob and let it swing out, then back to your face. Don't flinch. Then comment on your confidence in one of the most central of the physical laws — the *conservation of energy*. The study of energy begins with a related concept, *work*. (If you can't do this, describing the situation has merit.)

Work: Define work and relate it to the lifting of a barbell, as shown in Figure 8.1. When work is done on the barbell two things happen: (1) a force is exerted on the barbell, and (2) the barbell is moved by that force. If the barbell is simply held still, the weightlifter would get tired, and feel like he is doing work. He may well be doing work on himself via tiny movements in his body tissues, but he is doing no work *on the barbell* unless the force he exerts *moves* the barbell. (Distinguish between work done on an object, and the work done by an object on something else; distinguish between work done by you, on you, and *in* you.)

> CHECK QUESTION: Work is done lifting a barbell. How much more work is done lifting a twice-as-heavy barbell the same distance? [Twice as much.] How much more work is done lifting a twice-as-heavy barbell twice as far? [Four times the work in lifting the first barbell.]

Compare work to impulse of the previous chapter. In both concepts, a force is extended — in time for impulse, in distance for work. Return to previous examples of drawn slingshots and long cannons, where the added length produced greater speeds. We can describe this speed and mass in terms of two concepts — momentum and energy. Failure to distinguish between these two gave rise to much controversy in Europe after the time of Newton. (The concept of KE was after Newton's time.)

Potential Energy: Attach a spring balance to the pendulum bob at its equilibrium position. Show how a small force pulls it sideways from its equilibrium position. Make a comparison between this force and the force that would be necessary to lift it vertically (its weight). Show how as the bob is pulled farther up the arc, the force to move it increases. This is because it is being pulled against gravity, which has no vector component along the pendulum path when it is hanging at its lowest point, but which increases as the pendulum is raised. More work is required to move it equal distances the farther it is raised.

> CHECK QUESTION: Keeping the spring balance always perpendicular to the string, predict what the force will be if the string is pulled through 90 degrees and is horizontal? [The pull force will be equal and opposite to the force of gravity on the bob — its weight.]

Point out that the arc path to any elevation is longer than the vertical path. State that to compute the work done along the arc path is complicated because the force continually varies with distance. The computation requires a form of mathematics (integral calculus) that progressively adds a succession of tiny work segments. But this advanced mathematics can be short circuited, for the same answer is obtained by simply multiplying the weight of the bob by the vertical distance it is raised! The work done against gravity in elevating the pendulum bob is the same along either path, straight up or along the arc. Gravitational potential energy depends only on weight and height — not on the path taken to get it there.

Discuss the elevated boulder in Figure 8.3.

> CHECK QUESTIONS: Does a car hoisted for lubrication in a service station have PE? [Yes, any elevated body has PE with respect to any chosen reference level (usually the "ground level")] How much work will raise the car twice as high? [Twice, and it will have twice as much PE] How much work is required to raise it three times as high, and how much PE will it have? [Three times as much.]

Kinetic Energy: A moving body can do work because of its motion. It has motion energy, or in Greek, kinetic energy (KE). Relate KE to force x distance. Discuss Figure 8.5. State that later in the course you will apply the idea of KE to molecules and speak of heat and temperature. KE underlies heat [haphazard motion of molecules], sound [vibratory motion of molecules], and light [emitted by the vibratory motion of electrons in an atom].

> CHECK QUESTIONS: Does a car moving along a road have KE? [Yes, any moving object has KE (KE is a relative quantity, as is speed. The cup of tea you hold in a high-flying jet liner has KE with respect to the ground, but no KE with respect to the saucer in which it sits)]. If the speed of the car doubles, by how much does the KE increase? [By 4] If the speed triples? [By 9].

(This is a good break place.)

Conservation of Energy: When you rub two sticks together to start a fire you transform mechanical energy into heat energy. When you do work and wind a spring in a toy cart you give it PE which then transforms to KE when the cart speeds up on the floor (Figure 8.6). When the speed becomes constant, the continued transfer of PE is transformed to heat; to work against friction (without friction, KE would keep increasing with decreasing PE).

> DEMONSTRATION [8-1] : Swing a pendulum to and fro and cite the transformations from PE to KE and so on. Acknowledge the role of friction in damping the pendulum motion (and the subsequent warming of the room!)

Discuss Figure 8.7.

DEMONSTRATION [8-2]: Preview electricity and magnetism and bring out the hand-cranked horseshoe-magnet generator that lights up the lamp. Have student volunteers note and state that more work is needed to turn the crank when the lamp is connected than when it is not. Then relate this to Think and Explain Question # 7.

Discuss the question about the miracle car in the middle of page 111. [Return to this question later when you discuss efficiency, and then repeat it for the case of a car that is 30 percent efficient, and how the car will therefore go 30 percent of the 20 km distance.]

Discuss the essentials for a follow through to energy conservation, the experiment *Releasing Your Potential*, or *Conserving Your Energy*.

[**Practice Book 8-3,** page 35 on bungee jumping and page 36 on cars going over a cliff, tie free-fall motion, momentum, and energy together.]

(This is a good break place.)

Machines: Apply energy conservation to the *lever* (Figure 8.9). [Do not confuse the distances moved with the lever-arm distances of torque later in Chapter 11 — *Fd* here refers to the force multiplied by the distance the "force moves," (parallel to the force) whereas in the case of torque *d* refers to the leverage distance that is perpendicular to the applied force.] Show how varying the position of the fulcrum changes the relative values of output force and distance moved. Stress that this is in accord with the rule "work input = work output."

CHECK QUESTION: Archimedes, the most famous scientist in ancient Greece, stated that given a long-enough lever, he could move the world. What is meant by this? [In accord with the lever equation $fD = Fd$, a force as great as the weight of the world could be lifted with the force he could muster (providing there was a place for him to stand and a place for the fulcrum!)]

[**Transparencies 13** and **14,** Figures 8.9, 8.10, and Figures 8.11, 8.12 here]

Acknowledge the different types of levers as shown in Figure 8.11, without overstating the distinction between the three types. The point to stress is the relationship $fD = Fd$, energy conservation.

CHECK QUESTION: In which type of lever is work output greater than work input? [NONE! In no system can work output exceed work input! Be clear about the difference between *work* and *force*.]

Show that a pulley is simply a lever in disguise, as shown in Figure 8.12. Show also $fD = Fd$

DEMONSTRATION [8-3]: Show with model pulleys the arrangements of Figure 8.12. A spring balance will show the relative forces needed to support the same load.

CHECK QUESTION: In what pulley arrangement can work output exceed work input? [NONE!]

Cite the cases of charlatans who devise complicated arrangements of levers, pulleys, and other gadgets such as magnets, to design a machine that will have a greater work output than work input. Such charlatans, very numerous in the past, are still at work today. They tell their "followers" that the oil companies and the patent office are conspiring against them, and that if they can raise sufficient funds, they can build their machine and usher in a better world. They prey on people who are ignorant of or do not understand the message of the energy conservation law. You can't get something for nothing. In fact you can't even break even, because of the inevitable transformation of energy to thermal energy.

Efficiency: It should be enough that your students are acquainted with the idea of efficiency and actual and theoretical mechanical advantage. It is easy to let the plow blade sink deeper in Section 8.8, and turn this chapter toward the burdensome side of study. I therefore recommend this section be treated lightly, and not used as primary examination fodder.

CHECK QUESTION: What does it mean to say a certain machine is 30% efficient? [It means it will convert 30% of the energy input to useful work — 70% of the energy input will be wasted.]

The efficiency of a light bulb underscores the idea of *useful energy.* To say an incandescent lamp is 10% efficient is to say that only 10% of the energy input is converted to the useful form of energy, light. All the rest goes to heat. But even the light energy converts to heat upon absorbtion. So all the energy input to an incandescent lamp is converted to heat. This means it is a 100% efficient device as a *heater* (but not as a device for emitting light)! We return to this idea in Chapter 24, Thermodynamics.

Fuels such as oil, gas, and wood are forms of concentrated energy. When they are used to do work, their energy is degraded. If all concentrations of energy are degraded, no more work can be done. Heat is the destiny of useful energy.

Section 8.9, *Energy for Life,* can be skimmed or be the topic of a lecture on how the conservation of energy underlies all biology.

More Think-and-Explain Questions:

1. Why does the force of gravity do no work on a bowling ball rolling along a bowling alley?
Answer: Work is done on an object only when a force (or some component of a force) acts in the direction of motion of the object. In the case of the bowling ball, the force is perpendicular to the motion, with no component parallel to the alley. (We will see later that for the same reason the force of gravity does no work on satellites in circular orbit.) [2]

2. What effect does a long barrel on a rifle have on the muzzle velocity of the bullets it fires, and why?
Answer: The long barrel provides a greater distance for the applied force of expanding gases. So more work is done on the bullet and it emerges with greater velocity and greater KE. (Of course there is a limit as to how long — expanding gases would dissipate in a barrel that was too long and friction would prevail.)

3. Can an object have mechanical energy without having momentum? Explain. Can an object have momentum without having energy? Explain.
Answer: First of all, all objects have internal heat energy (and also have energy of being in the form of mass, $E_0 = mc^2$). If the mechanical energy is due to motion, then a moving object has both KE and momentum. If the mechanical energy is PE and the object is at rest, then it can have mechanical energy without having momentum. But if an object has momentum, then by definition, it is moving and has KE also.

4. Why are the handles long and blades short for metal-cutting shears (just the oppostite for ordinary scissors)?

Answer: The long handles act as long levers and multiply the force applied to the blades. Such increased force is not needed for ordinary scissors, where the handles are much shorter.

5. Suppose you are at the edge of a cliff and throw one ball down to the ground below and another up at the same speed. The upward thrown ball rises and then falls to the ground below. How do the speeds of the balls compare when striking the ground? Neglect air resistance and use the conservation of energy to arrive at your answer.

Answer: The ball strikes the ground with the *same* speed, whether thrown up or down. Relative to the ground below, each ball starts with the same energy (PE + KE). When they reach ground level PE = 0, all the energy is the same KE. This can be seen by the analysis of Figure 2.6 back on page 18, where the ball that is thrown upward will return to its starting level with its launching speed. So its speed at the ground is the same whether the ball is thrown up or down. (Interestingly enough, the speed of the ball upon striking the ground will be the same if the ball is thrown horizontally, or in any direction! PE + KE at the top will equal KE at the bottom.)

6. Ideally, how much force must the man exert on the rope to lift the engine and pulley that weigh 100 N?
Answer: 50 N.

7. The two balls roll along the tracks shown, starting from rest. At the end of the tracks, which ball will have the most KE? Which will arrive at the end first?

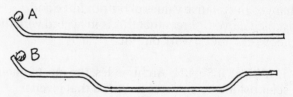

Answer. Both will have the same KE, but B will take the shortest time because its average speed is greater along the lower section (recall this question in Chapter 2).

8. If a cat and an elephant run down the road with the same KE, which is running faster?
Answer. The cat, for its small mass is compensated with a large speed if its KE is the same.

9. Molecules of different gases in a mix have the same average KE. Which are the faster molecules, the very massive ones or the less massive ones? Or the same?
Answer. Like the cat and the elephant, the small ones must be moving faster to have the same KE as the large ones.

10. We'll learn when we study heat that the temperature of a gas is proportional to the average molecular KEs of the molecules comprising the gas. In the mixture of nitrogen and oxygen molecules in the air, which has the most average speed?
Answer Nitrogen is slightly lighter than oxygen, so moves faster on the average.

11. Looking ahead to atoms a bit, what atom would you expect to have the greatest speed in air?
Answer Hydrogen, the lightest of the elements. Next is helium. Hydrogen rarely exists solo, but helium does. Helium's speed at room temperature is greater than escape speed for Planet Earth (Chapter 13). That's why there's practically no helium in the air we breath. Its gotten from below ground trapped with natural gas.

More Think and Solves

1. Relative to the ground below, how many joules of PE does a 1000-N boulder have at the top of a 5-m ledge? If it falls, with how much KE will it strike the ground? What will be its speed of impact?
Answer: PE = weight x height = 1000 N x 5 m = 5000 Nm = 5000 J. By the conservation of energy, it will have the same 5000 J of KE at impact. It will have a speed of 10 m/s upon impact, as any object will freely fall a distance of 5 m in its first second of fall (Chapter 2), and any object starting from rest will reach a speed of about 10m/s in its first second of fall (actually 9.8 m/s). Or, from KE = PE, $1/2\ mv^2 = mgh$, or $v^2 = 2gh$, or v $= \sqrt{2gh} = \sqrt{2(10)(5)} = \sqrt{100} = 10$ m/s.

2. Use the conservation of energy to find an equation for the speed of a freely falling object that falls from rest at a height h. That is, equate the PE to KE and solve for velocity v.
Answer: $v = \sqrt{2gh}$. The PE (mgh) of the object at the rest position will be converted to KE ($1/2\ mv^2$) after falling through a vertical distance h. From mgh = $1/2\ mv^2$, we see after cancelling m and rearranging term, $v = \sqrt{2gh}$.

3. A pole vaulter wishes to clear a 4 meter bar. How fast must he run? (Assume that all his kinetic energy is converted into gravitational potential energy.)

Answer: From $mgh = \Delta KE$, $v = \sqrt{2gh} = \sqrt{80} = 8.9$ m/s. Note the pole simply acts as a transforming agent from KE to PE. Here we neglect the energy transformed to heating of the pole.

4. Water drops about 50 m over the Niagra Falls. If 8 million kg of water fall each second, what power is available at the bottom?
Answer: 4000 MW. $P = W/t = mgh/t = (8,000,000$ x 10 x 50)J/s = 4,000,000,000 W or 4000 MW.

5. When a 1-kg projectile is fired at 10 m/s from a 10-kg gun, the momentum of the projectile and recoiling gun is the same (but in opposite directions). Show that the KE of the projectile is 10 times greater than the KE of the recoiling gun.
Answer: KE of projectile = $1/2\ mv^2 = 1/2$ (1 kg) (10 m/s)^2 = 50 J. The speed of the recoiling gun, by momentum conservation, must be 1 m/s. So the KE of the recoiling gun = $1/2\ mv^2 = 1/2$ (10 kg) (1 m/s) ^{2} = 5 J. Hence the KE of the projectile is 10 times the KE of the recoiling gun.

6. In the hydraulic machine shown, it is observed that when the small piston is pushed down a distance of 10 cm, the large piston is raised 1 cm. If the small piston is pushed down with a force of 200 N, how much force is the large piston exerting?

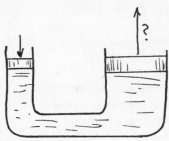

Answer:
From the $work_{input} = work_{output}$ relationship:
$(Fd)_{input} = (Fd)_{output}$
(200 N x 10 cm) = (F x 1 cm)
$F = 2000$ N

7. What is the scale reading for the right-hand rope that helps to support the 10-N weight? To increase the weight's PE by 10 J, what vertical distance must the right-hand side of the rope be raised?

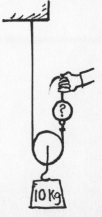

Answers: The scale reads 5 N (Chapter 4 and 5 stuff). To raise the weight 1 m requires the hand to rise 2 m. Then work input = work output.

8. What is the theoretical mechanical advantage of a 5-m long inclined plane that is elevated with one end 1 m? What is the actual mechanical advantage if 100 N of effort are needed to push a block of ice that weighs 400 N up the plane? What is the efficiency of the inclined plane?

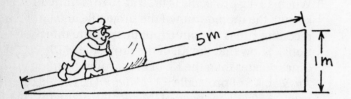

Answers: Theoretical mechanical advantage = (Input distance)/(output distance) = 5 m/1 m = 5. Actual mechanical advantage = (Output force)/(input force) = 400 N/100 N = 4. Efficiency = AMA/TMA = 4/5 = 0.8, or 80%.

9. In the pulley system shown,
a. what force is necessary to raise the 10 kg weight with a constant speed?
b. If the object raises 4 cm, how far does the puller's hand move?
c. If the system is 40% efficient, what force is necessary to raise the 10 kg block at a constant velocity?

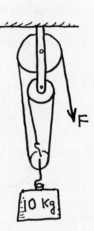

Answers: a. Note MA is 3, so the applied force is 1/3 the weight of the load; 1/3 mg = 33.3 N.
b. Three times as far, 12 cm.
c. 40% efficient means applied force must be greater by 1/0.4 or 2.5 (33.3) = 83.3 N.

10. What is the efficiency of the body when a cyclist expends 1000 watts of power to deliver mechanical energy to the bicycle at the rate of 100 watts?
Answer: Efficiency = Power output/power input = 100 W/1000 W = 0.10 or 10%.

I cover a lot of distance to get to class. When teaching physics I'll uncover a little — so they'll learn a lot. Good teaching is knowing more than what to cover — it's knowing what should be left out!

9 Circular Motion

Objectives

- Distinguish between rotate and revolve.
- Distinguish between linear speed and rotational speed, and explain what each depends on.
- Give examples of a centripetal force.
- Describe the resulting motion of an object if the centripetal force acting on it ceases.
- Explain why it is incorrect to say that a centrifugal force pulls outward on an object being whirled in a circle.
- Explain why a ladybug in a whirling can would experience what seems to be an outward force, and why a physicist would label this a fictitious force.
- Describe how a simulated gravitational acceleration can be produced in a space colony.

Possible Misconceptions to Correct

- Linear speed and rotational speed are the same.
- The linear speed on a rotating surface is the same at all radial distances.
- Things moving in a circular path are pulled outward by some force.
- If the string breaks on an object pulled into a circular path, the object will move radially outward (rather than tangentially).

Demonstration Equipment

- [9-1] A rotating turntable of any kind, and two coins.
- [9-2] Meter stick (or any stick) to swing as a pendulum.
- [9-3] A tin can (or similar object to whirl) tied to a piece of string (about 1 m).
- [9-4] Bucket of water to swing overhead.

Introduction

This chapter extends the translational ideas of Chapter 2 to rotation, and serves as an introduction to Chapter 11. A space habitat theme is briefly treated that opens the door to the myriad of interesting physics applications in a rotating frame of reference.

Note that this chapter omits entirely the "right hand rule," where fingers of the right hand represent the motion of a rotating body and the thumb represents the positive vector of motion. I have always felt that the reason for this rule in introductory physics courses was to provide the instructor the opportunity to easily make up tricky exam questions. Please spare undue emphasis on this material, which your students can get into in a follow-up course.

It is often said that rotational motion is analogous to linear motion and therefore should not be difficult to learn. But consider the many distinctions between 1) linear, 2) rotational, 3) revolutional, 4) radial, 5) tangential, 6) angular, and all related to a) speed, b) velocity, and c) acceleration. And we have centripetal and centrifugal forces, real and ficticious, not to mention torques that will be coming up soon. So there is a myriad of ideas to describe and understand. Is it any wonder why students who do well in linear motion fall apart here? A study of rotational motion is considerably more complex than a study of linear motion. Caution your students to be patient with themselves if they don't immediately catch on to what has taken centuries to master.

A neat activity for demonstrating centripetal force I learned from physics teacher Howard Brand is the following: Have a small group of students around a small table (ideally circular) blow air through straws at a Ping-Pong ball so that it will move in a circular path. They will experience the fact that the ball must be blown radially inward.

The lab *Going in Circles* should help "straighten out" student confusion about centripetal acceleration and force.

Suggested Lecture

Rotations and Revolutions: Without making a big deal of it, distinguish between a rotation [spin about an axis located within a body] and a revolution [axis outside the body]. A wheel rotates; its rim revolves. Cite the case of a spinning satellite [rotating] while it orbits the earth [revolving].

> CHECK QUESTIONS: Does a tossed football rotate or revolve? [It rotates (spins).] Does a ball whirled overhead at the end of a string rotate or revolve? [It revolves about you.]

[**Practice Book 9-1** here]

Rotational Speed and Tangential Speed: Distinguish between rotational speed and linear speed by the examples of riding at different radial positions on a merry-go-round. When the linear speed is tangent to a curved path, we speak of *tangential speed*.

> DEMONSTRATION [9-1]: Place coins on the top of a turntable, one near the center and the other near the edge. Rotate the table and show how the outer

has a greater linear speed. Point out that both have the same rotational speed — they undergo the same number of revolutions persecond. Compare the speeds of the coins to the speed of different parts of a phonograph record beneath the stylus. Linear velocity that is perpendicular to the radial direction is the same as tangential velocity [$v = r\omega$] Cite examples such as being able to see detail on the hub cap of a moving car while not seeing similar detail on the tire. Cite the motion of "tail-end Charlie" at the skating rink.

DEMONSTRATION [9-2]: Let a meterstick supported at the 0-cm mark swing like a pendulum from your fingers. How fast at any given moment is the 100-cm mark moving compared to the 50-cm mark? [The 100-cm mark is twice as far from the center of rotation than the 50-cm mark and has twice the linear speed.]

Liken this idea to the speed of the end of a flyswatter (the relatively long handle greatly amplifies the speed of your hand).

[NTQ 9-1, the object sliding off the rotating turntable, calls for vectors — and good thinking!]

The Tapered Wheels of Rail Road Cars: The two Doing Physics activities on pages 125 and 126 in the text nicely lead into a fascinating concept — how the tapered wheels of railroad cars keep the train on the track. After your class has done these activities, draw the sketch below, which illustrates the Link to Technology box on page 126. (This is the most interesting consequence of $v = r\omega$ that I know of, and students find the concept fascinating!)

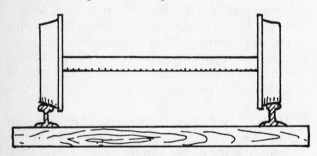

Centripetal Force: Define centripetal force as any force that causes a body to move in a circular path — or in part of a circular path, such as rounding a corner while riding a bicycle.

DEMONSTRATION [9-3]: Whirl an object such as a tin can securely fastened at the end of a string above your head. Don't simply discuss this: DO IT!

Expand on the idea that a centripetal force is exerted on the whirling can at the end of a string. The string pulls radially inward on the can. By Newton's 3rd

Law, the can pulls outward on the string — so there is an outward-acting force on the string. Stress the fact that this outward force does not act on the can. Only an inward force acts on the can.

DEMONSTRATION [9-4]: Swing a bucket of water in a vertical circle and show that the water doesn't spill. All your students have heard of this demonstration, but only a few have actually seen it done. They will particularly enjoy seeing YOU do it, and the prospect of seeing you "all wet!" [You're copping out if you only talk about it. DO IT!]

The water doesn't spill at the top when the centripetal force is at least equal to the weight of the water. But before invoking this explanation, ask why the water doesn't fall. After some thought state that your question is misleading, for the water indeed does fall! The "trick" is to pull the bucket down as fast as the water falls so both fall the same vertical distance in the same time. Too slow a swing produces a wet teacher. Interestingly enough, the water in the swinging bucket is analogous to the orbiting of a satellite. Both the swinging water and a satellite such as the orbiting space shuttle are falling. Because of their tangential velocities, they fall in a curve; just the right speed for the water in the bucket, and just the right greater speed for the space shuttle. Tying these related ideas together is good teaching!

CHECK QUESTION: A motorcycle runs on the inside of a bowl-shaped track (see sketch). Is the force that holds the motorcycle in a circular path an inward- or outward-directed force? [It is an inward-directed force — a centripetal force. An outward-directed force acts on the inner wall, which may bulge as a result, but no outward-directed force acts on the motorcycle.]

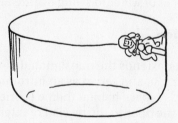

[**Transparency 15**, Figures 9.5, 9.7 on centripetal force here]

Centrifugal Force: Centrifugal force is the name given to a radially-outward-acting force, and it is useful only in a rotating frame of reference. The inward push feels like an outward pull to the occupants in a rotating system, as if a big mass were out there causing gravity. State how it differs from a real force in that there is no interaction — that is there is no mass out there pulling on it. The magnetic force between a paper clip and a magnet, for example, requires both the clip and magnet. They pull on each other and comprise a real interaction. Whereas a real force is an interaction between one body and another, there is no reaction counterpart to the centrifugal force that is felt. Distinguish centrifugal force from the action-reaction pairs of forces at the feet of an astronaut in a rotating habitat.

CHECK QUESTION: A person in a spinning space habitat feels a force like that of gravity and does pushups against the floor just as at home. Is the force that is felt a centrifugal or centripetal force? [Centrifugal force.] How does it differ from gravity? [Unlike gravity, there is no interaction with a "mass" or other thing that supposedly does the pulling.]

So we see that the centrifugal force is not a real force, but is the effect of rotation. This may be a difficult distinction to make with your students.

[**Practice Book 9-2b** nicely relates centripetal force with the parallelogram rule of vectors. This comes from CCSF colleague Jim Court's similar creation which he graciously shared with me. Thanks Jim!]

Applications: Discuss rotating space habitats. Show how g varies with the radial distance from the hub, and with the rotational rate of the structure. The earth has been the cradle of humankind; but humans do not live in the cradle forever. We may eventually leave our cradle and inhabit structures of our own building; structrues that will serve as lifeboats for the planet earth. Such a prospect is exciting from both technological and social points of view.

[**Practice Book 9-3** nicely illustrates some interesting physics in a rotating habitat. Controversy will be generated by the first question, where the question is asked about whether Bob sees Suzie rotating clockwise or counterclockwise. Suzie sees Bob rotating clockwise, and relative to Bob, Suzie rotates opposite. But Bob is facing Suzie, so he sees her rotating clockwise. You'll have fun with this! This idea was given to me by chemistry teacher Bob Becker in St. Louis. Bob reasoned that a jogger in a rotating habitat would press against the floor differently when jogging in different directions. When he found that his friends

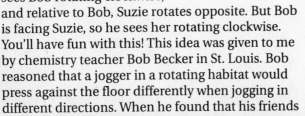

disagreed with him, he phoned me for my opinion. When he related his frustration with other teachers about this, I realized this would make an excellent practice page. Thank you, Bob Becker!]

More Think-and-Explain Questions

1. What is an advantage of the tapered shapes of birds eggs?
   Answer: The tapered shape ensures they'll roll in a curved path, which is an advantage for eggs that roll out of a nest in precarious places.

2. Somebody says that the reason the moon doesn't fall to earth is because the centrifugal force that acts on it exactly counteracts gravity. What do you say about this?
   Answer: No, no, no! First, no centrifugal force acts on the moon. The only force that holds it in orbit around the earth is a centripetal force, directed toward (not away from) the earth. This centripetal force *is* the gravitational force. Second, the moon does fall toward the earth, but because of its tangential velocity, it falls around rather than into the earth.

3. Is the centripetal force that holds the moon in earth orbit exactly equal to the gravitational force? Why?
   Answer: The centripetal force that holds the moon in earth orbit *is* the gravitional force, so of course it is exactly the same in magnitude and in every other respect. It is a mistake to assume there is both a gravitational *and* a centripetal force acting on the moon.

4. We humans and everything else in the world travel in a circular path as the earth rotates daily about its polar axis. Does this mean there is a centripetal force acting on us and everything else?
   Answer: Yes; the centripetal force is supplied by the force of gravity. If gravity were not as strong as it is, centripetal force may not be great enough to hold things to the earth. The first to go would be things closest to the equator, which travels faster than other parts of the world and requires greater centripetal force. The exception is the poles, where no centripetal force is required because there is no tangential speed there. [Caution: The centripetal force that acts on objects at the earth's surface is the full force of gravity only at the equator. Only there is the radial distance the same as the earth's radius. At other latitudes the centripetal force is the component of gravitational force perpendicular to the earth's axis ($mg \cos \theta$, where θ is the number of degrees from the equator). At the

45th parallel, for example, it is 0.707 the pull of gravity; at the poles, zero. (Advanced stuff at this point.)]

5. If the earth rotated 17 times faster, objects at the equator would have no weight. What of objects at higher or lower latitudes? Explain.
Answer: Gravitation would still exceed the "centrifugal force" at latitudes away from the equator, so things there would still hug the earth.

Think and Solves

1. From the equation $F = mv^2/r$, calculate the tension in a 2-m length of string that whirls a 1-kg mass at 2 m/s in a horizontal circle.
Answer: $F = mv^2/r = [1 \text{ kg} \times (2 \text{ m/s})^2]/2 \text{ m} = 2 \text{ N}$.

2. Answer the previous question for the case of (a) twice the mass, (b) twice the speed, (c) twice the length of string (radial distance), and (d) twice mass, twice speed, and twice distance all at the same time.
Answer: (a) Twice, 4 N; (b) Four times; 8 N; (c) Half; 1 N; (d) Twice, 4 N (because 2 x 4 x 1/2 = 4 N).

3. a. What is the centripetal force acting on you in "Spin Out" if the radius of the cylinder is 7 meters, your mass is 50 kg, and you are traveling at 5 m/s?
b. What force keeps from sliding downward and how does that force relate to the above spinning speed?

Answer: a. $F = mv^2/r = (50 \text{ kg})(5 \text{ m/s})^2/7 \text{ m} = 179 \text{ N}$ b. friction and it increases with the increased normal force with increased speed.

4. Suppose you tie a rock to the end of a 1 meter long string and spin it in a vertical circle. What is the minimum speed it can travel and "just" get around the top? (Hint: the rope will just start to go "slack" and the only force acting on the rock, downward, is gravity.)
Answer: At the top, with no string tension, the only force acting is mg, which provides the centripetal force. So from $mg = mv^2/r$, $v = 3.13 \text{ m/s}$.

5. Suppose you are standing in a circular rotating space station, in outer space, with a tangential speed of 300 m/s. If the radius of the station is 9184 meters, what will you weigh? (Hint: Find v^2/r and compare it to g)

Answer: Weight will be your normal force, which = mv^2/r. Note that $v^2/r = 300 \text{ m/s})^2/9184 \text{ m} = 9.8 \text{ m/s}^2$, the same as earth g. So your weight would be what it is on the earth's surface.

10 Center of Gravity

Objectives

- Describe center of gravity.
- Describe how a plumb line and bob can be used to find the center of gravity of an irregularly shaped object.
- Given the location of the center of gravity and the area of support of an object, predict whether the object will topple.
- Distinguish among stable equilibrium, unstable equilibrium, and neutral equilibrium.
- Give examples of how a human is affected by the need to keep the body's center of gravity over the support base.

Possible Misconceptions to Correct

- The center of mass of an object must be where physical mass exists.
- The center of gravity of a person is at a fixed place inside the body.

Demonstration Equipment

- [10-1] Small ball and a piece of wood or plastic cut into an L shape (about the size of this book so it can be clearly seen).
- [10-2] An irregularly-shaped piece of plywood somewhat larger than the size of this book, with 3 strings fastened to different locations along the edge.
- [10-3] Same L-shaped object, a baseball bat, and any other irregular shapes to show CG.
- [10-4] Any assortment of CG toys such as Fig 10.18.
- [10-5] A container of dried beans and a Ping Pong ball (Figure 10.20).
- [10-6] A chair.

Introduction

Toppling is treated in this chapter before the concept of torque is introduced (next chapter). Toppling is treated as a result of a nonsupported center of gravity (CG). I suggest you treat it as the text does, and save the concept "torque" until the following Chapter 11, Rotational Mechanics. Or else introduce torque when you discuss toppling, as sort of a preview to the next chapter.

A nice extension of Activity 2 on page 148 (sliding two fingers to the center of a balanced

meterstick), is to do the same to a horizontally balanced plate on three fingers. Bring your fingers together and the plate remains in balance!

A neat demo is to attach a heavy weight to the edge of a basketball. Then give it a slight spin and toss it across the room.

A nice prop is a cutout of your state, suspended as the cutout of the U.S. in Figure 10.8. [For contiguous U.S. (48 states) the CG is near Lebanon, Smith County, Kansas. For the whole U.S., including Alaska and Hawaii, the CG is in South Dakota; Butte County, west of Castle Rock.] You can show where the CG of your homestate is. You can go a step further and stick nails or other heavy weights where population densities lie, in such a way that you can find the "CG" of your state in terms of population. (In 1980 the "center of population" for the United States was 1/4 mile west of De Soto in Jefferson County, Mo.) Construction makes a good project for energetic students.

Another good prop is the variable incline, block, and plumb bob arrangement shown in Figure 10.10. Another student project!

An impressive demonstration is the following: Place a wind-up (spring action) stop watch on top of an upside-down watchglass with a tiny mirror siliconed to the watch. Shine a laser beam on the mirror; watch the beam move back and forth with the rocking motion of the watch. The CG is slightly displaced with each tick! The same is true of a person lying still on a table. The table vibrates slightly with the heart beat.

This chapter can be skimmed or skipped if your time is tight.

Suggested Lecture

Begin with the following demonstration:

DEMONSTRATION [10-1]: Toss a small ball from one hand to the other and call attention to the smooth parabola it traces. Then toss an L-shaped piece of wood or other material. State that in doing so it doesn't seem to follow a smooth parabola — that it wobbles all over the place. A very special place, nontheless — the place that this chapter is about — the CG.

[**Transparency 16**, Figures 10.1 and 10.4 here]

Center of Gravity and Center of Mass:
Define center of gravity as the average positon of weight, and center of mass as the average position of matter. For our purposes, they describe the same point. Show that the CG of a book is at the geometrical center, which is easily found by the intersection of diagonal lines from opposite corners. But what of an object with more than 4 corners?

DEMONSTRATION [10-2]: Show a piece of irregular-shaped plywood (somewhat larger than the book) that has about 5 corners. Three short pieces of string are fastened at different places along its edge. Ask how the CG of this shape can be found. Certainly not by connecting the corners, for the lines would not have a common intersection. Solution: Suspend the plywood by one of the strings and draw a vertical chalk line beneath the point of suspension. Do this with a second string and the intersection is the CG. Double check by suspending it by a third string.

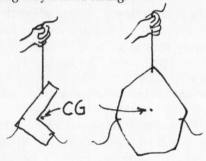

DEMONSTRATION [10-3]: Attempt to balance the L shape with its small end on the table and watch it topple. That's because it wasn't supported at its "average position of weight" — its CG. Illustrate CG with a baseball bat and other objects.

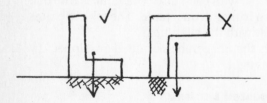

State that when the "average position of mass" is considered, one speaks of the center of mass. For most cases, the two are indistinguishable, so CG will be taken to mean both.

Stability: Distinguish between unstable, neutral, and stable equilibrium.

DEMONSTRATION [10-4]: Show how the CG of an object is either raised, not changed, or lowered when the object is tipped. Also demonstrate, if available, the devices shown in Figures 10.17 and 10.18.

Work and Raising CG: A floating iceberg will not tip over because its CG is below the water line. If it were to tip, its CG would be raised, which requires a work input. This is true for Sutro Tower in San Francisco, that easily withstands strong winds. Its base is so heavily buried into concrete that it in a sense is "already tipped over." Similarly for the Space Needle in Seattle. Work input is needed to raise the CG of a system. Relate this idea to Figures 10.20 and 10.21.

DEMONSTRATION [10-5]: Shake a container of dried beans with a Ping Pong ball at the bottom, as shown in Figure 10.20. [Here the density of the beans is greater than the density of the Ping Pong ball, so it's like "panning gold." For objects of the same density, smaller ones will fill in the open spaces between larger ones and similarly produce a greater effective density of space. The CG lowers.]

The shaking beans demo can be extended to the Ping Pong ball in a glass of water. The CG of the system is lowest when the Ping-Pong ball floats. Push it under the surface and the CG is raised. If you do the same thing with something more dense than water, the CG is lowest when it is sunk at the bottom. (More about this in Chapter 19.)

[**NTQ 10-2**, about the shaken berries, parallels the shaking beans topic.]

CG of People: Ask your students if they have a CG. Acknowledge that the CG in men is generally higher than in women (1% - 2%), mainly because women tend to be proportionally smaller in the upper body, and heavier in the pelvis. The CG of men and women can be likened to the CG of a baseball bat standing on end; with its heavy end toward the ground it is similar to the build of an average woman. With its narrow end toward the ground it is similar to the build of an average man. Point out that this may apply to most people, but not to all people. People come in a variety of sizes and proportions, a diversity that makes for a more interesting world. For most adults, the CG with arms at the side lies about 6 inches above the crotch, a bit below the bellybutton. [If your students have done the lab activity *Where's Your CG?* they have presumably discovered this.] In children, the CG is about 5% higher because of their proportionally larger heads and shorter legs. The central location of the CG is important in a fetus, for unborns rotate. The CG of a person is not located in a fixed place, but depends on body orientation. Just as the CG of a boomerang is outside the material, your CG is outside your body when you bend over and make a U or L shape. Whatever your body orientation, to remain stable your CG must be above (or below) a support base area. Show how this support base is enlarged when you stand with your feet wide apart (Figure 10.23).

DEMONSTRATION [10-6]: Attempt to stand from a seated postion without putting your feet under the chair. [This cannot be done unless your feet provide a support base area that lies beneath your CG.]

DEMONSTRATION [10-7]: Challenge your students to the following home project: Tell them to stand facing a wall with toes against the wall and simply stand unaided on tiptoes for a couple of seconds. If they can do this in your next class meeting, they will receive an A for the course! [This cannot be done, because the CG will be farther from the wall than the support base provided by the toes. With a bit of "trickery" this can be done near a doorway when you hold a heavy weight from your extended arm into the doorway in front of yourself so that the CG is above the narrow support base. But nonaided, you'll award no A grades for this feat.

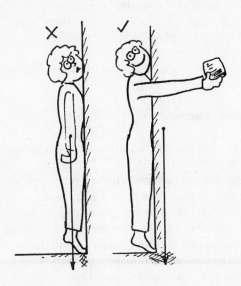

In the following chapter, the same examples can be explained with torques.

More Think-and-Explain Questions

1. Why is the middle seating most comfortable in a bus traveling along a bumpy road?
   Answer: The bus will tend to rock about its CG. The closer one's seat is to the CG, the less up and down motion as the bus rocks. (The CG of the bus will depend also on whether the motor is in the front or the back.)

2. Why does a hiker carrying a heavy backpack lean forward?
   Answer: Leaning forward puts the CG above the feet.

3. What is the role of the heavy tail of dinosaurs with respect to CG?
   Answer: With tail extended the dinosaur's CG is above its feet when running.

4. How does a heavy tail enable a monkey standing on a branch to reach to farther branches?
   Answer: With tail extended backward, the monkey's CG is above its feet even when its arms are extended forward.

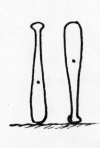

5. The CG of a baseball bat is not in the middle of the bat, but toward the more massive end. When the bat is stood upright with its massive end down, its CG is lower to the ground than when stood upright with its massive end up. How is this similar to the different CGs of broad-shouldered men and broad-hipped women?
   Answer: Standing upright with massive end up is similar to the higher CG of the man; standing with massive end down is similar to the lower CG of the woman.

11 Rotational Mechanics

Objectives

- Define torque and describe what it depends on.
- Describe the condition for one torque to balance another.
- Given the location of the center of gravity of an object and the position and direction of the forces on it, tell whether the forces will produce rotation.
- Describe what the rotational inertia of an object depends on.
- Give examples of how a gymnast changes the rotational inertia of the body in order to change the spin rate.
- Define angular momentum and describe the conditions under which it a) remains the same and b) changes.
- Give an example of a situation in which the rotational speed changes but the angular momentum does not.

Possible Misconceptions to Correct

- Torque and force are the same concept.
- Inertia and rotational inertia are much the same concept.

Demonstration Equipment

- [11-1] L shape (used in previous chapter demo).
- [11-2] Your own body.
- [11-3] Disk with lead in it so its CG if off center, and inclined plane.
- [11-4] Two drinking glasses, a candle, and two pins or needles.
- [11-5] A very heavy plank (a considerable fraction of your weight).
- [11-6] A wooden stick, about 1 m long, with about 1 or 2 kg of mass attached at one end — or a broom or sledge hammer.
- [11-7] A pair of plastic pipes, about 1 m long; one with 2 massive lead inserts in its center, the other with the same massive lead inserts in each end. (Hidden version of Figure 11.9.)
- [11-8] Hoop and solid cylinder, and inclined plane (a 1-m or more board will do).
- [11-9] Cans of food, liquid and solid, and the same inclined plane.
- [11-10] Rotating platform and a pair of masses of about 2-kg.
- [11-11] Gyroscope (prefertably bicycle-wheel kind).

Introduction

This chapter may be difficult for your students because it consists of a lot of hardcore physics that takes time to assimilate. It may be omitted without consequence.

Chapter 10, Center of Gravity, may be combined with this chapter. In Chapter 10 toppling was explained without torques in terms of the CG of a system extending beyond a base of support. The concept of torque is now introduced here.

The formulas for the rotational inertias of common shapes are given in Figure 11.14 on page 157. They are intended to serve interesting information about relative rotational inertias. For some of your students, however, they may be seen as a threat — for considerable complexity is evident that may be used in examinations — particularly closed book exams. It would be counterproductive for your students to learn the different formulas, or to think they are learning any physics at all if they memorize them. Please make this clear to your class, and do not use the formulas as examination material.

An excellent resource for examples of rotational mechanics is *Sport Science* by Peter Brancazio (Simon & Shuster, 1984). Brancazio's book is an excellent source of physics applications, with emphasis on the human body.

The labs *Weighing an Elephant* and *Keeping in Balance* are classic lever-principle labs.

Suggested Lecture

Torque: Extend the lab-manual activity *Torque Feeler* to other "twisting forces," such as prying a lid off a can with a screwdriver, turning a wrench, or even opening (rotating) a door. Cite how a steering wheel is simply a modified wrench, and explain why trucks and heavy vehicles without power steering use large-diameter steering wheels. In all these cases there are two important considerations: (1) the application of a force, and (2) leverage.

DEMONSTRATION [11-1]: Place the L-shaped object on the table and show how it topples in different positions (as you did in Demo [10-2] in the previous chapter).

On the board sketch the L shape as shown in the first sketch and define torque.

[**Transparency 17**, Figure 11.4 here]

Torque and Your CG: Recall from the previous chapter that the location of one's CG depends upon body configuration.

DEMONSTRATION [11-2]: Stand against a wall and ask if it is possible for one to bend over and touch their toes without toppling forward. When you attempt to do so your body position approximates the L shape. Sketch this on the board next to the L-shape as shown. By now your chalkboard looks as follows:

Discuss a remedy for such toppling, like longer shoes or the wearing of snowshoes or skiis. Sketch a pair of skiis on the feet of the person in your drawing.

The Pregnant Woman: Seem to change the subject and ask why a pregnant woman often gets back pains. Sketch a woman before and after getting pregnant, showing how the CG shifts forward — beyond a point of support for the same posture. Make a third sketch showing how the woman adjusts her posture so that her CG is above the support base bounded by her feet, sketching lastly, the "marks of pain." Ask the class how she could prevent these pains, and if someone in class doesn't volunteer the idea of wearing skiis, do so yourself and sketch skiis on her feet in the second drawing.

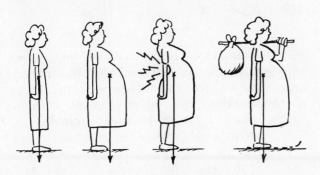

Lead your class into an alternate solution, that of carrying a pole on her shoulder, near the end of which is a load. Erase the skiis and sketch in the pole and load as shown. Acknowledge the objection that she would have to increase the mass of the load as the months go by, and ask what else can be done. Someone should volunteer that she need only move the load closer to the end, which in effect shifts the overall CG in a favorable direction (or produces

more counter torque). This routine is effective and sparks much class interest. However, you must be very careful that you don't offend your students, particularly your female students. Whenever you single out any "minority (?)" you run the risk of offending members of that minority group or those sensitive to the feelings of members of that group. We instructors are for the most part conscious of this, and therefore make our examples as general as possible — mixing "shes" and "hes" whenever these pronouns come up. But in the case of a person becoming pregnant, its a definite "she." At the risk of being too defensive, you might acknowledge this point. Any classroom laughter that your presentation elicits should be, after all, directed to the situation and not particularly toward the woman. In any event, we are in sad shape when we cannot laugh at ourselves occasionally. A similar story can be made of a man with a paunchy stomach.

Torque and CG Examples: Return to your chalkboard sketches of L-shaped objects and relate their tipping to the torques that exist. Point out the lever arms in the sketches.

CHECK QUESTION: An L-shaped object with CG marked by the X rests on a hill as shown. Draw this on your paper and mark it appropriately to determine whether the object will topple or not. Comment: Be prepared for some students to incorrectly sketch in the "vertical" line through the CG *perpendicular* to the slope as shown. Vertical lines should be vertical!

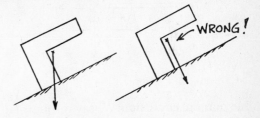

Cite examples involving the CG in animals and people — how a walking pigeon moves its head back and forth with each step, thereby keeping its CG above the foot it momentarily stands on — how the long tails of monkeys enable them to lean forward without losing balance — and how people lean backwards when carrying a heavy load at their chests, and how the coolie method with the load distributed in two parts suspended at the ends of a pole supported in the middle is a better way.

Ask why a ball rolls down a hill. State that "because of gravity" is an incomplete answer. Gravity would have it slide down the hill. The fact it rolls, or rotates, is evidence of an unbalanced torque. Sketch this on your chalkboard.

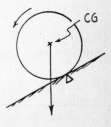

DEMONSTRATION [11-3]: Show how a "loaded disk" rolls *up* an inclined plane. After class speculation, show how the disk remains at rest on the incline. When at rest, the CG is above the point of support. Show this on your chalkboard sketch to show how both the CG with respect to the support point is altered. This means there is no absence of a lever arm and therefore the absence of a torque.

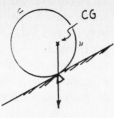

[**Practice Book 11.2**, which begins with torques that emphize the lever-arm construction, end with the spool and ball rolling down a hill situations. Fun!]

See Saws: Extend rotation to see-saws. Show this first on the board with a sketch of equal-weight players (a similar sketch to Figure 11.5 on page 152). Cite how the force x distance on the left side of the fulcrum that tends to make the see saw rotate counterclockwise = the force x distance on the right side. Then discuss the case of the twice-as-heavy boy (Figure 11.5 on page 152). Same idea.

CHECK QUESTION: If the boy in Figure 11.5 weighed 600 N, how far would he have to sit from the fulcrum for equilibrium? [1 m.]

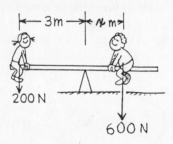

(Possible point of confusion: We say Torque = *Fd*, and in the previous chapter we said Work = *Fd*. The distance for torque is altogether different than the distance used for work. In work the distance *d* is the distance the "force moves" (parallel to the force). In torque the distance *d* refers to the leverage distance (perpendicular to the force). The ratios *d / d* for levers and see saws, however, turn out to be the same.)

Explain how participants on a see-saw can vary the net torque by not only sliding back and forth, but by leaning. In this way the location of their CGs and hence the lever arm distance is changed.

[**NTQ 11-1**, the sawed-off broom, nicely distinguishes between force and torque.]

DEMONSTRATION [11-4]: Do as Cindy Dube at Farmington High School in Conneticut does and make a candle see saw. Trim with the wick ex-

posed at both ends, and balance the candle by a needle through the center. Rest the ends of the needle on a pair of drinking glasses. Light both ends of the candle. As the wax drips, the CG shifts, causing the candle to oscillate.

Solitary See Saw: Thus far, the CG of the see saw has been at the axis of rotation. The weight of the see saw contributed no torque because of the 0 lever arm. When the fulcrum is not at the CG the situation becomes somewhat more complicated (more interesting?).

Cite the case of the obnoxious boy who cannot find a playmate to join him playing see-saw. He simply moves the middle of the see-saw beyond the fulcrum and uses the weight of the see-saw, at its CG, as his "invisible partner." Once balanced, he is able to rotate up and down by leaning toward and away from the fulcrum. This "solitary see-saw" idea will require repeated explanation, and is the concept treated in the lab experiment, *Weighing an Elephant*.

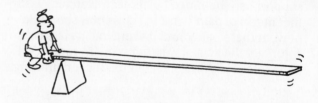

DEMONSTRATION [11-5] : Place a heavy plank on your lecture table so that it overhangs. Walk out on the overhanging part and ask why you don't topple. (Or simulate this with a smaller version — a heavy weight and a board that overhangs your table.) Relate this to the solitary see-saw example.

This is difficult for students who don't see this is a version of the solitary see saw. If person and board have the same weight, then the fulcrum is midway between the CGs of both, like the simpler case of two twins on a see saw. Likewise, if you and the board have equal weights, the edge of the table will be midway between you and the CG of the board — at the 1/4 mark (one half the distance from the end to the CG). If you are heavier than the board, then the fulcrum (edge of the table) must be closer to you so that the board's CG has more leverage.

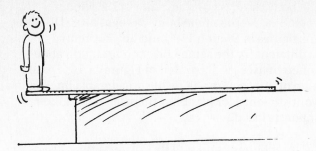

Rotational Inertia: Compare the concept of inertia and its role in linear motion to rotational inertia (sometimes called "moment of inertia") and its role in rotational motion. The difference between the two involves the role of *radial distance* from a rotational axis. The greater the distance of mass concentration, the greater the resistance to rotation.

DEMONSTRATION [11-6]: Have students try to balance on a finger an upright long stick with a massive lead weight at one end. Try it first with the weight at the finger tip, then with the weight at the top. [Rotional inertia is greater for the stick when it is made to rotate with the massive part far from the pivot than closer — the farther the mass, the greater the rotational inertia — which is to say, the more it resists a change in rotation.] Or you can use a broom, or long-handled hammer. Relate this to the ease with which a circus performer balances a pole full of people doing acrobatics, and cite how much more difficult it would be for the performer to balance an empty pole!

Relate this demonstration and the continued adjustments you have to execute to keep the object balanced to the similar adjustments that must be made in keeping a rocket vertical when it is first fired. Amazing.

DEMONSTRATION [11-7]: Have two 1 meter pipes, one with two lead plugs in the center, the other with plugs in each end. They appear identical. Weigh both to show the same weight. Give one to a student (with plugs in ends) and ask her to rotate it about its center (like in Figure 11.9). Have another student do the same with the pipe that has the plugs in the middle. Then have them switch. Good fun. Then ask for speculations as to why one was noticeably more difficult to rotate back and forth.

Explain how the location of an object's mass with respect to its axis of rotation determines its rotational inertia. Hence the large rotational inertias of flywheels with mass concentrations along the rim. The rotational inertia of an object is a measure of how much it resists turning, a fact employed by tightrope walkers who carry long poles.

Cite the similarity of training wheels on a bicycle for a beginner, to a long pole for a beginning tightrope walker. Suppose the ends of the long pole could slide along supporting slots as a tightrope walker walked along the wire. If the pole has adequate rotational inertia, the slots provide psychological comfort as well as actual safety. Just as the training wheels could be safely removed without the rider's knowledge, the slots could be safely removed without the walker's knowledge. Angular momentum aids the cyclist and rotational inertia aids the tightrope walker.

State the law of rotational inertia: an object rotating about an axis tends to keep rotating in the absence of an external torque.

CHECK QUESTION: Why are spiral grooves cut in the bores of guns? [Once spinning about an axis, the bullet tends to remain spinning about that axis. This prevents a flip flop and avoids greater air resistance.]

Show how a longer pendulum has a greater period and relate this to the different strides of long and short legged people. Imitate these strides yourself — or at least with your fingers walking across the desk.

[**Transparency 18**, Figure 11.4 here]

Discuss the variety of rotational inertias shown in Figure 11.14 on page 157. Stress the formulas are for comparison, and point out why the same formula applies to the pendulum and the hoop (all the mass of each is at the same distance from the rotational axis). State how reasonable the smaller value for a solid disk is, given that much of its mass is close to the rotational axis. State that learning the formulas has little value. Comparing the effort needed to change the rotation of the various figures, on the other hand, is good physics.

CHECK QUESTION: Supposing the shapes in Figure 11.14 all have the same mass and radius (or length), which would be the easiest to start spinning about the axes indicated? [The stick about its CG, as indicated by its small rotational inertia.] Which would be the most difficult to start (or stop) spinning? [The simple pendulum or the hoop about its normal axis, as indicated by the relatively large rotational inertia.]

Relate the acceleration of a rolling object down an incline with its rotational inertia. For similar masses, shapes with the greater rotational inertia (the "laziest") lag behind shapes with less rotational inertia.

DEMONSTRATION [11-8]: Roll hoops and cylinders down an incline after asking your students to predict which rolls faster? (This is the lab activity *Rotational Derby*.) [Any cylinder will beat any hoop. Mass does not play a role just as it doesn't play a roll in the acceleration of free fall or the acceleration of a block down a frictionless plane. The acceleration down an incline has to do with the rotational inertia *per kilogram*. In effect the mass cancels out. That's why regardless of mass, any cylinder will beat any hoop.]

DEMONSTRATION [11-9]: Roll various cans of food down an incline and ask why different cans roll at different accelerations. Does a can of chicken soup beat vegetarian vegetable? How do Chinese noodles compare with pineapple juice? [A can of low-viscosity liquid rolls faster than a can of beans — the beans are made to turn with the turning can, and are therefore "lazy," while a liquid doesn't turn with the can and behaves like a sliding block — no rotation, no rotational inertia! Contents of various compositions and viscosities will produce varying performances (again, the object of *Rotational Derby*).]

Going Further with Rolling: Rolling things have two kinds of kinetic energy: that due to linear motion, and that due to rotational motion. So an object rolling down an incline will lag behind a freely sliding object because a part of a rolling object's kinetic energy is in rotation. If this is clear, the following question is in order for your better students.

NEXT-TIME QUESTIONS: Which will roll with the greater acceleration down an incline, a can of water or a frozen can of ice? Double credit for a good explanation of what is seen. [The can of water will undergo appreciably more acceleration because the liquid is not made to rotate with the rotating can. It in effect "slides" rather than rolls down the incline, so practically all the KE at the bottom is in linear speed with next-to none in rotation. Fine, one might say, then if the liquid doesn't rotate, the can ought to behave as an empty can, with the larger rotational inertia of a "hoop" and lag behind. This brings up an interesting point: The issue is not which can has the greater rotational inertia, but which has the greater rotational inertia compared to its mass (note the qualifier in the legend of Figure 11.15.) The liquid content has appreciably more mass than the can that contains it; hence the non-rolling liquid serves to increase the mass of the can without contributing to its rotational inertia. It gives the can of liquid a relatively small rotational inertia compared to its mass.]

[NTQ 11-2 parallels the above.]

Rotational Inertia and Gymnastics: State that just as the body can change shape and orientation, the rotational inertia of the body changes also. Discuss the figures in Section 11.5, and how rotational inertia is different for the same body configuration about different axes, as illustrated in Figure 11.16. Discussion of this section will be of considerable interest to your students, for it's about themselves and their interests in a direct way.

Angular Momentum and its Conservation: Just as inertia and rotational inertia differ by a radial distance, and just as force and torque also differ by a radial distance, so momentum and angular momentum differ by a radial distance. Relate linear momentum to angular momentum for the case of a small mass at a relatively large radial distance — the object you previously swung overhead.

For the more general case, angular momentum is simple the product of rotational inertia I and angular velocity ω. This is indicated in Figure 11.24.

DEMONSTRATION [11-10]: With weights in your hand, rotate on a platform as shown in Figure 11.26. Show angular momentum conservation by drawing your arms in and speeding up.

Cite the fact that much mass flows down the Mississippi River as mud that is deposited in the Gulf of Mexico. Ask what effect this tends to have on the earth's rotation. [It tends to slow the earth, which you can simulate on the rotating table with one weight held outstretched at about 45° and lowered toward the horizontal. Students will see a slowing of rotational speed.] Cite also the fact that when polar ice melts, the melted water tends to flow toward the equatorial parts of the earth, effectively spreading the mass of ice away from the polar axis. Ask what effect this tends to have on the earth's rotation. [Again, it tends to slow the earth, which you can simulate on the rotating table with two weights held outstretched overhead and lowered toward the horizontal. Students will see even more slowing of rotational speed.]

DEMONSTRATION [11-11]: Show the operation of a gyroscope — either a model or a rotating bicycle wheel as my late son James demonstrates in Figure 11.23. You can demonstrate angular momentum conservation nicely if you stand on the turntable and show different orientations of the spinning wheel. Begin with the axes of spinning wheel and stationary rotating platform perpendicular [no effect]. Then turn the axis of the spinning wheel so it is parallel to the axis of the platform. If you had no angular momentum initially, you'll rotate in a direction opposite to that of the spinning wheel to produce the same zero angular momentum. Different angles produce different components of angular momentum with interesting effects. (The angular momentum vector is along the axis of rotation. Let the spin be in the direction of your curled fingers on your right hand. Then the angular momentum vector is in the direction of your thumb.)

More Think-and-Explain Questions

1. If you place any weight on a balanced see-saw it will topple — unless the weight is placed directly above the fulcrum. Why will weight added there not upset the balance?
Answer: At this place, the added force passes through the CG of the seesaw and the fulcrum — no lever arm — no torque — no rotation.

2. A basketball player wishes to balance a ball on his fingertip. Will he be more successful with a spinning ball or a stationary ball? What physical principle supports your answer?
Answer: A spinning ball is more easily balanced, in accord with the law of rotational inertia — a spinning body tends to remain spinning.

3. You'd hold your finger in the middle of a horizontal meter stick, at the 50-cm mark, to balance it. Suppose you hang an identical meter stick vertically from one end, say the 0-cm end. Where would you place your finger to balance the horizontal stick?

?

Answer: At the 25-cm mark, where equal weights would each be 25 cm distant.

4. Suppose you sit in the middle of a large freely rotating turntable at an amusement park. If you crawl toward the outer rim, does the rotational speed increase, decrease, or remain unchanged? What physical principle supports your answer?
Answer: Rotational speed decreases, in accord with the conservation of angular momentum.

5. Why is it incorrect to say that when you execute a somersault and pull your arms and legs inward that your angular momentum increases?
Answer: It is your rotational speed that increases, not your angular momentum. Angular momentum remains the same. [The confusion is likely with the many terms in this chapter, rather than the concepts.]

6. When a car accelerates forward, why does its front end rise? Why does its front end dip when braking?

Answer: The force by the road on the tires rocks the car about its CG. When the force is forward, the car rocks nose up; when the force is bacward, the car rocks nose down. When speed is constant, the nose levels off.

More Think and Solves

Do all work on a separate sheet. Be complete and show the logic of your solutions.
A ruler is balanced as shown in the diagram with the fulcrum at the 50 cm mark.

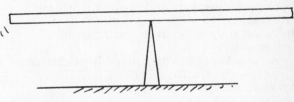

1. If a 200 gram weight is placed at the 20 cm mark (30 cm from the fulcrum) at what mark should a 500 gram be placed so that the system balances?
Answer: 1. 62 cm mark

2. If a 100 gram weight was placed at the 25 cm mark, a 20 gram weight at the 10 cm mark, where should a 500 gram weight be placed to balance the system?
Answer: 56.6 cm mark

3. Come up with an arrangement of a 50 gram, a 100 gram, a 200 gram and a 500 gram weight that balances. Show all the math and indicate the positions the weights should occupy (like in problems 1 and 2)
Open ended

4. A 200 gram weight is placed at the 30 cm position and a 500 gram weight at the 60 cm position. If we neglect the mass of the meter stick where is the center of mass of the two weights? (You are looking for the balance point!)
Answer: 51.4 cm mark

5. If the meter stick weighs 200 grams, now where is the center of mass of the system? (Hint: The two weights (200 gram + 500 gram = 700 grams) act as though they *both* were at their center of mass.)
Answer: 51.1 cm. mark

12 Universal Gravitation

Objectives

- Explain Newton's idea that the moon, like an apple, falls toward the earth.
- Explain why the moon does not fall into the earth, nor the planets into the sun.
- State Newton's law of universal gravitation.
- Explain the significance of an inverse-square law.
- Explain the connection between gravitation and the idea that the universe may stop expanding and begin to contract.
- Give examples of how Newton's theory of gravitation affected the thinking of philosophers of the eighteenth century.

Possible Misconceptions to Correct

- Newton discovered gravity (rather than discovering that gravity was universal).
- Above the atmosphere of the earth there is no earth gravity.
- The moon and planets are beyond the pull of earth gravity.
- Gravity gets stronger with altitude, as evidenced by objects carried up a flight of stairs feeling heavier at the top.

No Demonstrations for this Chapter

Introduction

This chapter presents a good climate for discussion of the meaning of a scientific theory, referred to in the footnote of page 171. The last chapter on *Cargo Cult Science* of Feynman's book, *Surely You're Joking, Mr. Feynman* (Norton, 1985), expands nicely on this. Read this entertaining book; also his *What Do You Care What Other People Think* (Norton, 1987).

Although the formula for Newton's law of gravitation is not shown until five pages into the chapter, I have found considerable success in lecture by beginning with the law right away. All the examples throughout the lecture relate to the formula. The formula focuses on what might be seen as diverse phenomena. (Acknowledge that many other texts and references use the symbol r instead of the d used in this text. The r is used to indicate the radial distance from a body's CG, and to emphasize the center-to-center rather than surface-to-surface nature for distance, and to prepare for r as a displacement vector. We don't set our plow that deep, however, and use d for distance.)

There are no demos for this chapter, nor are there labs. Keep class participation and interest via the check-your-neighbor routine. (By now have you noticed that this routine dows more than engage your class — allowing *you* ample time to check your own notes, collect your thoughts, and improve your pacing?)

Suggested Lecture

Begin by briefly discussing the simple codes and patterns that underlie the complex things around us, whether musical compositions or DNA molecules, and then briefly describe the harmonious motion of the solar system, the Milky Way and other galaxies in the universe — stating that the shapes of the planets, stars, and galaxies, and their motions are all governed by an extremely simple code, or if you will, a pattern. Then write the formula for universal gravitation on the board.

Formula Supported by Examples: Give examples of bodies pulling on each other to convey a clear idea of what the symbols in the equation mean and how they relate.

CHECK QUESTIONS: How is the gravitational force between a pair of planets altered when the mass of one is doubled? [Twice the force.] When both are doubled? [The force is four times as great.] When they are twice as far apart? [Twice as far apart decreases the force to 1/4 as much.] When they are three times as far apart? [To 1/9 as much.] Ten times as far apart? [To 1/100 as much.]

Development of the Formula: Talk of how Newton developed the law, going from falling apples to the falling moon. Explain what is meant by *tangential* speed or velocity. The physics of the falling earth is explained in more detail in Chapter 14. (Perhaps call attention to the comic strip, "Satellite Physics" ahead on page 201 if questions are raised about satellite motion.)

[**Transparency 19**, Newton's drawing of satellite paths about the earth, Figure 12.2 here. Follow this up with **Transparency 20**, Figure 12.10]

[**Next-Time Question 12-1** on the cable to replace gravity between the earth and moon should spark interest]

Inverse-Square Law: Discuss the inverse square law and go over Figure 12.10 or its equivalent for candle-light or radioactivity.

CHECK QUESTIONS: A space probe is a certain distance, center to center, from a massive star. If it instead is four times as far from the star, how does its gravitational force toward the star compare? [1/16 as much.] A sheet of photographic film is exposed to a point source of light that is a certain distance away. If the sheet were instead exposed to the same light four times as far away, how would the intensity on the film compare? [1/16 as much.] A radioactive detector registers a certain amount of radioactivity when it is a certain distance away from a small piece of uranium. If the detector is four times as far from the uranium, how will the radioactivity reading compare? [1/16 as much.]

Plot to scale an inverse-square curve on the board, showing the initial steepness of the curve and how it quickly "levels off" as it goes from 1/4 to 1/9, to 1/16 for twice, thrice, and four times separation. This is shown in Figure 12.11.

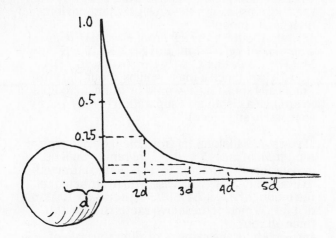

[**Practice Book 12-1** develops the inverse square law]

CHECK QUESTIONS: True or false: The force of earth gravity on the space shuttle in orbit is zero or nearly zero. [False! The force of earth gravity on the shuttle in orbit is nearly the same as the force of earth gravity on the shuttle at sea level. At an altitude of 200 km, well above the earth's atmosphere, the space shuttle is only 3% farther from the earth's center and experiences 94% the gravitational pull at the earth's surface.] True or false: At the far reaches of the universe, a body would experience zero earth gravity. [False! The equation guides thinking here: As distance d approaches infinity, force F approaches (but does not reach) zero. As a practical matter, at such a distance the force due to earth gravity may be negligible in comparison to the influences of closer and more massive bodies, but strictly speaking, the gravitation of the earth extends to infinity. No matter how far you go, earth gravity is your companion.]

Gravitational Constant G: Explain the gravitational constant G by comparing it to the constant π for circles. Begin by writing $C \sim D$, draw several different-size circles on the board, and show how circumference and diameter are proportional. State how if you divide the circumference C by the diameter D for any circle, you get the same number; 22/7. This constant number is called π. So the proportion can be written as the exact equation, $C = \pi D$.

Similarly for the constant G in Newton's equation. When the force of gravity F between two bodies of mass m_1 and m_2 and separated by distance d is divided by $m_1 m_2 / d^2$, the number that results is a constant (6.67×10^{-11} Nm^2/kg^2). So the proportion $F \sim m_1 m_2 / d^2$ can be written as the exact equation $F = G m_1 m_2 / d^2$. Call attention to von Jolly's method, Figure 12.8.

Universal Gravitation: Discuss the expanding theory of matter in the universe, and its possible oscillating mode. You can get class interest into high gear with speculations as to the possibility of past and future cycles. After discussion, you can end your class on a high note by doing the following: State that you wish to represent a single cycle with the positions of the chalk you are holding in your hand above the lecture table. Place the chalk on the table and let that represent the time of the primordial explosion. Then as if the chalk were projected upward, raise the chalk to a point just above your head and state that this position represents the point where the universe momentarily stops before beginning its inward collapse, the "big crunch" — then move your hand slowly down, speeding up and back to its starting point — the completion of one cycle. Then hold the chalk a foot or so above the table, to a point corresponding to where we are today — a point representing about 15 to 20 billion years from the beginning of the cycle. Holding the chalk steady, and purposefully, ask where the chalk should be positioned to represent the dawning of civilization. Then move the chalk very intently to a position about a quarter of an inch below the present point. State that that's where we were, and this is where we are, as you move the chalk back to the present position. Still holding it there, ask for a speculation of where humankind will be and what the world will be like when we move to ... and then raise the chalk upward about a quarter of an inch. That point, of course, represents a time on earth difficult to comprehend. It is conceivable that by then we will have evolved to beings with such an intelligence as to be completely beyond present human imagining — to a point that by today's standards would be deemed God-like.

The continued evolution of humankind holds much promise.

More Think-and-Explain Questions

1. The earth and the moon gravitationally attract each other. Does the more massive earth attract the moon with a greater force, the same force, or less force than the moon attracts the earth?
Answer: The force on both is the same, in accord with Newton's 3rd law. Note also from Newton's formula for gravitation that the force does not depend on the order of the masses, but simply the product.

2. What is the magnitude and direction of the gravitational force that acts on a woman who weighs 500 N at the surface of the earth?
Answer: The force is 500 N straight downward, her weight.

3. Somewhere between the earth and moon, gravity on a space pod would cancel. Is this location nearer the earth or moon?
Answer: Nearer the moon.

4. Gvavitational force acts on all bodies in proportion to their masses. Why, then, doesn't a heavy body fall faster than a light body?
Answer: The answer to this goes back to Newton's 2nd law. Acceleration of free fall equals the *ratio* of force to mass, which is the same for all bodies. Remember?

More Think and Solves

1. A light source located 1 m away from a one-square meter opening will cover 4 m^2 at a distance of 2 m from the source. How many square meters will it cover 3 m away? 5 m away? 10 m away?
Answers: At 3 m it will cover 3^2 or 9 square meters; at 5 m it will cover 5^2 or 25 square meters; at 10 m it will cover 10^2 or 100 square meters.

2. The value g at the earth's surface is 9.8 m/s^2. What is the value of g at a distance from the center four times the earth's radius?
Answer: g/16, or 0.6 m/s^2.

3. Calculate the force of gravity between the earth (6 x 10^{24} kg) and the sun (2 x 10^{30} kg, which are 1.5 x 10^{11} m distant).
Answer: $F = GmM/d^2 = [(6.67 \times 10^{-11})(6 \times 10^{24})(2 \times 10^{30})]/(1.5 \times 10^{11})^2 = 3.6 \times 10^{22}$ N.

4. Pretend the force of gravity between the sun and earth vanishes. Instead a steel cable between these two bodies keeps the earth in orbit. Estimate the thickness of such a cable. You need to know that the strength of steel is 5 x 10^8 N/m^2 (called the elastic modulus). That is, a steel cable with a 1 square meter cross-section will support a force of 5 x 10^8 N.
Answer: Nearly 1000 km thick! From the ratio 3.6 x 10^{22} N/x =5 x 10^8 N/1 m^2, x = (3.6 x 10^{22})/(5 x 10^8) = 7.2 x 10^{13} m^2. This would be the cross-sectional area of the cable. From the area of a circle, A = $\pi D^2/4$, we find its diameter D = $\sqrt{4A/\pi}$ = 9.6 x 10^6 m = 960 km.

5. With how much force is a 1-kg mass on earth attracted to the moon? (The moon's mass is 7.4 x 10^{22} kg and its distance is 3.8 x 10^5 km.)
Answer: $F = GmM/d^2 = (6.67 \times 10^{-11})(1)(7.4 \times 10^{22})/(3.8 \times 10^8)^2 = 3.4 \times 10^{-5}$ N.

6. Use the results of the previous problem to calculate how great a mass located 1 m away from the 1-kg mass exerts as much gravitational force on it as the moon.
Answer: About 5 x 10^5 kg. From $F = GmM/d^2$, where m = 1 kg, d = 1 m, and F = 3.4 x 10^{-5} N, M = Fd^2/Gm = (3.4 x 10^{-5})(1)^2/[(6.67 x 10^{-11})(1)] = 5 x 10^5 kg. (Such a mass weighs about 500 tons! Practically speaking, it would be quite incredible to arrange a distance of separation of only 1 m for so massive an object.)

7. If you stand 1 kilometer from the base of a typical mountain of mass 5 x 10^{11} kilograms, you'll be gravitationally attracted to it (as you're attracted to everything else). Likewise, you're attracted to the moon (of mass 7.4 x 10^{22} kg and 3.8 x 10^5 km distant). Which of these two exerts the greatest force on you?
Answer: About the same. Consider the ratio of mountain F to moon F':
$F/F' = (GmM/d^2)/(GmM'/D^2) = (M/d^2)/(M'/D^2) = [(5 \times 10^{11})/(1)^2]/[(7.4 \times 10^{22})/(3.8 \times 10^5)^2] = (5 \times 10^{11})/(5 \times 10^{11}) = 1$. (Note here that because they canceled anyway, we left the distances in km. Their ratio would be the same in m or any other pair of consistent units.)

13 Gravitational Interactions

Objectives

- Distinguish between g (the acceleration due to gravity) and G (the universal gravitational constant).
- Describe a gravitational field.
- Describe the gravitational field of the earth both inside and outside the earth's surface.
- Explain why an astronaut in earth orbit seems weightless even though there is a gravitational force on the astronaut.
- Explain how the moon and sun cause the ocean tides.
- Give examples of tides other than those in water.
- Describe how a black hole is formed.

Possible Misconceptions to Correct

- The fact that the same side of the moon faces earth is evidence the moon doesn't spin about its axis.
- The crescent shape of the moon is created by the earth's shadow.
- The fact that the moon is the chief cause of ocean tides is evidence that the moon's pull on the earth is greater than the sun's pull.
- Just as the moon greatly affects the oceans, it also affects the fluids in our bodies.

No Demonstrations in This Chapter

Introduction

The concept of force field introduced in this chapter is a good background for the electric field treated later in Chapter 33. The gravity field here is applied to regions outside as well as inside the earth. You may expand on the "tunnel all-the-way-through-the-earth" bit and explain how ideally the period of oscillation of a body traveling in such a tunnel under the influence of only gravity would be the same for any straight tunnel — whether from New York to Hawaii, or from New York to China. You can support this with the analogy of a pendulum that swings through different amplitudes with the same period. In non-vertical tunnels, of course, the object must slide rather than drop without friction. The timetables for travel in this way would be quite simple; any one-way trip would take 43 minutes!

In the answer to check question 1 on page 185 the text states without explanation that a body dropped in a tunnel bored through the earth will undergo simple harmonic motion. The condition for simple harmonic motion is that the restoring force be directly proportional to displacement, as is the case for a bob at the end of a spring (restoring force is $-kx$, Hooke's law). It turns out that the force of gravity on a body inside a planet of uniform density is directly proportional to the distance from its center (not the distance squared from its center).

Here's the explanation: We know that the gravitational force F between a particle m and a spherical mass M, when m is outside M is simply $F = GmM/d^2$. But when m is inside a uniform density solid sphere of mass M, the force on m is due only to the mass M' contained within the sphere of radius r ($< R$), represented by the dashed line in the figure. Contributions from the shell $> r$ cancel out . So, $F = GmM'/d^2$. From the ratio of M'/M, you can see that $M' = Mr^3/R^3$. [that is, $M'/M = V'/V = (4/3\,\pi r^3)/(4/3\,\pi R^3) = r^3/R^3$.] Substitute M' in Newton's equation for gravitation and you get $F = GmMr/R^3$. All terms on the right are constant except r. So $F = kr$; force is linearly proportional to radial distance when $r < R$.

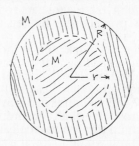

Compared to the gravitational attraction to local buildings and the like, the pull to the moon is appreciable. Consider the ratio of the mass of the moon to its distance squared:

$$7.4 \times 10^{22}\text{kg}/(4 \times 10^5\text{km})^2 = 5 \times 10^{11}\text{kg/km}^2$$

This is a sizable ratio, one that buildings in your vicinity cannot match (city buildings of greatest mass are typically on the order of 10^6 or 10^7 kilograms). However, if you stand 1 kilometer away from the foot of a mountain of typical mass 5×10^{11} kilograms, then the pull between you and the mountain and the pull between you and the moon are the same. Interestingly enough, with no friction you would tend to gravitate from your spot toward the mountain — but you experience no tendency to gravitate from your spot toward the moon! That's because the spot you stand on undergoes the same gravitational acceleration toward the moon as you do. Both you and the whole earth are in lunar free fall, accelerating toward the moon. Whatever the lunar force on you, it has no tendency to pull you off a weighing scale — which is why your weight has nothing to do with the positions of the sun or moon. When you step on a weighing scale, the interaction is only between you and the mass of the earth.

One new feature of this edition compared with previous editions is the treatment of the inverse-cube nature of tidal forces. The relationship is stated in the text on page 190, and students are led to its derivation in Practice Book 13-3b. Plug and Chugs and Think and Solves at chapter end make this point further. The point should be clear that any claims that the moon's tidal influence on people, or the tidal influence of any planets or stars, is enormously weak in comparison with that due to common things around us. This culminates with students comparing the tidal force of a 1-kg melon held 1 meter away with the tidal force of the moon. The melon wins by a factor of almost 200!

It is interesting to expand upon the zero-g field inside a hollow planet, and speculate about the living conditions of a civilization in such an environment. If the shell is uniform, g is everywhere zero inside, and not just at the center as indicated in Figure 13.5.

This chapter is a good place for students to learn some of the principles of creating a scientific theory by means of an imaginary model — for example, ocean tides. Main points are, (1) making the model simple, (2) consider only one effective element at a time, (3) explore the limits of the variables from small to large (or zero to infinity), and (4) take time, proceed step by step, and give imagination a chance.

A brief treatment of black holes is included in this chapter. It is interesting to note that light bends in any gravitational field, and not simply in the enormous gravitational fields near black holes. Einstein stated that light bends in a gravitational field as does a thrown baseball. According to Einstein, if you could throw a baseball as fast as light (you can't), both would follow the same trajectory! We say light travels in straight lines much for the same reason that some people say that a high-speed bullet doesn't curve downward in the first part of its trajectory. Over short distances the bullet doesn't *appear* to drop only because of the short time involved. Likewise with light, which we don't notice because of the vast distance involved compared to the brief time it is in the strong part of the earth's gravitational field.

While the information in this chapter is useful as a background for force fields in general, it may be skipped without complicating the treatment of other material. This is an interesting chapter, for the material is interesting in itself, is interesting historically, and is closely related to space science, currently in the public eye.

Lab activity *Apparent Weightlessness* helps students understand the notion that zero-g means lack of support forces and NOT the absence of gravity. Measures of g are made with *Acceleration of Free Fall*, and if you have computer facilities, *Computerized Gravity* is the way to go. Here the students will find the slope of a velocity versus time graph to find g, making use of the same technique used in the motion lab, *Conceptual Graphing*, with the sonic ranger.

Suggested Lecture

g and G: Distinguish between the acceleration due to gravity, g, and the universal gravitational constant, G. Although they represent completely different quantities, they are related. The derivation of g in terms of G is presented on page 183. [This is the first place in the text where a derivation is not tucked away in a footnote.] Relate this to Phillip von Jolly's method shown in Figure 12.8

of the previous chapter. If you haven't done so before, make this sketch on the board and explain that all values except G were measured. Explain how once G was found, the mass of the earth was known also. [Equate the weight of anything, mg, to the force of gravity, GmM/d^2. Then $M = gd^2/G$, where d is the earth's radius, g is 9.8 m/s^2, and G is 6.67 x 10^{-11} Nm^2/kg^2.]

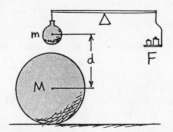

Discuss the questions on page 184, and their footnoted answers.

CHECK QUESTION: If the earth had the same size, yet twice the mass, what would be the acceleration of freely-falling objects at its surface? [Twice g, or nearly 20 m/s^2.] If the earth had the same mass yet half the size, what would be the acceleration of freely-falling objects at its surface? [Four times g, or nearly 40 m/s^2.] If the earth had twice the mass, and half the size, what would be the acceleration of freely-falling objects at its surface? [Eight times g, or nearly 80 m/s^2.]

[**Practice Book 13-2** presents a concept-by-formula development]

Gravitational Field: Show or call attention to the altered space that surrounds a magnet — a kind of aura, called a magnetic field. A magnetic field is a force field, for magnetic materials in it experience a force. Also with the gravitational field about the earth, or about any mass. A mass in the field region experiences a gravitational force. The field is strongest at the surface of the earth, and its strength falls off as the inverse square of distance from the earth's center.

CHECK QUESTIONS: What evidence would you look for to tell whether or not you were in a gravitational field? [The presence of a gravitational force.] Compared to on the surface of the earth, how strong is the gravitational field twice as far from the earth's center? [By the inverse-square law, 1/4 as much.]

Field Inside the Earth: It is interesting to consider a tunnel bored clear through the earth. It's easy to convince your students that the gravitational force on a body located at the exact center of the tunnel is zero — a chalkboard sketch showing a few symmetrical force vectors does this. The gravitational field at the earth's center is zero. Then consider the magnitude of force the body would experience away from the center, somewhere between the center and the surface. A few more carefully-drawn vectors will show that the forces don't cancel to zero. The gravitational field is between zero and the value at the surface. If the density of the earth were uniform, the field would be linear from the center to the surface — the earth's field would be half at the halfway mark, 3/4 at the 3/4 mark, and so on, as shown by the straight line in the sketch. (Actually the field is not linear because the density is much greater at the earth's center. The actual shape of the curve is more like that indicated in the right-hand sketch.)

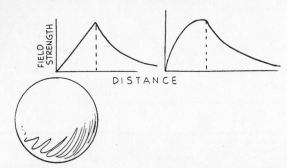

Earth Tunnel: You may want to go beyond the text coverage and discuss the motion of a body dropped in a tunnel bored completely through the earth and how it would keep rhythm with a circularly moving satellite of the same "amplitude". It takes nearly 90 minutes for a satellite to make a complete trip around the earth in close orbit, exactly the same time it would take a body dropped from the same altitude into the tunnel through the earth (page 184). It should be enough to state the oscillating case without going into the mathematics of simple harmonic motion (discussed briefly in the second paragraph at the beginning of this chapter here in the Teaching Guide).

CHECK QUESTION: If you dropped a rock into a tunnel through the earth, would the rock shoot out the other side like it was fired from a "gravity gun"? [No, it would gain speed until it reached the earth's center, and then lose speed the rest of the way. Its speed at the far end of the tunnel would be the same as its initial speed at the beginning. It would then fall back and repeat the motion in cyclic fashion.]

CHECK QUESTION: As the velocity of fall increases when falling into the earth tunnel, does the acceleration increase, decrease, or remain unchanged? [The acceleration decreases as the gravitational field decreases, and is zero at the earth's center. The falling body has its maximum velocity at the earth's center, where both the field and acceleration is zero.]

[**Practice Book 13-1b** treats the notion of falling through the earth]

Weight and Weightlessness: Define weight in terms of support force. According to this definition, we are as heavy as we feel. Contrast this to apparent weightlessness and relate it to the queasy feeling your students experience when in a car that goes too fast over the top of a hill. State that this feeling is what an astronaut is confronted with all the time in orbit! Ask how many of your class would still welcome the opportunity to take a field trip to Cape Canaveral and take a ride aboard the shuttle. What an exciting prospect!

CHECK QUESTION: Why would you feel weightless in an elevator with a broken cable? [There would be an absence of a support force — the floor would fall as fast as you.]

Freely-Falling Elevator: Cite the apparent weightlessness of astronauts orbiting in the space shuttle, and how videocasts show things floating around as if no gravity were present. Imitate an astronaut removing a pen from his or her shirt pocket and releasing it only to find it floating where it is released. Then ask your class to consider a video camera fixed to the inside of an elevator. Pretend you are in the elevator and remove your pen and drop it. The video records the dropping of the pen. No big deal. But now consider what the camera would see if you repeated the pen-drop maneuver in an elevator that is in free fall. The camera would show the pen floating beside you, as you, pen, camera, elevator and all fall at *g*. Ask if there is a force of gravity on you in this case (as evidenced by the sudden stop!). Does the camera show the dropping motion? Isn't this what occurs in orbit? Viola!

(This is a good break place.)

Ocean Tides: Begin your treatment of tides by asking the class to consider the consequences of someone pulling your coat. If they pulled only on the sleeve, for example, it would tear. But if every part of your coat were pulled equally, it and you would accelerate — but it wouldn't tear. It tears when one part is pulled harder than another — or it tears because of a *difference* in forces acting on the coat. In a similar way, the spherical earth is "torn" into an elliptical shape by differences in gravitational forces by the moon — stronger between the moon and the near side of the earth, and weaker between the moon and the far side of the earth. Similarly for the sun, but with less differences in force.

Explain why the moon "out-tides" the stronger-pulling sun [because the *difference* in pulls on either side of the earth is greater for the closer moon]. Explain why tides are extra high when the moon and sun are lined up [the pulls add and the two tides due to the moon and sun overlap]. Explain why the tides are not as high when the moon and sun are at right angles to each other [the high tide of the sun overlaps the low tide of the moon, and vice versa].

CHECK QUESTION: Which pulls harder on the oceans of the earth, the sun or the moon? [The sun.] Which is most effective in raising tides, the sun or the moon? [The moon.] (This question is a good one to distinguish who is reading the book and who isn't!)

Explain how the earth turns daily beneath the two ocean bulges to give us the two high and two low tides per day. This is best discussed with a globe of the earth on your lecture table. Designate a moon across the room, and a high tide on the earth in its direction. Then rotate the globe and show how different parts of the earth pass "beneath" the moon and experience high tides. Similarly, with the opposite side of the earth.

CHECK QUESTION: At the time of extra high tides, will extra low tides follow in the same day? [Yes, by the "conservation of water". There is only so much water on the earth — extra high tides in one part of the world means extra low tides in another. If students don't see this, ask them to imagine they are sloshing water back and forth while taking a bath in a bathtub. When the water is extra deep in the front part of the tub, doesn't this mean the water level will be extra low in the back part? Similarly for the ocean!]

[**Practice Book 13-3** develops the concept of tides, and 13-3b sets the groundwork for the analytical questions and problems about tidal forces in the chapter backmatter. These are somewhat heavyweight, so assign with care and appropriate preparation.]

Tides and the Inverse-Square Law (Optional) A roughly plotted graph of the gravitational force on an object near the earth's surface, versus distance from the earth, is useful in explaining tidal forces. Make a chalkboard sketch like that ar the right and show the inverse-square decline with distance.

Consider tides via the accelerating ball of taffy as in the text.

Equal pulls result in an undistorted ball as it accelerates, but unequal pulls cause a stretching. This stretching is evident in the earth's oceans, where the side nearest the moon is appreciably closer to the moon than the side farthest away. Modify your graph of gravitational force versus distance to that of the sun on the board.

Understanding this inverse relationship explains why closeness is so important for tides. Your graph shows that the size of ΔF rather than F itself is responsible for tidal effects. Hence the greater attraction of the distant sun produces only a small *difference* in pulls on the earth, and compared to the moon makes a small contribution to the tides on earth. Explain why the highest high tides occur when the earth, moon, and sun are aligned — at the time of a new and a full moon. Discuss tides in the molten earth and in the atmosphere.

Amplify this graph with a comparison of ΔFs for both the sun and the moon as shown. Clearly ΔF is smaller for the larger but farther sun.

[**Transparency 21**, Figures 13.14 and 13.16 on tides here]

Misconceptions About the Moon: This is an appropriate place for you to dispel two popular misconceptions about the moon: (1) Since one side of the moon's face is "frozen" to the earth, it doesn't rotate about its polar axis. (2) The crescent shape commonly seen is the earth's shadow. To convince your class that the moon does rotate about its polar axis, simulate the situation by holding your eraser at arms length in front of your face. Tell your class that the eraser represents the moon and your head represents the earth. Rotate slowly keeping one face of the eraser in your view. Call attention to the class that from your frame of reference, the eraser doesn't rotate as it revolves about you — as evidenced by your observation of only one face, with the backside hidden. But your students occupy the frame of reference of the stars (each of them *is* a star). From their point of view they can see all sides of the eraser as it rotates because it turns about its axis as often as it revolves about yours. Show them how the eraser, if not slowly rotating (frozen with one face always facing the same stars) would show all of its sides to

you as it circles around you. See one face, then wait 14 days later and the backside is in your view. The moon has a rotation rate that is the same as its revolution rate. The footnote on page 188 gives an explanation for the same side of the moon facing earth.

Misconception 2: Draw a half moon on the board. The shadow is along the diameter and is perfectly straight. If that were the shadow of the earth, then the earth would have to be flat, or be a big block shape! Discuss playing "flashlight tag" with a suspended basketball in a dark room that is illuminated by a flashlight in various locations. Ask your class if they could estimate the location of the flashlight by only looking at the illumination of the ball. Likewise with the moon illuminated by the sun!

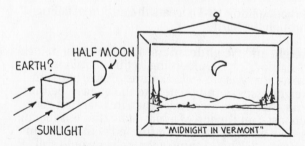

CHECK QUESTION: Sketch the picture above on the board and ask what is wrong with it. [The moon is in a daytime position as evidenced by the upper part of the moon being illuminated. This means the sun must be above the horizon (at about "11 O'clock"). Dispel notions that the crescent shape of the moon is a partial eclipse by considering a half moon and the shape of the earth to cast such a shadow

Suggest that students observe the phase of the moon and compare it to the phases shown on wall calendars. Don't be shocked to learn that some students may have never noticed the moon in the daytime sky!

Tides in the Earth and in the Atmosphere: For the same reason we have ocean tides, there are tides of the earth, which after all, is mostly molten lava. Mount Everest rises and falls about 30 cm twice a day.

Biological tides are addressed in Think and Explain question #9. Many people attribute special significance to the gravitational pull of the moon on themselves, and support this with the fact that the moon raises the ocean an average of 1 meter each 12 hours. Repeat the reason for the tides: half the water is closer to the moon than the other half. To be subject to any measurable lunar tides in our bodies, then part of our bodies must be appreciably closer to the moon than other parts. Detectable lunar tides in body fluids would occur only in tall people — like many kilometers tall!

If your students have done the Plug and Chugs for this chapter, and Practice Book 13-3b, they may be less likely to share most people's misconceptions about the effect of tides on us. Let your students not add to the ranks of those who incorporate nonsense into their view of nature.

Add to the text material by discussing the consequences if the moon were closer — ocean tides would be higher and by the same token, the tidal forces on the moon's crust would be greater. Too close, and the earth's tidal forces would tear the moon into a billion pieces, forming a ring around the earth similar to that of Saturn. Saturn's rings are thought to be the debris left over from bodies torn apart by tidal forces.

Black Holes: Tidal forces reach an extreme in the case of a black hole. The unfortunate fate of an astronaut falling into a black hole is not encountering the singularity, but the tidal forces encountered far before getting that close. Approaching feet first, for example, the closer feet would be pulled with a greater force than the midsection, which in turn would be pulled with a greater force than the head. The tidal forces would stretch the astronaut who would be killed before these forces literally pulled the body apart.

[**Transparency 22**, black hole, here]

Describe how a collapsed star represents condensed mass and therefore condensed gravity. The mass of a black hole is no more than the mass of the star that collapsed to form it. Hence the gravitational field of the star and the black hole are the same at distances greater than the original radius of the star. It is only at closer distances that the enormous field occurs. Discuss Figure 13.19 on page 194.

CHECK QUESTION: Consider a satellite companion to a star that collapses to become a black hole. How will the orbit of the companion satellite be affected by the star's transformation to a black hole? [Not at all. No terms in the gravitational equation change.]

[**Next-Time Question 13-1** treats this concept]

More Think-and-Explain Questions

1. The gravitational field strength at the earth's surface is 9.8 N/kg. What is the field strength at the center of the earth? At a distance one earth radius beyond the surface?
   Answers: Zero at the earth's center, and 1/4 or 2.45 N/kg twice as far from the center (one earth radius from the surface).

2. How would the gravitational field at the earth's surface be affected if the earth shrank in size without any change in mass? What would be its relative strength at the new surface if the earth shrank to half size? To one-tenth size?
   Answers: At half size, strength would be increased by 4; at one-tenth, strength would be 100 fold. [Can you see why gravitation is so intense at the surface of a collapsed star?]

3. How is stepping off a curbstone similar to taking a ride aboard the space shuttle?
   Answer: In both cases you experience weightlessness. The principle difference is in the times involved. Stepping off a curbstone involves an apparent weightlessness of such short duration that it not noticed.

4. The sun exerts almost 200 times more force on the oceans of the earth than the moon. Why then, is the moon more effective in raising tides?
   Answer: Tides are caused by the *difference* in gravitational pulls. The moon pulls with proportionally more force on the near side of the earth to the moon than on the far side. This difference in pulls is greater than the corresponding difference in pulls by the more distant sun.

5. From a point of view at the sun, does the moon circle the earth, or does the earth circle the moon?
   Answer: Neither; both the earth and the moon circle a common point, the center of mass of the earth-moon system (called the barycenter), located about 3/4 the earth's radius from its center (about 1600 km deep). It is the center of mass that smoothly orbits the sun, while the earth and moon wobble monthly about this center.

6. What would be the effect on the earth's tides if the diameter of the earth were very much larger than it is? If the earth were as it presently is, but the moon very much larger but with the same mass?
   Answers: Tides would be greater if the earth's diameter were greater because the difference in pulls would be greater. Tides on earth would be no different if the moon's diameter were larger. The gravitational influence of the moon is as if all the moon's mass were at its CG. Tidal bulges on the solid surface of the moon, however, would be greater if the moon's diameter were larger — but not on the earth.

7. Does the strongest tidal force on our bodies come from the earth, moon, or sun?
   Answer: The nearest body, the earth.

8. If the moon didn't exist, would the earth still have ocean tides? If so, how often?
   Answer: Yes, the earth's tides would be due only to the sun. They'd occur twice per day as now due to the earth's daily rotation.

More Think and Solves

1. The mass of Saturn is 95 times that of the earth and its radius is 9 times that of the earth. Calculate the acceleration due to gravity at the surface of Saturn. Express your answer in g's.
   Answer: About 1.2 g. On earth, $g = GM/R^2$, where M is the earth's mass, and R its radius. Saturn's mass is 95M, and its radius is 9R. Then on Saturn, the acceleration due to gravity $= G(95M)/(9R)^2 = 95/81\ GM/R^2 = 95/81\ g = 1.2\ g$.

2. The mass of the earth is about 80 times that of the moon and its radius about 3.7 times that of the moon. Calculate the acceleration due to gravity at the surface of the moon. Express your answer in g's.
   Answer: About 0.17 g. On earth, $g = GM/R^2$, where M is the earth's mass, and R its radius. Moon's mass is M/80, and its radius is R/3.7. Then on the moon, the acceleration due to gravity $= G(M/80)/(R/3.7)^2 = 3.7^2/80\ GM/R^2 = 13.7/80\ g = 0.17\ g$. (That's about $g/6$.)

3. If you drop a 1-kg mass just above the earth's surface, it accelerates downward at 9.8 m/s^2. But the force that pulls the 1-kg mass downward, is also the force that must pull the 6 x 10^{24}-kg earth upward. Compute the acceleration of the earth as it "races upward" to meet the 1-kg mass.
   Answer: $a = GM/R^2 = 1.6 \times 10^{-23}$ N/kg
   $\qquad\qquad\qquad\quad = 1.6 \times 10^{-23}$ m/s^2
   where N/kg = m/s^2. That's why the upward acceleration of the earth is not observable — much too small!

CALCULATOR TIME!

Objectives

- Explain how the speed of a satellite in circular orbit around the earth is related to the distance an object falls in the first second due to gravity.
- Explain why the force of gravity does not cause a change in the speed of a satellite in circular orbit.
- Describe how the speed of a satellite changes for different portions of an elliptical orbit.
- Apply the energy conservation law to describe changes in the potential and kinetic energies of a satellite for different portions of an elliptical orbit.
- Describe what is meant by an escape speed.

Possible Misconceptions to Correct

- Satellites are beyond the main pull of a planets gravitational field.
- Satellites are held up by a centrifugal force.

Demonstration Equipment

- [14-1] Piece of string with two suction cups or tacks to show ellipse construction.

Introduction

The idea of satellite motion as an extension of projectile motion was introduced in Chapter 6. And the idea of the "falling moon" was introduced in Chapter 12. The comic strip, *Satellite Physics* on page 201 says it all. The rest is embellishment.

The excellent NASA 15-minute film, *Zero-g* is a must. It is historic footage taken aboard Skylab in 1978, narrated by astronaut Owen Garriott. An overview of Newton's laws of motion are treated with excellent examples, and with a touch of humor. Your students will enjoy this educational film. Note that Kepler's laws are not covered in the text. Your students will "discover" Kepler's third law using the computer and the lab *Trial and Error*. It is best to introduce Kepler and his laws of planetary motion after your students do this great computer activity. The lab *Getting Eccentric* makes a good home activity.

When discussing the elliptical paths of satellites, you may point out that when we toss a baseball into the air we say its path is parabolic, but strictly speaking, it is a segment of an ellipse. The earth's center is at the far focus of this ellipse. If nothing were in the way, the baseball would follow an eccentric elliptical path and return to its starting point! The earth's center is at the near focus for satellites that trace external elliptical paths around the earth. In this case, nothing occupies the other focal point.

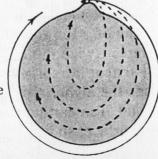

Suggested Lecture

Introduce satellite motion as an extension of simple projectile motion, as shown in the comic strip "Satellite Physics." Draw a world on the board, with a hypothetical mountain at the top as shown in the sketch. Call this, "Newton's Mountain," high enough to poke through the atmosphere so that cannonballs fired from it encounter no air resistance. Show how successively greater speeds result in a circular orbit. State that Isaac Newton thought of this idea and calculated the required speed of a cannonball for circular orbit. And that you expect that many in your class will be able to do the same before the class period is over. You will provide them with some information about the world that will help them make the calculation.

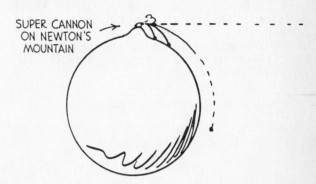

[**Transparency 23**, Figures 14.3 and 14.4 here]

Calculation of Orbital Speed: Sketch Figure 14.4 on the board. Pretend to place a laser on a 1-meter-high tripod and to aim it over a perfectly level desert floor. The beam is straight, but the desert floor curves 4.9 meters over an 8000-meter (8 km) tangent, as shown in the sketch below (certainly not to scale!).

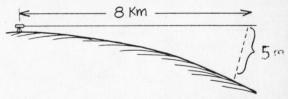

After you have drawn this on the chalkboard, replace the laser with a super cannon positioned so it aims along the laser line. Ask your class how far along the laser line would a cannonball go if fired at 2 km/s, with no gravity and no air drag. Be sure they see it will travel 2 km before you continue. Ask if this is fast enough for earth orbit in the presence of earth gravity, with no air drag. [It's speed is insufficient for earth orbit, for it will crash into the sand before it can reach the 2-km point.] Ask how far vertically the cannonball will fall beneath the laser line providing the sand weren't in the way. [4.9 m.] Then draw the sketch shown to show this case. You shovel sand out of the way if it is not to strike the earth's surface.

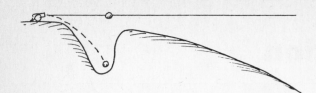

Next consider a cannonball fired at 4 km/s. Without gravity or air drag it will travel 4 km down the laser path in 1 second. Ask if this is fast enough for earth orbit. [No, because it will hit the sand before 1 second is up. Emphasize the cannonball will fall a vertical distance of 4.9 (or 5) m in 1 second whatever its horizontal speed.] So you dig some sand out of the way and your sketch now looks like this:

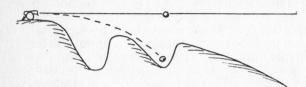

Continue by considering a greater muzzle velocity — great enough so the cannonball travels 6 km in one second. This is 6 km/s. Ask if this is fast enough not to hit the sand (or equivalently, if it is fast enough for earth orbit!) Then repeat the previous line of reasoning, again having to dig a trench, and your sketch looks like this:

Continue by considering a still greater muzzle velocity — 8 km/s. Ask for a neighbor check about this speed. Ask if you'll have to dig sand out of the way at this speed. Then after a pause, and with a tone of importance, ask the class with what speed must the cannonball have to orbit the earth. Done properly, you have led your class into a "derivation" of orbital speed about the earth with no equations or algebra!

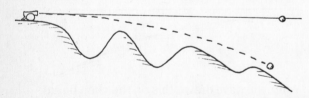

Acknowledge that gravitational force is less on satellites in higher orbits so they need not go so fast. This is acknowledged in the footnote on page 302 ($v = \sqrt{GM/d}$; so a satellite at 4 times the earth's radius need travel half as fast, 4 km/s).

Tangential Motion: Establish the idea that gravity does not change the tangential speed of a satellite — that there is no tangential component of gravitation. Do this by considering the effect of gravity on a bowling ball rolling along a level bowling alley. The pull is down, perpendicular to the alley and perpen-

dicular to the direction of motion. Therefore gravity does no work on the ball (Figure 14.5). Consider a bowling alley that completely encircles the earth — elevated so it is above air drag. The ball would roll indefinitely — always "level."

CHECK QUESTION: How fast would the bowling ball have to be moving for it to clear a broken span and continue moving along the alley on the other side? [8 km/s — in fact, you could remove the whole alley!]

CHECK QUESTION: Would a cannonball fired *upward* at 8 km/s go into earth orbit? [No, it would simply act as a projectile and crash back into the earth at 8 km/s. To circle the earth it must have a *tangential* speed of 8 km/s.]

{This is a good place to break}

[**Next-Time Question 14-1** addresses the non-work by gravity for circular moving satellites]

Elliptical Orbits: Begin your treatment of elliptical orbits with the following demo:

DEMONSTRATION [14-1]: With a loop of string, a pair of small suction cups stuck to the chalkboard, trace an ellipse (as is done in Figure 14.7).

Return to Newton's Mountain and consider greater cannonball speeds, starting with say 9 km/s. Show how this speed causes the cannonball to overshoot the path it would take for circular orbit. Ask if the 9 km/s value will increase, decrease, or remain the same on the first part of its outward trip. [Since it is going against gravity, the cannonball will slow to a speed less than its initial speed — a quite different situation than when in circular orbit.] Trace a full ellipse. As you retrace the elliptical path, show with a sweeping motion of your arm how the satellite slows as it recedes from the earth, moving slowest at its furthermost point; then how it speeds up as it falls toward the earth, whipping around the earth at its closest point. The cycle repeats. Point out the similarity of this to how a stone thrown upward at an angle slows on the way up, and speeds up on the way down. Planets orbiting about the sun do similarly. Kepler didn't understand the slowness of planets when farthest from the sun because he did not view them as bodies freely falling around the sun.

CHECK QUESTIONS: If a cannonball is fired horizontally from Newton's mountain at a tangential velocity less than 8 km/s it soon strikes the ground below. Will its speed of impact be greater, the same, or less than its muzzle speed? [Greater because of a component of its velocity is along the gravitational field of the earth. Similarly, any object tossed horizontally that moves downward will pick up speed for the same reason.] State that only if it is fired at 8 km/s will its speed remains at 8 km/s. If it is fired at 9 or 10 km/s, how does its speed change? [Speed decreases because a component of its velocity is against the gravitational field — simply put, it is going against gravity.]

Summarize by stating that for close earth orbit, tangential satellite speeds must range between 8 km/s to 11.2 km/s.

Escape Speed: Toss something straight upward. Point out that if air drag does not play a role, then the launching speed and the speed of return are the same. Fired upward at 8 km/s will result in a return speed of 8 km/s (if no air drag). Kinetic energy lost going up is equal to the kinetic energy gained in returning. But beyond 11.2 km/s, the story is different. This speed is sufficient for a no-return situation. This is escape speed.

CHECK QUESTION: If an object located at a distance beyond Pluto were dropped from a position of rest to earth, what would be its maximum speed of impact if its increase in speed is due only to earth gravity? [Interestingly, 11.2 km/s, the same speed it would need to bounce from the earth to return to its original distance.]

Acknowledge that the term *escape speed* refers to "ballistic speed," the speed a body must have after the thrusting force ends. If the thrusting force were somehow continuous, then any speed could provide escape if maintained over a sufficient time.

Energy Conservation: Sketch a large ellipse on the board to represent an elliptical orbit around the earth. Place the earth in the appropriate place (it is invariably closer to the perigee than most people would place it — see the position of the focus in Figure 14.11). Now place a satellite at the perigee, and write a large "KE" beside it. That's where the satellite is traveling fastest. But it's also closest to the earth, so write a small "PE" next to the "KE." Draw the satellite at other points. Ask for relative values of KE and PE at these points. Express these with the exaggerated-symbol technique. After discussion, erase the board.

[**Transparencies 24 and 25,** Figures 14.10-14.12]

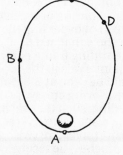

CHECK QUESTION: Draw another ellipse on the board, with planet appropriately placed. Sketch several satellite positions [as shown] and label them A, B, C, and D. Ask where the satellite has the maximum: (1) speed; (2) gravitational force to earth; (3) kinetic energy; (4) momentum; (5) gravitational potential energy; (6) total energy; (7) acceleration. [(1) A; (2) A; (3) A; (4) A; (5) C; (6) same everywhere; (8) A. You can expect the greatest number of wrong answers on the last question — where the guide for thinking, $a = F/m$, comes in handiest.]

[**Practice Book 14-1** develops both circular and elliptical orbits in terms of velocity and force vectors, and energy conservation. Caution: A poor practice is shown here — placing force and velocity vectors on the same diagram. Take care that you don't combine such vectors for resultants, for you can't combine a velocity with a force. Ouch!]

More Think-and-Explain Questions

1. Do the speeds of planets around the sun depend on the planets' masses? On the sun's mass? On their distance?
   Answer: The speeds depend only on the sun's mass, and on their distance from the sun.

2. If a projectile were launched from the surface of the earth at a vertical speed of 10 km/s, would it orbit the earth?
   Answer: No, it would simply rise and then fall back to earth, just as a vertically thrown baseball would do. It must have a horizontal component of 8 km/s to orbit — lesser speeds at greater distances from the earth.

3. If Pluto were somehow stopped dead in its orbit, it would fall into rather than around the sun. How fast would it be moving when it hits the sun?
   Answer: It would hit the sun with very nearly the escape speed from the sun — 620 km/s.

4. What would be the consequences of the sun momentarily stopping in its apparent path across the sky?
   Answer: It would be the earth that stops, not the sun. With no tangential speed, the earth would then fall directly toward, rather than around the sun.

5. The orbiting space shuttle moves at 8 km/s with respect to the earth. Suppose it projects a capsule rearward at 8 km/s with respect to the shuttle. Describe the path of the capsule with respect to the earth.
   Answer: Its tangential speed would be zero and it would fall vertically to the earth's surface.

More Think and Solves

1. The force of gravity between the earth and an earth satellite is given by $F = GmM/r^2$, where m is the mass of the satellite, M the mass of the earth, and r the radial distance between the satellite and the center of the earth. If it follows a circular orbit, the force is a centripetal force, given by $F = mv^2/r$. Equate the two expressions for force to show that the speed $v = \sqrt{GM/r}$.
   Answer: $GmM/r^2 = mv^2/r$, cancelling m and r we get $GM/r = v^2$; taking the square root of both sides gives $v = \sqrt{GM/r}$.

2. The speed of a satellite in circular orbit is given by the equation, $v = \sqrt{GM/r}$, where G is the gravitational constant, M is the mass of the earth, and r the radial distance between the satellite and the center of the earth. Equate this to the other expression for speed, $v = $ *distance travelled/time*. Find the equation for the time it takes to completely orbit the earth — the period T. Use the complete orbit, $2\pi r$, for the distance travelled, and T for the period of revolution.
   Answer: $T = 2\pi\sqrt{r^3/GM}$. Begin with $v = \sqrt{GM/r} = 2\pi r/T$; invert both sides and we have $\sqrt{r/GM} = T/2\pi r$, and rearange to find $T = 2\pi r\sqrt{r/GM}$. Since $r = \sqrt{r^2}$, this can be written $T = 2\pi\sqrt{r^3/GM}$.

15 Special Relativity — Space and Time

Objectives

- Give examples of relative and non-relative motion.
- Define and give examples of Einstein's first and second postulate of Special Relativity.
- Give an example of time dilation.
- Reconcile the concept that observers in different frames of reference moving uniformly with respect to each other each observe time dilation in the other frame with the example of the twin trip, in which both twins agree that the traveling twin does not age as fast.
- Explain how a space traveler could live long enough to travel a distance that it takes light 200 years to travel.

Possible Misconceptions to Correct

- Objects can go faster than the speed of light from some frames of reference.
- There is no upper limit of speed for material objects.
- Our rate of aging does not depend on the frame of reference.
- The farthest one can travel in a time of say 1 year, at the speed of light, is 1 light year, regardless of the frame of reference.

No Labs or Demos for this Chapter

Introduction

For those who will not be covering all the chapters of the text, I expect this and the following chapter will be omitted. They can be omitted without consequence to the chapters that follow. The ideas discussed in these chapters are perhaps the most exciting in the book. But they are difficult to comprehend. Regardless of how clearly and logically this material is presented, students may find that they do not "understand" it in a manner that satisfies them. This is understandable for so brief an exposure to a part of reality untouched by conscious experience. The intention of these chapters is to develop enough insight into relativity to stimulate further student interest and inquiry.

Time is one of those concepts we are all familiar with yet are hard pressed to define. A simple yet less than satisfying way to look at it is like our definition of space; that which we measure with a measuring stick — and time, that which we measure with a clock. Or we may quip, time is nature's way of seeing to it that everything doesn't happen all at once!

Should you get into a discussion of the relativity of time NOT as meant in the special theory, an interesting point to bring up is the different lives of mammals — for example, the short life of a mouse and the longer life of an elephant. Based on the internal clocks of their own hearts or the rhythm of their own breathing, all mammals live about the same time — about 200 million breaths, and about 800 million heartbeats. So don't feel sorry for pets that from our point of view live for such short lifespans. (The exception, interestingly or luckily enough, is humans, who have about three times as many heartbeats and breaths on the average.)

Note the important significance of "The Twin Trip" Section 15-7 in the text, in that it completely bypasses mathematical equations for time dilation and the relativistic Doppler effect. The reciprocity of relativistic Doppler frequencies for approach and recession stems only from Einstein's 1st and 2nd postulates and is illustrated with a 4-step presentation that involves only simple arithmetic in the following suggested lecture.

This reciprocal nature of the relativistic Doppler effect does not hold for waves that require a medium, such as sound, where the "moving" frame is not equivalent to the "rest" (relative to air) frame. If the ratio of frequency received to frequency sent for hearing in the rest frame is 2, the ratio for hearing in the moving frame is 3/2 (clearly not 2!). For sound, the speed as well as the frequency depends on the motion of the receiver. If the receiver moves toward a sound source then the speed of sound encountered is greater; moving away, less — very much unlike the case for light.

With the simple flash-counting sequence, time dilation is shown without the use of any mathematical formulas. The results of the twin-trip flash sequence agree with Einstein's time dilation equation. So this treatment is completely independent of the time dilation equation and the relativistic Doppler equation! (Who says that good physics can't be presented nonmathematically?)

If your class is in a more mathematical mood, you may wish to show an alternative approach to The Twin Trip and consider straightforward time dilation plus corrections for the changing positions of the emitting or receiving body between flashes. Instead of bypassing the time dilation equation, use it to show that at 0.6c, 6-minute flash intervals in the emitting frame compute to be 7 1/2-minute flash intervals in the receiving frame. The flashes would be seen at 7 1/2-minute intervals if the ship were moving crosswise, neither approaching nor receding, such that each flash travels essentially the same distance to the receiver. In our case the ship doesn't travel crosswise, but recedes from and then approaches the receiver — so corrections must be made in the time interval due to the extra distance the light travels when the spaceship is receding and the lesser distance the light travels when the ship is approaching. This turns out to be 4 1/2 minutes;

$$\Delta t = \frac{\text{extra distance}}{c} = \frac{0.6c \times 7.5 \text{ min}}{c} = 4.5 \text{ min}$$

So when receding, the flashes are seen at 7 1/2 + 4 1/2 = 12-minute intervals; when approaching, the flashes are seen at 7 1/2 - 4 1/2 = 3-minute intervals. The results of this method are the same as those of the 4-step conceptual presentation in the following suggested lecture.

Conceptual Physics Alive!, both in videotape and videodisk features my 12-minute animated film, *Relativistic Time Dilation*, which details the section on The Twin Trip.

[**Practice Book 15-1** complements The Twin Trip]

[There are no transparencies for this and the following chapter on Special Relativity]

Suggested Lecture

After discussing Einstein and a broad overview of what special relativity is and is not, point out somewhere along the line that the theory of relativity is grounded in *experiment*, and in its development it explained some very perplexing experimental facts (constancy of the speed of light, muon decay, solar energy, the nature of mass, etc.). It is not, as some people think, only the speculations of one man's way of thinking. Newspapers during the early part of the century used to report that there were only 12 people in the world who understood special relativity. This in inaccurate, for although in 1905 there was only one person to understand it, Einstein himself, after he published his paper and explained it, large numbers of people in the community of physicists understood it.

Motion is Relative: Ask your class to pretend they are in a parking lot playing ball with someone driving toward them and away from them in an open vehicle (Figure 15.5, page 215). A pitcher in the vehicle tosses a ball to them, always with the same pitching speed — no variation. Ask for the relative speed of catching a ball when the car approaches and again when it recedes. They know there will be a difference. Ask how they would react if the speed of the ball during catching were the same, whether the thrower was moving toward them, at rest, or moving away from them. This would be most perplexing. State that a similar occurrence was presented to the physicists at the turn of the century by the null result of the Michelson-Morley experiment.

Michelson-Morley Experiment: The experiment that first showed that the speed of light is invariant was the 1887 Michelson-Morley experiment. Avoid information overload by not treating the details of their experiment and the development of the interferometer. Instead direct your students' mental energies to the broad ideas of special relativity. Explain what it means to say that the velocity of light is invariant — that it is the same for all observers.

First Postulate: The laws of physics are the same in all uniformly moving reference frames. A bee inside a fast-moving jet plane executes the same flying maneuvers regardless of the speed of the plane. If you drop a coin to the floor of the moving plane, it will fall as if the plane were at rest. A flight attendant need make no adjustments in pouring tea because of the plane's high speed. Physical experiments behave the same in all uniformly moving frames. This leads, most importantly, to the development of

special relativity, to the speed of light that is seen to be the same to all observers.

Second Postulate: Stand still and toss a piece of chalk in the air, catching it as you would when flipping a coin. Ask the class to suppose that, in so doing, all measurements show the chalk to have a constant average speed. Call this constant speed *c*, for short. Then proceed to walk at a fairly brisk pace across the room and again toss the chalk. State that from your frame of reference the measured speed is

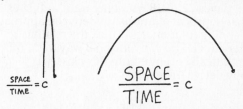

again the same. Ask if the speed looked different to them. They should respond that the chalk was moving faster this time. Ask them to suppose instead that their measurement of speed was the same. They may be a bit perplexed, which again is similar to the perplexed state of physicists at the turn of the century. Write on the board, with uniformly sized letters,

$$c = \frac{\text{SPACE}}{\text{TIME}}$$

This represents speed as seen by you in your frame of reference. State that from the frame of reference of the class, the space covered by the tossed chalk was seen to be greater, so write the word SPACE in correspondingly larger letters. Underline it. State that if they measure the same speed, that is, the same ratio of space to time, then such can be accounted for if the measured time is also greater. Then write the enlarged word TIME beneath the underline, equating it to *c*. Just as π, the ratio of circumference to diameter, is the same for all sizes of circles, all observers similarly measure the same ratio of space to time for light waves in free space.

Relate the analogy of your chalk-tossing sequence to the light clock discussed on page 219 and in Figures 15.11 through 15.14 and in the boxed material on page 221.

Relativistic Doppler Effect: Sketch a simple version of Figure 4 (ahead page 79) on the board. Explain that for a ship *at rest* relative to the two observers on the distant planets, light flashes emitted at 6-min intervals would be seen by both to also be at 6-min intervals. But with motion, the situation is different. Give examples of the Doppler effect: the changing pitch of a car horn when it approaches and when it recedes; the pitter patter of a slanting rain when you run into the rain versus when you run away from it. Ask your class to suppose the ship moves so fast toward the right observer that the flashes reach the observer at twice the frequency — with flashes closer together so they appear at 3-min intervals. The time between flashes is crimped in half. Ask how the time between flashes would be seen by the observer on the left — who sees the source receding. Is it reasonable to say the opposite occurs? That instead of being crimped in half, the flashes are spread apart twice as much so that the time between flashes is stretched by two?

That if 6-min flash intervals are crimped to 3-min for approach, they'll be stretched to 12-min intervals for recession? If this is acceptable to your class, you can then go on to discuss the Twin Trip, as is done in the both the text and the videotape. Or depending on the level of your class, you may wish to derive this halving and doubling of time intervals with the method that follows.

Option: Derivation of Relativistic Doppler Effect:
Before treating the light-flash sequence of The Twin Trip on pages 222-228, you may want to first establish the reciprocal relationship between approaching and receding frequencies — i.e., the relativistic Doppler effect. The conventional way to do this in mathematically oriented physics classes is to algebraically derive the expression

$$f = f_0 \sqrt{\frac{1 + v/c}{1 - v/c}}$$

This derivation can be found in many physics texts. But you can derive the same result without using a single mathematical expression and show that the reciprocity of frequencies is a natural consequence of the invariance of the speed of light. Try this with the following four-step conceptual presentation:

Step 1: Consider a person standing on earth directing brief flashes of light at 3-min intervals to a distant planet at rest relative to the earth. Some time will elapse before the first of these flashes reaches the planet, but since there is no relative motion between the sender and receiver, successive flashes will be observed at the distant planet at 3-min intervals. While you are making these remarks, make a sketch on the board of Figure. 1.

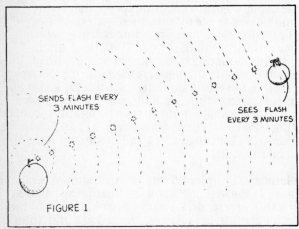

FIGURE 1.

Step 2: How frequently would these flashes encounter an observer in a fast-moving spaceship traveling between the earth and the planet? Although the *speed* of the flashes would be measured by the spaceship to be *c*, the *frequency* of flashes would be greater than or less than the emitting frequency depending on whether the ship were receding or approaching the light source. After supporting this idea with some examples of the Doppler effect (car horns, running into versus away from a slanting rain, etc.) make the supposition that the spaceship recedes from the light source at a speed great enough for the frequency of light flashes to decrease by half — so they're seen from the ship only half as often, at 6-min intervals. By now your chalkboard sketch looks like Fig. 2.

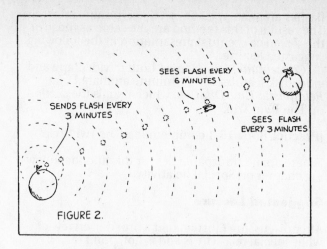

FIGURE 2.

Step 3: Suppose further that each time a flash reaches the ship, a triggering device activates a beacon on the ship that sends its own flash of light toward the distant planet. According to a clock in the spaceship then, this flash is emitted every 6-min. Since the flashes from earth and the flashes emitted by the spaceship travel at the same speed c, both sets of flashes travel together, and an observer on the distant planet sees not only the earth flashes at 3-min intervals, but the spaceship flashes at 3-min intervals as well (Fig. 3). At this point you have established that 6-min intervals on the approaching spaceship are seen as 3-min intervals on the stationary planet.

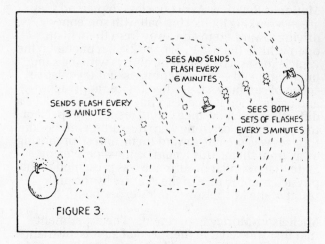

FIGURE 3.

Step 4: To establish that the 6-min flashes emitted by the spaceship are seen at 12-min intervals from the earth, go back to your earlier supposition that 3-min intervals on earth are seen as 6-min intervals from the frame of reference of the receding ship. Ask your class: If instead of emitting a flash every 3-min, the person on earth emits a flash every 6-min, then how often would these flashes be seen from the receding ship? [12 min] And then ask if the situation would be any different if the ship and earth were interchanged—if the ship were at rest and emitted flashes every 6 min to a receding earth? [No] After a suitable response erase from your chalkboard drawing all the flashes emitted from the earth. Replace the earth-twin's light source with a telescope while asking how often the 6-min flashes emitted by the moving spaceship are seen from earth. Student response should show that you have established the reciprocity of frequencies for the relativistic Doppler

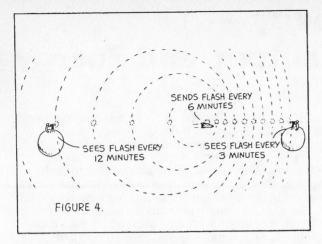

FIGURE 4.

effect without using a single equation. This is summarized in Fig. 4.

Note that you have employed Einstein's postulates in the last two steps, i.e., the second postulate in Step 3 (constancy of the speed of light) and the first postulate in Step 4 (equivalence of the earth and ship frames of reference).

Whether you have established this reciprocity from the Doppler equation or from the preceding four steps, you are now ready to demonstrate time dilation while also presenting a resolution to the so-called twin paradox. Do this by reviewing the treatment The Twin Trip in Section 5.7.

Show the 12-minute cartoon, *Relativistic Time Dilation*, which is Part I on the Conceptual Physics videotape.

Applications of Time Dilation: Discuss the prospects of "century hopping," a scenario in which future space travelers may take relatively short trips of a few years or so, and return in decades, centuries, or even thousands of years. This is, of course, pending the solution to two major problems: sufficient rocket engines and fuel supplies for prolonged voyages, and a means of shielding the radiation that would be produced by impact with interstellar matter.

Present this interesting but fictitious example of time dilation: Suppose that one could be whirled in a giant centrifuge up to relativistic speeds without physical injury. (Of course in reality one would be crushed to death in such a case, but pretend that somehow one is physically unaffected by the crushing centripetal forces — the fictitiousness of this example). Then cite how one taking a "ride" in such a centrifuge might be strapped in a seat and told to press a button on the seat when he or she wishes the ride terminated. And suppose that after being whirled about at rim speeds near the speed of light the occupant decides that 10 minutes is enough. So he or she presses the button, signaling those outside to bring the machine to a halt. After the machine is halted, those outside open the door, peer in, and ask, "Good gosh, what have you been doing in there for the past 3 weeks!" In the laboratory frame of reference, 3 weeks would have elapsed during a ten-minute interval in the rotating centrifuge. The point: one doesn't have to necessarily travel through wide expanses of space for time dilation to be significant. Motion in space, rather than space itself is the key factor.

More Think-and-Explain Questions

1. Could a person who has a life expectancy of 70 years possibly make a round-trip journey to a part of the universe thousands of lightyears distant?
   Answer: If a person travels at relativistic speeds, distances as far as those that light takes thousands of years to travel (from our frame of reference) could be traversed well within an average lifetime. This is because distance is relative to the frame of reference from which it is measured. Long distances from a rest frame may be quite short from a moving frame.

2. A twin who makes a long trip at relativistic speeds returns younger than his stay-at-home twin sister. Could he return before his twin sister was born? Defend your answer.
   Answer: A twin who makes a long trip at relativistic speeds returns younger than his stay-at-home twin sister only in the sense that he has not aged as much as his sister during the duration of his trip. If they could watch each other during the trip, there would be no time where either would see a reversing of age, only a slowing or speeding of aging. A reversal would appear only for speeds greater than the speed of light. So age will slow down, not reverse. This means the twin could not return to a time before his or his twin sister's birth.

Objectives

- Describe the conditions under which lengths contract.
- Describe the meaning of mass-energy relationship
- Correctly interpret the equation $E_O = mc^2$.
- Explain how it is still correct to say that mass is conserved and that energy is conserved.
- Explain why the equivalence of mass and energy is not noticed for everyday events such as the throwing of a baseball.
- Explain how the correspondence principle is a good test of the validity of any new theory.

Possible Misconceptions to Correct

- Objects can go faster than the speed of light from some frames of reference.
- $E_O = mc^2$ means that energy is mass traveling at the speed of light squared.
- The mass of an object does not change with speed.
- The momentum of an object is always simply its mass x velocity.

There are no Labs or Demos for this Chapter

Introduction

This chapter is a continuation of the previous chapter. It (or both) may be omitted from your course without consequences to the chapters that follow. Mass-energy is treated again in Chapter 40, so if you omit this chapter, bring up the concept at that time.

As the text states, push an object that is free to move and it accelerates in accord with Newton's 2nd law, $a = F/m$. Interestingly enough, Newton originally wrote the 2nd law not in terms of acceleration, but in terms of momentum, $F = \Delta p/\Delta t$, which is equivalent to the familiar $F = ma$. (Not until this chapter do we assign the symbol p to momentum. It wasn't introduced in Chapter 7 only to avoid presenting another abstract symbol to the student's early vocabulary. It wouldn't have simplified anything then, but it seems to now. Hence we say $p = mv$, or when high speeds are involved, $p = mv/\sqrt{1 - v^2/c^2}$).

In accord with the momentum version of Newton's 2nd law, push an object that is free to move and we increase its momentum. The acceleration or the change-of-momentum version of the 2nd law give the same result. But for very high speeds, it turns out that the momentum version is more accurate. $F = \Delta p/\Delta t$ holds for all speeds, from everyday speed to speeds near the speed of light — as long as the relativistic expression for momentum is used.

The first edition of Conceptual Physics, and some other physics textbooks, speak of *relativistic mass*, given by the equation $m = m_0/\sqrt{1 - (v^2/c^2)}$. The concept here is that the mass of an object increases as energy is supplied to it. This idea is now losing favor to the somewhat more complex idea of relativistic momentum. One problem with the idea of increased mass is that mass is a scalar: it has no direction. When particles are accelerated to high speeds, their increase in mass is directional. Increase occurs in the direction of motion in a manner similar to the way that length contraction occurs only in the direction of motion. Moving mass is, after all, momentum. So it is more appropriate to speak of increases in momentum rather than mass. Either treatment of relativistic mass or relativistic momentum, however, leads to the same description of rapidly moving objects in accord with observations.

Suggested Lecture

Length Contraction: Hold up a meter stick, horizontally, and state that if your students made accurate measurements of its length, their measurements would agree with your own. Everyone would measure it as 1 meter long. People at the back of the room would have to compensate for its shorter appearance due to distance, but nevertheless, they would agree on its 1-m length. But now walk across the room holding the meter stick like a spear. State that your measurements and those of your students would differ. If you were to travel at 87% the speed of light, relative to the class, they would measure the stick to be half as long, 0.5 m. At 99.5% the speed of light, they would see it as only 10 cm long. At greater speeds, it would be even shorter. At the speed of light it would contract to zero length. Write the length-contraction formula on the board:

$$L = L_O\sqrt{1 - (v^2/c^2)}$$

State that contraction takes place only in the direction of motion. The stick moving in spear fashion appears shorter but it doesn't appear thinner.

Contrast their view of the stick with yours. Since you move with the stick you se no contraction, whatever the speed. From your frame of reference (the same as the stick's), the v in the above equation is zero, and $L = L_O$. Hence contraction depends on the frame of reference.

Consider traveling by a 1-km long building at very high speed. From your frame of reference in the traveling vehicle, the length of the building is shorter. At 87% the speed of light, for example, the building would be seen half as long, 0.5 km. Likewise with space travel between stars. Their distance as seen from our rest frame of reference is quite different as seen from the frame of reference of a moving spaceship. If 20 lightyears separates a pair of stars from our frame of reference, a spaceship traveling at .087c between them would see them as only 10 lightyears apart.

CHECK QUESTION: Consider a pair of stars, one on each "edge" of the universe. That's an enormous distance of separation from our frame of reference. Now consider a photon traveling from one star across the entire universe to the other. From the frame of reference of the photon, what is the distance of separation between stars? (How big is the universe?)[Zero! From a frame of reference traveling at c, the length contraction reaches zero.]

The implication of the above question is that at high speeds, future space travelers may not face the restrictions of traveling distance that seem formidable without relativity! There is much food for thought on this!

The Mass-Energy Relationship

Write $E_O = mc^2$ on the board, the most celebrated equation of the twentieth century. It relates energy and mass. Every material object is composed of energy "energy of being." This "energy of being" is appropriately called *rest energy*, which is designated by the symbol E_O. (We distinguish here between rest energy E_O and the total energy E that may include potential and kinetic energies.) So the mass of something is actually the internal energy within it. This energy can be converted to other forms, light for example.

On the 4 1/2 million tons of matter that is converted to radiant energy by the sun every second: that tonnage is carried by the radiant energy through space, so when we speak of matter being "converted" to energy, we are merely converting from one form to another — from a form with one set of units perhaps, to another. Because of the mass and energy equivalence, in any reaction that takes into account the whole system, the total amount of mass + energy does not change.

Discuss the interesting idea that mass, every bit as much as energy, is delivered by the power utilities through the copper wires that run from the power plants to the consumers.

From a long view, the significance of the twentieth century will be most likely seen as a major turning point with the discovery of the $E_O = mc^2$ relationship. It may be interesting to speculate what the equation of the 21st century might be.

Relativistic Momentum: State that if you push an object that is free to move, it accelerates in accord with Newton's 2nd law, $a = F/m$. As it turns out, Newton originally wrote the 2nd law not in terms of acceleration, but in terms of momentum, $F = \Delta p/\Delta t$, which is equivalent to the familiar $F = ma$. Here we introduce the symbol p for momentum. $p = mv$. In accord with the momentum version of Newton's 2nd law, push an object that is free to move and we increase its momentum. The acceleration or the change-of-momentum version of the 2nd law give the same result. But for very high speeds, it turns out that the momentum version is more accurate. $F = \Delta p/\Delta t$ holds for all speeds, from everyday speed to speeds near the speed of light — as long as the relativistic expression of momentum is used.

Write the expression for relativistic momentum on the board:

$$p = \frac{mv}{\sqrt{1 - (v^2/c^2)}}$$

Point out that it differs from the classical expression for momentum by the denominator $\sqrt{1 - (v^2/c^2)}$. A common interpretation is that of a relativistic mass $m = m_0/\sqrt{1 - (v^2/c^2)}$, multiplied by a velocity v. Because the increase in mass with speed is directional (as is length contraction), and momentum rather than mass is a vector, the concept of momentum increase rather than mass increases is preferred in advanced physics courses. Either treatment of relativistic mass or relativistic momentum, however, leads to the same description of rapidly moving objects in accord with observations.

A good example of the increase of either mass or momentum for different relative speeds is the accelerated electrons and protons in high-energy particle accelerators. In these devices speeds greater than 0.99c are attained within the first meter, and most of the energy given to the charged particles during the remaining journey goes into increasing mass or momentum, according to your point of view. The particles strike their targets with masses or momentum thousands of times greater than the physics of Newton accounts for. Interestingly enough, if you traveled along with the charged particles, you would note no such increase in the particles themselves (the v in the relativistic mass equation would be zero), but you'd measure a mass or momentum increase in the atoms of the "approaching" target (the crash is the same whether the elephant hits the mouse or the mouse hits the elephant).

Cite how such an increase must be compensated for in the design of circular accelerators such as cyclotrons, bevatrons, and the like, and how such compensation is not required for a linear accelerator (except for the bending magnets at its end).

Point out to your class that the form of the relativistic momentum equation is very much like that for time.

Show how for small speeds the relativistic momentum equation reduces to the familiar mv (just as for small speeds $t = t_O$ in time dilation). Then show what happens when v approaches c. The denominator of the equation approaches zero. This means that the momentum approaches infinity! An object pushed to the speed of light would have infinite momentum and would require an infinite impulse (force x time), which is clearly impossible. Nothing material can be pushed to the speed of light. The speed of light c is the upper speed limit in the universe.

Cars, planes, and even the fastest rockets don't approach speeds to merit relativistic considerations, but subatomic particles do. They are routinely pushed to speeds beyond 99% the speed of light whereupon their momenta increase thousands of times more than the classical expression mv predicts. This is evidenced when a beam of electrons directed into a magnetic field is appreciably deflected from its normal path. The greater its speed, the greater its "moving inertia" — its momentum, and the greater it resists deflection (Figure 16.4). High-energy physicists must take relativistic momentum into account when working with high-speed subatomic particles in atomic accelerators. In that arena, relativity is an everyday fact of life.

Relativistic Kinetic Energy: The principal value of this section is to answer the question, "From where did Einstein's equation $E_O = mc^2$ originate?" Einstein was the first to derive the relativistic expression for kinetic energy, KE = $mc^2/\sqrt{1 - v^2/c^2} - mc^2$ and the first to note the term mc^2, which is independent of speed. This term is the basis of the celebrated equation, $E_0 = mc^2$.

Interestingly enough, for ordinary low speeds the relativistic equation for kinetic energy reduces to the familiar $KE = 1/2\ mv^2$ (via the binomial theorem). As the footnote suggests, in many situations where the momentum or energy of high-speed particles is known rather than speed, the expression that relates total energy E to the relativistic momentum p is given by $E^2 = p^2c^2 + (mc^2)^2$. This expression is derived by squaring the relation $E_0 = mc^2$ to obtain $E^2 = m^2c^4 = m^2c^2(c^2 + v^2 - v^2)$, and combining the relativistic equation for momentum.

Like the argument for a speed limit via the infinite impulse required to produce infinite momentum, we find that doing more and more work to move an object or particle increases its kinetic energy disproportionately to its increase in speed. The accelerated matter requires more and more kinetic energy for each small increase in speed. An infinite amount of energy would be required to accelerate a material object to the speed of light. Since an infinite amount of energy is not available, we again conclude that material particles cannot reach the speed of light.

The Correspondence Principle: This is one of the neater principles of physics and is a guide to clear and rational thinking — not only about the ideas of physics, but for all good theory — even in areas as far removed from science as government, religion, and ethics. Simply put, if a new idea is valid, then it ought to be in harmony with the region it overlaps.

Show your students that when small speeds are involved, the relativity formulas reduce to the everyday observation that time, length, and the momenta of things do not appear any different when moving. That's because the differences are too tiny to detect.

More Think-and-Explain Questions

1. As a meter stick moves past you, your measurements show its relativistic momentum to be twice that of its classical value of momentum. If your measurements also show it to have a length of 1 meter, what is the orientation of the stick?
   Answer: The stick must be oriented in a direction perpendicular to its motion, unlike that of a properly-thrown spear. This is because it is traveling at relativistic speed (actually 0.87c) as evidenced by its increased momentum. The fact that its length is unaltered means that its long direction is not in the direction of motion. The thickness of the stick, not the length of the stick, will appear shrunken to half size.

2. In the preceding question, if the stick is moving in a direction along its length (like a properly-thrown spear), how long will it appear to you?
   Answer: The stick will appear to be one-half meter long when it moves with its length along the direction of motion. Why one half its length? Because it is moving fast enough for its mass to be doubled, which is 0.87c.

3. How does the measured density of a body compare when at rest and when moving?
   Answer: The density of a moving body is measured to increase because of a measured increase in mass and decrease in volume.

4. What does the formula $E_0 = mc^2$ mean?
   Answer: $E_0 = mc^2$ means that energy and mass are equivalent to each other. The c^2 is the proportionality constant that links the units of energy and mass. In a practical sense, energy and mass are one and the same. When something gains energy, it gains mass. When something loses energy, it loses mass. Mass is simply congealed energy.

5. *Muons* are elementary particles that are formed high in the atmosphere by the interactions of cosmic rays with gases in the upper atmosphere. Muons are radioactive and have average lifetimes of about two-millionths of a second. Even though they travel at almost the speed of light, they are so high that very few should be detected at sea level — at least according to Newtonian physics. Laboratory measurements, however, show that muons in great proportions *do* reach the earth's surface. Can this be explained?
   Answer: This can be explained by time dilation or by length contraction. Time dilation: At the muons' high speeds they have about ten times as much time, or twenty-millionths of a second, to live. From the stationary earth frame of reference, the muon's "clock" is running ten times slower than earth clocks, allowing sufficient time to make the trip. Length contraction: From the muon's frame of reference, the distance to earth is contracted by ten times, so it has sufficient time to get there.

17 The Atomic Nature of Matter

Objectives

- Describe the relation of atoms and elements.
- Compare the age of atoms to the age of the materials they compose.
- Give examples that illustrate the small size of atoms.
- Cite evidence for the existence of atoms.
- Distinguish between an atom and a molecule.
- Distinguish between an element and a compound.
- Identify the three basic building blocks that make up an atom and tell where in the atom each is found.
- Explain the significance of the horizontal rows and the vertical columns in the periodic table.
- Describe how the plasma state of matter differs from the solid, liquid, and gaseous states.

Possible Misconceptions to Correct

- Material things are made of thousands of different kinds of atoms.
- The atoms that make up a newborn baby were made in the mother's womb.
- The age of atoms in a baby is less than the age of atoms in an old person.
- Molecules are actually big atoms.

No Demo Equipment for this Chapter

Introduction

The treatment of atoms in this chapter is basic, and provides a good background for the chapters on heat. It also provides background for Chapters 28, 32, and Unit VI. An extended treatment of atoms is given in Chapters 38 and 39. This chapter is the most important chapter in Unit II, and should not be skipped.

Interesting info not in the text: The ten most abundant elements in our environment are in order, oxygen, silicon, aluminum, iron, calcium, sodium, potassium, magnesium, titanium, and hydrogen. There are 4×10^{-6} grams of gold in a metric ton of seawater.

(The lovely girl in Figure 17.1 is my daughter Leslie when she was 16, who is presently a geologist and a teacher.)

Atoms, of course, are not the smallest particles that exist. Smaller than protons, neutrons, and electrons are neutrinos. As you are reading this sentence, a thousand billion neutrinos emanating from the sun pierce through your body. This is true day or night, since at nighttime the solar neutrinos travel through the earth and pierce you from below — interesting tid bit!

An excellent 10-minute film is *Powers of Ten,* by Charles and Ray Eames, and narrated by Philip Morrison. (Pyramid Films, 1978). This film makes an excellent tie from the solar system, galaxies, and the universe, discussed briefly in the previous chapters, to the atom — comparing sizes as positive and negative powers of ten.

The lab activity *Flat as a Pancake,* followed by *Extra Small,* is an excellent example of a pre-experiment activity making the experiment meaningful. Here students estimate the size of a molecule — and quite accurately.

Practice Book 17-1 can go anywhere with this chapter.

Next-Time Questions 17-1 and **17-2** are questions that require knowledge of the period table.

Suggested Lecture

Begin by posing the situation of breaking a boulder into rocks, rocks into stones, stones into pebbles, pebbles into gravel, gravel into sand, sand into powder, and so forth until you get to the fundamental building block — the atom. Give examples to convey the idea of the smallness of the atom, i.e., an atom is as many orders of magnitude smaller than a person as an average star is larger than a person — so we stand between the atoms and the stars. The size of an atom is to the size of an apple as the size of an apple is to the size of the earth. So if you want to imagine an apple full of atoms, think of the earth, solid-packed with apples.

Elements: State that although the number of atoms that exist is enormous, the number of different kinds of atoms is about 100. These are the elements, beginning with the simplest and lightest, hydrogen, to the most complex and heaviest normally found in the earth's crust, uranium. Elements heavier than uranium are not normally found in the earth's crust — the "transuranic elements."

Smallness of Atoms: You can lead into the idea of more molecules in the air in your lungs than there are lung-fulls of air in the world with the following: State that if you put a drop of ink in a bathtub full of water, you can very soon sample any part of the water and find ink in it. The atoms of ink spread out. We can get an idea of the smallness of atoms from this fact: There are more atoms in a thimbleful of ink than there are thimblefuls of water in all the lakes and rivers of the world. That means if you throw a thimbleful of ink into one of the Great Lakes, eventually it will mix, and then if you dip anywhere in the lake with a thimble, you'll have many atoms of ink in your sample.

Atoms are so tiny that you inhale billions of trillions with each breath, nearly a trillion times more atoms than the total population of people since humans emerged. [There are about 10^{23} atoms in a breath (a liter), and the present human population of the world is about 10^9, probably no more than 10^2 times the human population since time zero.] Assuming that most of the atoms previously breathed by people are still part of the atmosphere, then you inhale billions of atoms exhaled by every person who ever sighed, sneezed, laughed, and generally breathed! So in this sense we are all one!

About 6 years are required for molecules released in the atmosphere to become uniformly mixed. Sneeze, then in 6 years travel anywhere in the world and inhale. More than likely, one of the molecules from that sneeze will be in that breathful of air!

CHECK QUESTION: When you die, what ultimately becomes of the atoms of which you are made? [The atoms that make up your body and become part of the atmosphere will be breathed by and incorporated into the bodies of everyone else on earth — for all future generations!]

Cite how the process of cremation quickens the process of getting your atoms into the life cycle. Don't feel bad about those who have been buried in air-tight vaults. Most of the atoms that made up their bodies passed through them before they died and are in circulation now.

Historical Notes: Relate how from the earliest days of science people wondered how far the idea of breaking boulders into stones, pebbles, sand, powder, and so on, would go. Does the process of subdividing ever end? Hundreds of years ago, people had no way of finding out, and they instead carried on with philosophical speculation. Not until the late 1700's did people begin to get indirect evidence of some basic order in the combinations of things. The first real "proof" for atoms was given by Einstein in 1905, the same year he published his paper on relativity. He calculated what kind of motion there ought to be in Brownian motion, based on ideas we've already considered, like energy and momentum conservation, and the idea of heat as atomic motion. Many leading scientists at that time didn't believe in atoms until Einstein's work.

Evidence for Atoms: Ask what an atom would "look like" if viewed through a vertical bank of about 40 high-powered optical microscopes stacked one atop the other. Atoms don't *look* like anything — they don't have an appearance. You can qualify this by stating they have no appearance in the range of frequencies we call light. Discuss Figures 17.3 and 17.4, techniques that have opened new doors in fields such as medicine and biology. No longer will the positions of atoms in complex molecules be guesswork.

You might allude to the later study of Chapter 38 and state that the electron beam in the electron microscope has the properties of high-frequency light. (The electron microscope that had its heyday more than two and three decades ago is a fundamentally different device than today's scanning electron microscopes and scanning tunneling microscopes.) Acknowledge the wave nature of matter — the fuzziness in the distinction between particles and waves at the atomic level — that particles seem to be also congealed standing waves of energy — a "wavicle".

Molecules: Distinguish between atoms and molecules. There are a limited number of different atoms, but there are innumerable different molecules — and more are being discovered and constructed.

CHECK QUESTION: What is the number of elements in a water molecule? What is the number of atoms in a water molecule? [Two elements (hydrogen and oxygen), and three atoms, two of hydrogen and one of water.]

Interestingly enough, whereas an individual atom cannot be seen by the naked eye, some molecules can. One such molecule, called a macro-molecule, is a diamond. A diamond is actually one big carbon molecule!

[**Transparencies 26, 27, 28** here. These are of the Rutherford experiment (Figure 17.8), atomic shells (Figure 17.10) and the periodic table (Figure 17.11)]

The Atomic Nucleus: Distinguish among protons, neutrons, and electrons. Discuss Rutherford's discovery of the nucleus (Figure 17.8), and the Bohr model of the atom (Figure 17.9) and the electrical role of the nucleus and surrounding electrons. Stress the emptiness of the atom and lead into the idea of solid matter being mostly empty space. State how our bodies are 99.999% empty spaces, and how a particle, if tiny and not affected by electrical forces, could be shot straight through us without even making a hole! Neutrons do just that. From a beam of neutrons, a few may make bull's-eye collisions with some of our atomic nuclei — this can do damage so we wouldn't want to really do this. However, all but a minute fraction in a beam of neutrons would pass unhindered through the body.

Discuss the role of electrical forces in preventing us from oozing into our chairs and so forth. Ask the class to imagine that the lecture table is a large magnet, and that you wear magnetic shoes that are repelled by the table you "stand" on. Then state that on the submicroscopic scale that this is indeed what happens when you walk on any solid surface. Only the repelling force isn't magnetic, its electric! Discuss the submicroscopic notion of things touching. Acknowledge that under very special circumstances the nucleus of one atom can actually touch the nucleus of another atom — that this is what happens in a thermonuclear reaction.

CHECK QUESTION: True or False: There exists a large air gap between the nucleus of an atom and the orbiting electrons. [False, there is a void, but not an air gap. Air is far from being a void, and is a substance that consists principally of nitrogen and oxygen molecules.]

Schematically show the hydrogen atom, and add a proton and neutrons to build a helium atom, and then a lithium atom, and so on. Discuss atomic number, and the role that the number of protons play in the nucleus in dictating the surrounding electron configuration. Call attention to and briefly discuss the periodic table on page 254. Point out that the atomic configurations depicted in Figure 17.10 are simply models. Models are not complete or accurate. For example, if the nuclei were drawn to scale they would be scarcely visible specks. And the electrons don't actually orbit like planets as the drawings suggest — such terms don't seem to have much meaning at the atomic level. (Electrons don't exactly orbit because we lose the distinction between particle and wave. Can we say they "swarm" or "smear?" For your students that continue studying physics, they will later be up against the concept that something can be both a particle and a wave.)

You might state that the configuration of electrons and their interactions with each other is basically what chemistry is about.

Phases of Matter: Briefly discuss the phases of matter, and how different molecular speeds account for the solid, liquid, gaseous, and plasma phases. In the previous editions, and in the video series of Conceptual Physics, "states" of matter is spoken of. Either may be used. One ambiguity is that states also refers to the energy states of atoms. Phases avoids this.

Quarks: Just as the nucleus is composed of protons and neutrons, the protons and neutrons themselves are composed of quarks. Are quarks composed of still smaller particles? There doesn't seem to be reason to think so, but we don't know. This uncertainty is often cited as a weakness by people who do not understand what science is about. Science is not a bag of answers to all the questions of the world, but is a process for finding answers to many questions about the world. We continue to refine our models and add new layers to our understanding — sometimes building onto layers and other times replacing layers. It is unfortunate that some people see this as a weakness. This is remindful of Bertrand Russell, who publicly changed his mind about certain ideas in the course of his life — changes that were part of his growth, but were looked upon by some as a sign of weakness (as discussed back in Chapter 1). Likewise with physics. Our knowledge grows. And that's nice!

More Think-and-Explain Questions

1. How likely is it that at least one of the atoms exhaled by your very first breath at birth will be in your next breath?
   Answer: Highly likely, because the number of atoms exhaled is about the same as the number of liters of atmosphere in the world. And assuming you're more than 6 years old, they are uniformly mixed by now. That first breath, however, was less than a liter — your lungs were smaller then. So take two breaths, or three to be sure!

2. Which would produce a more highly valued element: adding or removing a proton from the element gold?
   Answer: Removing, gold turns into more valuable platinum. Adding a proton turns gold into less valuable mercury.

Think and Solves

1. How many grams of O are there in 18 grams of water?
   Answer: There are 16 grams of O in 18 grams of water. We can see from the formula for water, H_2O, there are twice as many H atoms (each of atomic mass 1) as O atoms (each of atomic mass 16). So the molecular mass of H_2O is 18, with 16 parts O by mass.

2. How many grams of H are there in 16 grams of methane (CH_4) gas?
   Answer: A carbon atom is 12 times as massive as a hydrogen atom, or 3 times as massive as four hydrogen atoms. A bit of reasoning will show that for every 4 grams of hydrogen there will be 3 x 4 = 12 grams of carbon, which when totaled gives 16 grams. So there are 4 grams of hydrogen in 16 grams of methane.

3. Gas A is composed of diatomic molecules (2 atoms to a molecule) of a pure element. Gas B is composed of monatomic molecules (1 atom to a "molecule") of another pure element. Gas A has 3 times the mass of an equal volume of gas B at the same temperature and pressure. How do the masses of elements A and B compare?
   Answer: The mass of element A is 3/2 the mass of element B. Why? Gas A has three times the mass as Gas B. If the equal number of molecules in A and B had equal numbers of atoms, then the atoms in Gas A would simply be three times as massive. But there are twice as many atoms in A, so the mass of each atom must be half of three times as much — that is, 3/2.

Good teaching is knowing what to cover. Better teaching is knowing what to omit.

18 Solids

Objectives

After studying Chapter 18, students will be able to:
• Cite evidence that many solids are crystals.
• Define density and explain why it is the same for different volumes or masses of the same material.
• Distinguish between an elastic material and an inelastic material.
• Predict the stretch for an applied force, given the stretch produced by a different force.
• Explain why the center of a horizontal steel girder need not be as wide as the top and bottom.
• Explain why making something larger by the same factor in all dimensions changes its strength in relation to its weight.

Possible Misconceptions to Correct

• Density is the same as weight, but expressed in different units.
• When a structure is scaled up or down in size, its properties go up or down in direct proportion.
• Doubling the volume of an object means doubling the surface area, or halving the volume means halving the surface area: Surface area and volume scale up or down in direct proportion.
• An animal scaled up in exact proportion, like King Kong, would be proportionally stronger.

Demonstration Equipment

• [18-1] Two springs; a stiff one to compress, and a thinner one to elongate. Spring stand and weights to demonstrate Hooke's law.
• [18-2] Balls of different materials to drop on a hard surface (like an anvil) to show elasticity.
• [18-3] Paper or plastic drinking straws and a potato.
• [18-4] Spherical flask and cylindrical flask of same volume (500 or 1000-ml).
• [18-5] Eight cubes (Styrofoam, wood, plastic, etc.)

Introduction

The crystal nature of solids are very briefly treated.

Hooke's law is treated in regard to elasticity and the stretches and compressions of solids. In many courses it is treated in mechanics. If you wish to treat Hooke's law earlier, it could go with the material in Chapters 4 or 6.

Density is introduced in this chapter, and also could be treated earlier, perhaps when mass was treated in Chapter 3. It works nicely here, however, for it plays a central role in the following chapters. (I like introducing ideas when they are needed, so they aren't considered excess baggage.) Table 18-1 lists the densities of some common materials. Not included is the density of atomic nuclei that comprise so tiny a fraction of space within matter, about 2×10^{14} gm/cm^3, and in a further crushed state, the interior of neutron stars, about 10^{16} gm/cm^3. That's dense!

Interesting tidbit also not in the text: Materials denser than lead are very expensive (platinum, gold, mercury, etc.), so are generally not used when denseness is wanted. A lead fishing weight may not be as dense as a gold fishing weight, but it is certainly more practical. Uranium, on the other hand, is relatively cheap, and is used as a substitute for lead in some cases — like bullets in electronically fired naval Gatling guns, or low-volume but heavy weights at the bottom of boat keels.

Students should find Section 19-4, *Scaling*, of particular interest. Many more examples of the implications of surface to volume can be explored(*On Being the Right Size*, by J.B.S. Haldane, and *On Magnitude*, by Sir D'Arcy Wentworth Thompson. Both are readings in J.R. Newman, ed. *The World of Mathematics*, Vol. II, Simon & Schuster, 1956).

Scaling is becoming enormously important as more and more devices are being miniaturized. Researchers are finding that when something shrinks enough, whether an electronic circuit, a motor, a film of lubricant, or an individual crystal of metal or ceramic, that thing stops acting like a miniature version of its larger self and starts behaving in new and different ways. Palladium metal, for example, which is normally composed of grains about 1000 nanometers in size, is found to be five times as strong when formed from 5 nanometer grains.

Our technology is changing from "top down" to "bottom up." In the top-down method, relatively large pieces of material are carved into smaller pieces. Such has been the era of milling machines and lathes. In the bottom-up method, matter is assembled an atom at a time — interestingly enough, nature's way. Trees grow an atom at a time. Will tomorrow's human-made devices in the era of nanotechnology do the same?

This chapter may be skipped with no particular consequence. If this chapter is skipped and Chapter 19 is assigned, the concept of density should be introduced then.

Stretch is a traditional Hooke's law lab in which students graphically calculate the spring constant. Introduce scaling to your students by having them do the lab *Geometric Physic*.

Suggested Lecture

Begin by showing evidence for crystal structure in solids, such as passing small sheets of galvanized iron around the room.

[**Transparencies 29** and **30**, Figure 18.2 of a salt crystal; Table 18.1 of densities]

Density: Pass around the room two objects that are about the same volume but vastly different mass, like a lead block and a wood block. Have your students shake each. This should dispel the notion mass is

volume. Go further for same mass and different volume to dispel the notion volume is mass. Note the difference between a vertical shake and a horizontal shake. Vertical involves weight, horizontal does not. This leads to outer space, and the vital concept, mass density is basic; weight density is not (depends on where we are).

Interesting fact not in the text: The three metals lithium, sodium, and potassium are all less dense than water and will float in water.

Using a large wooden cube, measure its dimensions in cm and find its mass with a pan balance. Define density = mass/volume. (Use the same cube when you discuss flotation in the next chapter.) Some of your students will unfortunately still confuse density as massiveness or bulkiness with massiveness-per-bulkiness, even when they give a verbal definition properly. Be prepared to find that you'll have students who can not correctly answer the question: How many faces does a cube have? Count them!

CHECK QUESTIONS: What happens to the density of each piece of an object when it is cut into pieces? [Each piece has the same density as the original object had.] Which has the greater density, a kilogram of lead or a kilogram of feathers? [Any amount of lead is more dense than any amount of feathers.] A single uranium atom or the world? [The uranium atom.]

Acknowledge weight density, common in the British system of units — like the density of water, 62.4 lb/ft^2. Discuss the boxed section on page 262 is the essence of the "Eureka" story of Archimedes and the gold crown.

Elasticity: Introduce elasticity with an activity version of *Stretch* (Experiment 43).

DEMONSTRATION [18-1]: Hang weights from a spring to illustrate Hooke's Law. Ask the class to predict the elongations before suspending additional masses. Also place weights on a spring and predict the compression. Hooke's law holds for both stretching and compression.

DEMONSTRATION [18-2]: Drop spheres of glass, steel, rubber, and other materials onto a hard surface and compare the elasticities. [Your students will be surprised to see that glass and steel are considerably more elastic than rubber!]

Compression and Stretching: Discuss Figures 18.7 and 18.8, and the reason for the I-beam cross section for construction girders.

Not mentioned in the text, one cubic inch of bone can withstand a 2-ton force.

DEMONSTRATION [18-3]: Show the weakness of a paper drinking straw when a force is applied

perpendicular to its length. A small load buckles the straw. But along its length, like vertical girders used in construction, the straw has great strength. Show this by grasping a straw firmly at its end with forefinger and thumb and slamming it spear wise against a potato held in your other hand. With very little practice you can pierce the potato. (Similarly, various reports have cited pieces of straw penetrating boards and other materials in hurricanes. If the straw strikes exactly perpendicular to the material it encounters, penetration rather than bending occurs.)

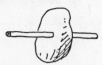

Not mentioned in the text, and an interesting follow-through to the text material is the ease with which tiny cracks can lead to big breaks in strong structures. This accounts for disasters such as ships breaking in two or wings falling off airplanes. Bonds between atoms are broken in a crack or scratch, which places greater stress upon neighboring bonds. A concentration of stress occurs at the tip of a crack, so that a relatively small force can cause the overstrained bond to break. The next bond in turn breaks, and like a zipper, the whole structure separates. The initial dislocation need not be a large one. A glass cutter wanting to cut glass needs only make a shallow scratch on the surface, and then the glass will break easily along the line of the scratch. Similarly, a piece of cloth is easily ripped if a small nick is first made in the material.

Area and Volume: Introduce the relationship between area and volume as Chelcie Liu does with the following demo:

DEMONSTRATION [18-4]: Have a 500-ml or 1000-ml spherical flask filled with colored water sitting on your lecture table. Produce a tall cylindrical flask, of same volume (unknown to your students), and ask for speculations as to how high the water level will be when all the water from the spherical flask is poured into it. Ask for a show of hands for those who think that the water will reach more than half the height, and for those who think it will fill to less than half the height, and for those who guess it will fill to exactly half the height. Your students will be amazed when they see that the seemingly smaller spherical flask has the same volume as the tall cylinder.

To explain the above, call attention to the fact that the *area* of the spherical flask is considerably smaller than the surface area of the cylinder. We see the greater area of the cylindrical surface and we tend to think that the volume of the cylinder should be greater. Be sure you do this; it is more impressive than it sounds.

[**Transparency 31**, Figure 18.10 on scaling]

[**Practice Book 18-1** and **18-2** feature scaling]

[**Next-Time Question 18-1** also features scaling]

Scaling: Get into the most interesting part of the chapter, explaining Figures 18.10 and 18.11 via the following:

DEMONSTRATION [18-5]: Display a bunch of toy cubical blocks, or a box of sugar cubes. Be sure to actually show cubes, and even pass sets of eight or more to groups of students. Playing with actual cubes will shed any last remnants of confusion between area and volume.

Regarding Figure 18.12 note that the span from eartip to eartip is almost the height of the elephant. The dense packing of veins and arteries in the elephant's ears finds a five-degree difference for blood entering and leaving the ears. A second type of African elephant that resides in cooler forested regions has smaller ears. Perhaps Indian elephants, with relatively small ears, evolved in cooler climates.

CHECK QUESTIONS: Which has more surface area, an elephant or a mouse? [Elephant.] 2000 kilograms of elephant or 2000 kilograms of mice? [2000 kg of mice.] Distinguish carefully between these different questions.

CHECK QUESTION: Cite two reasons why small cars are more affected by wind. [Less mass and more cross-sectional area compared to weight than larger cars.]

CHECK QUESTION: Why do Chinese cooks chop food in such small pieces for cooking quickly in a wok? [Since cooking occurs from the surface inward, the greater area per volume enhances cooking.]

CHECK QUESTION: In terms of surface to volume, why should parents take extra care that a baby is warm enough in a cold environment? [The baby has more surface per bodyweight, and will therefore cool more rapidly than a larger person.]

Related tidbits not mentioned in the text: The surface area of human lungs is about 20 times greater than the surface skin area. The digestive tract of an adult human is about 10 meters long.
Your lecture can continue by posing exercises from the chapter-end material, and involving the check-your-neighbor technique or general class discussion. The examples posed in the Think and Explain questions, and questions in the exploratory activity *Geometrical Physics* will perk class interest.

More Think-and-Explain Questions

1. Is a piece of lead necessarily heavier than a piece of wood? Explain.
   Answer: Although a piece of lead is denser than any piece of wood, it may or may not be heavier, depending on its size. A small piece of lead is obviously lighter than a full-grown tree. (Confusion often results when weight and density are not distinguished.)

2. Why can large fish generally swim faster than small fish?
   Answer: To understand why large fish swim faster than small fish, consider dropping a large and small fish through the air. The larger fish will more easily "plow through" the air like a heavier parachutist descends in air faster than a light parachutist. The situation is the same in water. The larger fish has more mass, and therefore more strength, compared to its surface area and resistance. So large fish feed by simply swimming with their mouths open after smaller fish.

3. Do the effects of scaling help or hinder a small swimmer on a racing team?
   Answer: The effects of scaling hinder small swimmers. Larger swimmers have more mass per surface area, and therefore more strength compared to the water resistance they encounter. Now you know why champion swimmers are larger than average people.

4. Who has more need for drink in a dry desert climate — a child or an adult?
   Answer: A child, for a child has more surface area per volume, and therefore loses disproportionally more water to the air.

Think and Solves

1. A one-cubic centimeter cube has sides 1 cm in length. What is the length of the sides of a cube of volume two-cubic centimeters?
   Answer: Each side is the cube root of 2, which is 1.26 cm.

2. Larger people at the beach need more suntan lotion than smaller people. Compared to a smaller person, how much lotion will a twice-as-heavy person use?
   Answer: About 1.6 times as much. Both have the same density, so the person twice as heavy has twice the volume, but not twice the surface area. The twice-as-heavy person has more area than the smaller person, but less than twice as much. (How much more surface area is there for a body with twice the volume? Consider the unit cube of the previous problem; twice the volume means each side is the cube root of two (1.26) times the side of the smaller cube. Its area is then 1.26 x 1.26 = 1.587 times greater than the smaller cube. So the twice as heavy person at the beach would use about 1.6 times as much suntan lotion.)

3. Consider eight one-cubic centimeter sugar cubes stacked two by two to form a single bigger cube.

What will be the volume of the combined cube? How does its surface area compare to the total surface area of the eight separate cubes?

Answer: The big cube will have the same combined volume of the eight little cubes, but have half their combined area. The area of each side of the little cubes is 1 cm^2, and for its six sides the total area of each little cube is 6 cm^2. So all eight individual cubes have a total surface area 48 cm^2. The area of each side of the big cube, on the other hand, is 2^2 or 4 cm^2; for all six sides its total surface area is 24 cm^2, half as much as the separate small cubes.

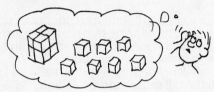

4. Consider eight little spheres of mercury, each with a diameter of 1 millimeter. When they coalesce to form a single sphere, how big will it be? How does its surface area compare to the total surface area of the previous eight little spheres?

Answer: The big sphere will have twice the diameter of the 1-mm spheres, and will have only one half as much surface area as the total surface area of the eight little spheres. This problem is very similar to the previous one for cubes, since the scaling principles illustrated in the text by cubes hold for any shapes. (This fact, that the total surface area is reduced when smaller parts combine to form a larger shape is employed by mice and other creatures who ball up in clusters to reduce their total surface area in cold weather.)

19 Liquids

Objectives

- Describe what determines the pressure of a liquid at any point.
- Explain what causes a buoyant force on an immersed or submerged object.
- Relate the buoyant force on an immersed or submerged object with the weight of the fluid it displaces.
- Describe what determines whether an object will sink or float in a fluid.
- Given the weight of a floating object, determine the weight of fluid it displaces.
- Describe how Pascal's principle can be applied to increase the force of a fluid on a surface.

Possible Misconceptions to Correct

- Liquid pressure depends on the total weight of liquid present.
- Immersed and submerged mean the same thing.
- The buoyant force that acts on a submerged object equals the weight of the object (rather than weight of water displaced).
- Heavy things (rather than denser things) sink in water, while light things float.
- Whether something sinks or floats depends on its weight (rather than density).

Demonstration Equipment

- [19-1]: Pascal's Vases.
- [19-2]: Overflow can, or graduated cylinder, or a liquid-measuring cup, and a metal or stone weight that can be lowered into the water-filled vessel by a string.
- [19-3] Pair of spring scales, metal block or stone, vessel filled with water, and smaller vessel to catch overflow (as shown in Figure 19.10, page 279).
- [19-4]: Cartesian diver (Activity 2, page 287).

Introduction

Knowledge of the ocean as well as of outer space is of current interest, so this and the following chapter should have special interest to your class. Liquids are a real part of your students' everyday world.

Consider doing the neat demo that Paul Robinson does to enchant his classes and mix some cornstarch with water in a shallow pan in front of your class. The gooey liquid state is evident as it is sloshed about in the pan. Then invite a student to strike the liquid with a rubber mallet. Instead of splashing, it thuds. Under pressure, the liquid mixture is puttylike, more solid than liquid, much like a pressure sensitive liquid crystal. For an explanation, see Jearl Walker's delightful book, *The Flying Circus of Physics, With Answers*, (Wiley, 1978).

The unit "ton" is used in several places in this text. It may be taken to mean a metric tonne, the weight of 1000 kilograms, or the British ton, 2000 pounds. Either interpretation is sufficient in treating the idea involved.

You may find that many students who have trouble with conceptualizing buoyant force are confused about the distinction between area and volume. Be sure to make this distinction clear. If you didn't pour the contents of the 500-ml or 1000-ml spherical flask into the tall same-volume cylinder as described in the suggested lecture of the last chapter, be sure to do it now.

Prerequisite to this chapter is knowledge of density, covered in the previous chapter. So if you skipped Chapter 18, discuss density now. This chapter is a prerequisite for the following chapter but not for the remaining chapters.

In the lab *Eureka!* students will discover that fluid displacement does not depend on weight whereas in *Sink or Swim* they learn to use and apply Archimedes' principle.

Suggested Lecture

Pressure: Begin by recalling from Chapter 4 the distinction between force and pressure. Illustrate with examples: Somebody pushing on your back with a force of only one newton — with a pin! As you're lying on the floor, a woman steps on your stomach — perched atop spike heels! Indian master lying on a bed of 1000 nails — apprentice considering starting with one nail! Why the importance of jewel bearings in watches (remember them, old timer?), diamond stylus (still around!) in record players (still around!), rounded corners on tables, sharp blades on cutting knives.

Have students compare in their hands the weights of a small steel ball and a large Styrofoam ball, and after agreeing that the little ball is heavier (since density was treated in the previous chapter), weigh them and show the Styrofoam ball is heavier! Another example of pressure (on the nerve endings).

Liquid Pressure: Recall the definition of density from the previous chapter. Consider the pressure at the bottom of a container of water, as is done via Figure 19.2. Liquid pressure = weight density x depth: After a few words about weight density, you may want to derive or call attention to the derivation of this relationship (footnote on page 274). Note that mass density x depth (or height) must be further multiplied by *g* to give pressure (N/m², not kg/m²). This "tacking on of *g*" is avoided when weight density rather than mass density is used to develop liquid pressure.

DEMONSTRATION [19-1]: Pascal's Vases — rationalize your results in terms of the supporting forces exerted by the sloping sides of the vases. [For wide-mouth conical vases, conical glass sides push upward on water, so pressure at bottom is effectively due only to weight of cylindrical part of water above. For the non-vertical part of the narrow-mouth vase, glass pushes down on water (reaction to water pushing on glass) with just as much force as the weight of a column of water above.]

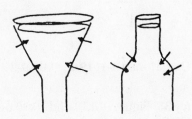

Ask why dams are built thicker at the bottom, and after discussing Figure 19.3 sketch the top view of a couple of dams on the board and ask which design is best. Then relate this to ideas of the previous chapter, the shape of stone bridges (which actually need no mortar), and the arched shape of the tops of windows in old brick buildings. Another illustration is the concave ends of large wine barrels.

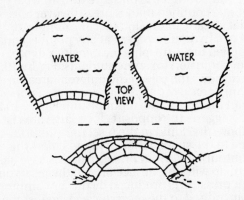

CHECK QUESTIONS: Would the pressure be greater swimming 3 meters deep in the middle of the ocean, than 3 meters deep in an ocean tidepool? [No.] Would the pressure be greater swimming 3 meters deep in the middle of the ocean, than 3 meters deep in a pond? [Yes, but only because salt water is more dense.]

Compare the densities of fresh and salt water (about 2% denser than fresh water.)
Cite how blood pressure is taken at the upper arm because it is at the same "depth" as the heart. Follow-up information: For the average human, blood takes only about 23 seconds to circulate through the body; every extra pound of fat you carry requires an extra 200 miles of capillaries (another reason for staying slim!).

Show that buoyancy is a consequence of pressure being depth dependent. Sketch Figure 19.6 on the board.

DEMONSTRATION [19-2]: Lower an object by string into water in an overflow can, a graduated cylinder, or a liquid-measuring cup, to show the idea of displacement and how an object's volume is nicely measured.

Distinguish between immersed and submerged. In a baptism the person is immersed, not submerged. The difference is in degree. Point out that more water is displaced when something is submerged than when immersed (partially submerged).

[**Transparencies** 32 and 33, Figures 19.6 and 19.10 on Archimedes' principle]

[**Practice Book** 19-1 and 19-2 are on Archimedes' principle]

Archimedes' Principle: State how one is buoyed upward when immersed or submerged in water. Call attention to Figure 19.11 — that because pressure depends on depth, the bottom of a submerged object experienced greater pressure than the top. This difference in pressures produces a difference in forces, that produce a resulting buoyant force. The amount of buoyant force is given by Archimedes' principle:

DEMONSTRATION [19-3]: Show Archimedes' principle with the apparatus in Figure 19.10.

Another way to state Archimedes' principle is to cite Newton's third law: If you put something in water that pushes say 100 N of water out of the way (displaces 100 N), then the water pushes back with 100 N. The buoyant force is equal and opposite to the weight of water you displace.

CHECK QUESTION: If an object is put into the water that pushes 500 N of water out of the way, how much force does the water exert on the object? [500 N] If you push 1000 N of water aside, how much force does the water then exert on you? [1000 N]

Point out that because a liquid is nearly incompressible its density is not depth dependent. A liquid is practically incompressible. The volume of water decreases by 50 one-millionths of its original volume for each atmosphere increase in pressure, or equivalently, for each addition 10.3 meters in depth. The density of water near the surface is practically the same as the density far beneath the surface. Greater variation occurs due to temperature difference. Usually a student will inquire about waterlogged objects that lie submerged yet above the bottom. Such objects are slightly denser than the warmer surface water and not quite as dense as the cooler water at the bottom. Stress that this is unusual, and that objects appreciably denser than water always sink to the bottom, regardless of the depth of the water. Scuba divers do not encounter floating rocks near the bottoms of deep bodies of water!

bodies of water!

CHECK QUESTION: Two solid blocks of the same size are submerged in water. One block is lead and the other is aluminum. Upon which is the buoyant force greater? [Both the same.]

After discussion, try this one:

CHECK QUESTION: Two solid blocks of identical size, one of lead and the other of wood, are put in the same water and released. Upon which is the buoyant force greater? [Because the wood floats, this time the BF is greater on the lead, because it displaces more water.]

The Role of Density: Discuss the three rules that describe the effect of density on submerged objects — top of page 281.

CHECK QUESTIONS: What is the approximate density of a fish? Of a person? What can you say of people who can't float? [The density of a fish = that of water; most people are slightly less dense than water; people denser than water can't float.]

It is interesting to note that mountains float on the earth's mantle, and are less dense than the molten mantle. Also, just as most of an iceberg is below the water line, most of a mountain is below the surface of the ground. The earth's crust is therefore deeper where there are mountains.

[**Transparency** 34, Figure s 19.14 and 19.17 on flotation]

Flotation: Explain how Archimedes' principle holds whether or not an object sinks or floats — but in the case of floating, the buoyant force equals not only the weight of liquid displaced, but also the weight of the floating object.

CHECK QUESTION: Is the above statement a coincidence? [No, the equilibrium of floating requires that the BF be equal and opposite to the gravity force — its weight.]

CHECK QUESTION: What is the buoyant force on a ten-ton ship floating in fresh water? In salt water? In a lake of mercury? [10 tons in each case (although the *volume* of liquid displaced differs).]

Discuss boats and rafts and the change of water lines when loaded.

Technically speaking we can say that a completely submerged object that doesn't sink and doesn't rise is floating, but we commonly consider floating as just breaking surface or higher. This distinction becomes evident when considering a balloon floating in the air. Air is a fluid and the same buoyancy principle applies (next chapter).

DEMONSTRATION [19-4]: Cartesian diver (Activity 2, page 287).

Discuss the compressibility of the human body in swimming — how the density of most people a meter or two below the surface of the water is still less than the density of water, and that one need only relax and be buoyed to the surface. But that at greater depths, the greater pressure compresses us to densities greater than the density of water, and we must swim to the surface. Simply relaxing, we would sink to the bottom! Relate this to the Cartesian diver demonstration. This is the crux of Think and Explain #8 (the weighted balloon that sinks when pushed beneath the surface).

[**Next-Time Questions 19-1, 19-2**, and **19-3** are on floatation]

[**Transparency 35**, Figures 19.19 and 19.20 on Pascal's principle]

Pascal's Principle: Begin by pushing against the wall with a meter stick and state that the stick affords a means of applying pressure to the wall — then state that the same can be done with a confined fluid. Explain how any external pressure applied to a liquid that tightly fills a volume is transmitted to all parts of the liquid equally. Discuss Figures 19.18 and 19.19. If a hydraulic press is available, crush a block of wood with it. Point out that the pressure transmitted throughout a confined fluid is pressure over and above that already in the liquid. For example, the pressure in a hydraulic system at any point is equal to the applied pressure, plus the density x depth.

Point of confusion for some students: Figure 19.19 in the text shows the role of the different areas in multiplying forces; the area of the output piston is larger than the area of the input piston. Figure 19.20, however, suggests the opposite, for a large area is shown above the liquid in the reservoir (input) compared to the smaller area of liquid below the piston (output). But input pressure in this case has nothing to do with the surface area in the reservoir. The input pressure is produced by the air compressor and is transmitted to the reservoir and against the output piston in accord with Pascal's principle.

More Think-and-Explain Questions

1. Next time you're near a farm, notice that a silo has metal bands around it to give it strength. Notice also that these bands are closer together near ground level and are spaced farther apart near the top of the silo. Why is this so?
   Answer: The bands are closer together at the bottom because the pressure of its contents against its sides is greater near the bottom of the silo.

2. Why does water seek its own level?
   Answer: Water seeking its own level is a consequence of pressure depending on depth. In a bent U-tube full of water, the water in one side of the

tube pushes water up the other side until the pressure in both sides is equal. Therefore the corresponding depth of water causing to these pressures is equal.

3. Suppose you wish to see if a point at the front of your house is at the same elevation as a point around the back. How can you use a garden hose filled with water to determine whether the elevation is equal?

Answer: The use of a water-filled garden hose as an elevation indicator is a practical example of water seeking its own level. The water surface at one end of the hose will be at the same elevation above sea level as the water surface at the other end of the hose. As in the previous question, the hose is simply a wide-spread U tube.

More Think and Solves

1. The depth of water behind the Hoover Dam in Colorado is 220 m. What is the water pressure at the base of this dam (neglect the pressure due to the atmosphere)?

Answer: P = weight density x depth = 9800 N/m^3 x 220 m = 2156 x 10^3 Pa = 2160 kPa. (to three significant figures).

2. The top floor of a building is 30 m above the basement. How much greater will the water pressure be in the basement than on the top floor?

Answer: Water pressure is 294 kPa greater at basement level than at the top floor.
P = weight density x depth = 9800 N/m^3 x 30 m = 294,000 N/m^2, or 294 kPa.

3. Which do you suppose produces more pressure on the ground, an elephant or a lady standing on high heels? Approximate a rough calculation for each.

Answer: A lady with high heels produces considerably more pressure on the ground than an elephant! Example: A 400-N lady with 1-cm^2 high heels puts half her weight on each foot and produces (200 N/1 cm^2) = 200 N/cm^2. A 20,000-N elephant with 1000 cm^2 feet yields one-fourth its weight on each foot produces (5000 N/1000 cm^2) = 5 N/cm^2; about 1/40 the pressure. (So a lady with high heels will make greater dents in a linoleum floor than an elephant.)

4. A 0.6 kg piece of metal displaces 1 liter of water when submerged. What is its density?

Answer: Density = m/V = 0.6 kg/1 l = 0.6 kg/l. (Since there are 1000 liters in 1 cubic meter, density may be expressed in units kg/m^3. Density = 0.6 kg/1 l x 1000 l/m^3 = 600 kg/m^3.)

5. Calculate the approximate volume of a person of mass 100 kg who can just barely float in fresh water.

Answer: 0.1 m^3. The person's weight density is about that of water, 9800 N/m^3. Then from the definition Density = weight/volume, rearrangement gives Volume = weight/density = (100 kg x 9.8 N/kg)/9800 N/m^3 = 980 N/9800 N/m^3 = 0.1 m^3.

6. A certain block of plastic is 0.6 as dense as water and therefore floats in water. What weight of water will be displaced by a 100-kg floating block of this plastic? What additional force would be required to poke it beneath the surface so it is completely submerged?

Answer: Since it floats, weight of displaced water = weight of block = *mg* = 100 kg x 9.8 N/kg = 980 N. Some thought will show that this is 0.6 the weight of water, W, that would be displaced if the block were completely submerged. That is, 980 N = 0.6 W. So W = 980 N/0.6 = 1633.3 N. The additional force to submerge the block is then 1633.3 - 980 = 653.3 N, or 653 N rounded. (Like so many problems, there are other ways to arrive at the same result.)

Objectives

- Explain what keeps the molecules in the earth's atmosphere from neither escaping nor settling to the ground.
- Describe the source of atmospheric pressure.
- Explain why water cannot be raised higher than 10.3 m with a vacuum pump.
- Describe the relation between pressure and density for a given amount of a gas at a constant temperature.
- Explain what determines whether an object will float in air.
- Describe the relation between the speed of a fluid at any point and the pressure at that point, for steady flow.
- Explain the principle source of lift on the wing of a bird or airplane.

Possible Misconceptions to Correct

- Air has no weight.
- The atmosphere of the earth extends upward for hundreds of kilometers.
- Things float in air for different reasons than things float in water.
- The faster a fluid moves, the greater is its pressure.
- Atmospheric pressure is greater during a hurricane or tornado.

Demonstration Equipment

- [20-1] Two or three empty aluminum soda pop cans, with heat source to boil a bit of water inside.
- [20-2] Floppy rubber with handle in middle.
- [20-3] Wooden shingle and sheet of newspaper.
- [20-4] Glass of water and two drinking straws.
- 20-5] Siphon.
- [20-6] A drinking glass to immerse upside down in water, with a Ping Pong ball or other floating object to fit in the glass.
- [20-7] Bernoulli examples: beach ball and blower or vacuum cleaner, Ping-Pong ball and hairdryer, a several feet long plastic bag, cardboard tube with sandpaper inside, Ping-Pong ball on piece of string and stream of water.

Introduction

The concepts of fluid pressure, buoyancy, and flotation introduced in the previous chapter are applied to the atmosphere in this chapter. You should point out that unlike a liquid, the density of the atmosphere is depth-dependent. It thins with increasing altitude.

To avoid information overload, the section on Boyle's Law avoids distinguishing between absolute pressure and gauge pressure. An example illustrating this distinction is the fact that a pres-

sure gauge will register zero pressure for a flat tire, when in fact the air pressure in a flat tire is atmospheric pressure. So absolute pressure = gauge pressure + atmospheric pressure.

Charles' Law is not covered, and reference is made to temperature effects only in a footnote. The plow can be set deeper in a follow-up course.

If you're into lecture demonstrations, this is the material for a show. There are two good sources I have found useful: *A Demonstration Handbook for Physics*, by G.D. Frier and F.J. Anderson, published by AAPT, and *Invitations to Science Inquiry*, by the late Tik L. Liem of St. Francis Xavier University, in Antigonish, Nova Scotia.

Blowing bubbles is always fun, and here's one from the Exploratorium that nicely illustrates Bernoulli's Principle. Question: Can you blow a 1-breath bubble bigger than your lungs? Answer: Yes, depending on how you do it. Here's how: Tape together two or three small juice cans that have had both ends removed.

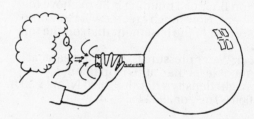

(You can use the cardboard core of a roll of paper towels, but this tube will not last through repeated uses.) Make up a soap solution that consists Joy or Dawn liquid dishwashing soap, glycerin, and water (recipe: 1 gallon of water, 2/3 cup of dishwashing soap, 3 tablespoons glycerin [available from any drug store].) Let the solution stand overnight, for better bubbles are produced by an "aged" mixture. Dip the tube to form a soap film over the end. To make a lung-sized bubble, take a deep breath and, with your mouth sealed against the non-soapy end of the tube, exhale and blow a bubble. Don't blow too hard or else the bubble film will break. You'll note the size of this bubble is nearly the volume of your lungs (you can't exhale *all* the air from your lungs).

You can do the same with a long plastic bag. Invite students to blow up the bag, counting their breaths. After two or three students have demonstrated that many breaths of air are required, announce that you can do it with one breath. The hold the bag a few centimeters in front of your mouth, not on it as your students likely did, and then blow. Air pressure in the air stream you produce is reduced, entrapping surrounding air to join in filling up the bag!

In the lab *Weighty Stuff* student will actually measure the weight of air that it takes to fill a basketball. You can extend this activity by having them then calculate the weight of air in their classroom.

Now dip the tube again and this time blow a full breath of air into the tube end, but keep your mouth about 10 cm away from the end. If you are careful, you can blow a bubble as big as your entire upper body! Here's the explanation: When you blow air into the tube, the moving air is at a lower pressure than the stationary air beside it. The stationary air is then drawn into the lower-pressure region (strictly speaking, is pushed in by the surrounding atmosphere). This extra air drawn into (or pushed into) the original stream further inflates the bubble, adding to the amount of air you exhale from your lungs. Very nice!

The text credits Bernoulli's principle and the airfoil shape of wings to explain wing lift, but as the footnote on page 301 suggests, wings would work without the airfoil. Remember those model planes you flew as a kid, that were constructed of flat wings? And do you remember that the slot to hold the wing was cut with an "angle of attack?" In this way, oncoming air is forced downward. Newton's 3rd law states the rest: If the wing forces air downward, the air simultaneously forces the wing upward. So birds were able to fly before the time of Daniel Bernoulli. The question is sometimes raised; could birds fly before the time of Isaac Newton?

Trying to explain Bernoulli's principle in terms the differences in molecular impacts on the top and bottom surfaces of the wings, turns out to be very challenging. Especially when experiments show that molecules don't make impact on the top surface anyway. A thin boundary layer of air is carried in this low pressure region. This is evidenced by the dust found on the surface of fan blades!

In discussing the global atmosphere, if you get into the abuses that the atmosphere is undergoing, acid rain, etc., please do not end on a sour note. Also get into what can be done to better the situation. Our students have no shortage of inputs telling them about the abuses of technology, and they hear less often about how technology can be used to improve the quality of life in the world.

The computer program *Gas* on the computer disk *Good Stuff!* complements this chapter: 125 gas atoms move about colliding with one another and with the walls of the container. Their speeds are graphed at the side of the picture and you can press "t" to trail one atom along its random path.

This chapter is not a prerequisite for the following chapters.

Practice Book 20-1 can go anywhere with this chapter.

Suggested Lecture

The Atmosphere and Atmospheric Pressure: Draw a circle as large as possible on the chalkboard, and then announce that it represents the earth. State that if you were to draw another circle, indicating the thickness of the atmosphere surrounding the earth to scale, that you would end up drawing the same line — for over 99% of the atmosphere lies within the thickness of the chalk line! (We compare a 30 km depth of atmosphere to the earth's radius 6370 km.) Then go on to discuss the ocean of air we live in.

[**Transparency 36**, Figure 20.1 of the atmosphere]

[**Next-Time Question 20-1** addresses air's weight]

DEMONSTRATION [20-1]: Here's a goodie, more dramatic than Figure 20.10! Heat some aluminum soda pop cans on a burner, empty except for a small amount of water that is brought to a boil to make steam. With a pot holder or tongs, pick up a can and quickly invert it into a basin of water. Crunch! The atmospheric pressure immediately crushes the can with a resounding WHOP! Very impressive. [Condensation of the steam and vapor occur and the interior pressure is reduced. This occurs even when the temperature of the water bath into which the can is inverted is nearly boiling temperature. What happens is a "flypaper effect" — water molecules in the vapor state condense when they encounter the water into which they're placed — even hot water. (Shown later in Figure 23.5 on page 342.)]

CHECK QUESTION: Open the door of a refrigerator and inside is a large lonely grapefruit. Which weighs more, the air in the frig or the grapefruit? [The inside volume of a common refrigerator is between 1/2 and 3/4 m^3, which corresponds to nearly a kilogram of cold air (about 2 pounds). So unless the grapefruit is more than a 2-pounder, the air weighs more.]

While this is going on, state that if you had a 30-kilometer tall bamboo pole of cross section 1 square centimeter, the mass of atmospheric air in it would amount to about 1 kilogram. The weight of this air is the source of atmospheric pressure. The atmosphere bears down on the earth's surface at sea level with a pressure that corresponds to the weight of 1 kilogram per square centimeter. That's nearly 10 N/cm^2. Since there are 10 000 cm^2 in 1 m^2, that's 100 000 N/m^2. Or put another way, ask your class to imagine a 30-kilometer tall sewer pipe of cross section 1 square meter, filled with the air of the atmosphere. How much would the enclosed air weigh? The answer is about 10^5N. So if you draw a circle of one square meter on the lecture table, and ask for the weight of all the air in the atmosphere above, you should elicit a chorus, silent or otherwise of "10^5N!" This is the atmospheric pressure at the bottom of our ocean of air. If your table is located above sea level, in mountain areas for example, then the weight of the atmosphere is correspondingly less (just as water pressure is less for a fish nearer the surface).

Then estimate the force of the air pressure that collapsed the metal can — both for a perfect vacuum and for a case where the pressure difference is about half an atmosphere. Estimate the force of the atmosphere on a person. You can estimate the surface area by approximating different parts of the body on the board — leg by leg, arm by arm, etc. (This can be quite funny, if you want it to be!)

DEMONSTRATION [20-2]: This great one consists of a square sheet of soft rubber with some sort of handle at its center. A 50-gram mass hanger poked through its center works well. Toss the rubber sheet on any perfectly flat surface — best on the top of a lab stool. Picking the rubber up by a corner is an easy task, because the air gets under it as it is lifted. But lifting it by the middle is another

region is formed because air cannot get in. The rubber sheet behaves as a suction cup, and the entire stool is lifted when the handle is raised. (Originated by John McDonald of Boise State University.)

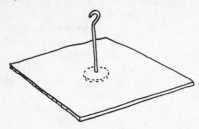

DEMONSTRATION [20-3]: Place a wooden shingle on the lecture table so that it overhangs the edge a bit. Cover the shingle with a flattened sheet of newspaper, and strike the overhanging part of the shingle with a stick or your hand (be careful of splinters). Promote more "discuss with your neighbor" activity. [Because parts of the paper are against the table with no air space, the downward force due to air pressure above the paper is greater than the upward force due to air pressure below the paper. So the stick breaks, as if someone held the end under the paper down during your blow. (Rotational inertia of the stick also contributes to this.)]

Barometer: Discuss Figure 20.8 where the girl shows that soda cannot be drawn through a straw unless atmospheric pressure acts on the liquid surface (or near-atmospheric pressure acts on the surface). Go a step further with the following demo:

DEMONSTRATION [20-4]: As the sketch shows, try sucking a drink through a straw with two straws; one in the liquid and the other outside. It can't be done because the pressure in your mouth is not reduced because of the second straw (although with some effort a bit of liquid can be drawn). Invite your students to try this, and to share this (and other ideas!) at parties.

The vacuum pump, such as the one that my brother and sister-in-law are demonstrating in Figure 20.9, operates by atmospheric pressure on the surface of water in the well. When the plunger is lifted, air pressure is reduced in the pipe that extends into the well [because the air is "thinned" as more volume is presented to the same amount of air]. The greater atmospheric pressure on the surrounding surface of the well water pushes water up the pipe, finally to overflow at the spout.

If all the air could be pumped out of the pipe, the atmosphere would push water up to a height of 10.3 meters. If the well contained liquid mercury, which is 13.6 times denser than water, the height of water needed to balance the atmosphere would be 1/13.6 of 10.3 meters = 76 cm. Now discuss the mercury barometer. If you have the opportunity, construct a mercury barometer in front of your class.

[**Practice Book 20-2** addresses the lift pump]

CHECK QUESTION: How would the barometer level vary while ascending and descending in the elevator of a tall building? [Answer: The level would drop when ascending, and rise when descending.]

Discuss ear popping in aircraft, and why cabin pressure is lower than atmospheric pressure at high altitudes.

DEMONSTRATION [20-5]: The siphon. This tube filled with water, with the short end in a reservoir, attracts attention because it is a device where water runs uphill. Water will flow continuously as long as the tube is full of water and the outlet is below the level of the surface of the water in the reservoir. The pressure of air on the surface of the reservoir keeps the tube full of water, as in a barometer. That's why the short end of the tube cannot extend upward more than 10.3 m. For a uniform tube the weight of water in the long end is always greater than the weight of water in the short end, so like a rope dangled over a pulley, the heavy side falls and the light side rises. This difference in weight together with the effect of air pressure in keeping the shorter side filled with water causes the continuous flow. (A more rigorous explanation involves pressures rather than weights of water in each side, and water always flows in the upward direction in the short tube, and downward in the long tube, whatever their diameters.)

Siphons are commonly used for drawing liquids from large containers to smaller ones. They may be used in bringing water from a pond or spring over higher terrain to any place lower than the source. By means of the *inverted siphon*, water in a pipe may be taken under a river and up on the other side. Water will flow through this pipe without the air of pumps if the outlet is lower than the place where water enters the pipe.

[**Transparency 38**, Figures 20.19 and 20.20 on Boyle's law]

[**Next-Time Question** 20-2 addresses compressibility of air in a balloon, Archimedes's principle, and density — a great one (and also T&E 8 in Chapter 19)].

Boyle's Law: Discuss and/or show Activity 1 on page 304 (dunking a glass mouth downwards in water to show the "empty" glass contains air — and how air is compressed with deeper depths) and relate this to the compressed air breathed by scuba divers. Discuss the reason for the difficulty of snorkeling at a depth of 1 meter and why such will not work for greater depths; i.e., air will not of itself move from a region of lesser pressure (the air at the surface) to a region of greater pressure (the compressed air in the submerged person's lungs). To breath we depress our diaphragm to reduce lung pressure so the atmospheric pressure outside insures a flow of inward air. But the increased pressure of the water beneath the surface results in a greater pressure in the lungs than atmospheric. Any flow of air is outward. That's why pumps must be used to supply air to divers below the surface of water.

DEMONSTRATION [20-6]: Tip a drinking glass upside down and immerse it in water. A Ping Pong ball or any floating object in the glass shows that the water level is depressed. This shows, for one thing, that air is substance that takes up space.

Relate the air space in the immersed drinking glass to the diving bells used in under-water construction. Workers are able to construct bridge foundations and so forth in such devices. They are in an environment of compressed air. How great is the air pressure in these devices? At least as much as the combined pressure of water and the atmosphere outside.

Buoyancy of Air: Archimede's principle applies to fluids, which includes gases as well as the liquids of the previous chapter. Objects immersed or submerged in water are buoyed up because there is greater pressure against the bottom of the object than against the top. This is simply because the bottom is deeper. Likewise for things buoyed upward by air. Ask the class if the atmospheric pressure is *really* greater at shoulder level than at the top of their heads. [It is, because shoulder level is deeper in the ocean of air than head level.] Ask for evidence of this greater pressure, and then produce a helium-filled balloon that has a size about that of one's head. The fact that the balloon is visibly buoyed upward is evidence that the atmospheric pressure against the bottom of the balloon (held at shoulder level) is greater than the atmospheric pressure against the top (at head level). Pressure really is depth dependent — in both gases and liquids.

CHECK QUESTION: Upon which is the greatest buoyant force: a Mack truck, or a child's helium-filled balloon? [The Mack truck, because it displaces more air.] Upon which is the buoyant force more effective? [The balloon, for the buoyant force is enough to make it rise.] Make the distinction between the thing itself (buoyant force) and the effect of the thing itself (floatation). Making such distinctions is thinking critically.

Ask if there is a buoyant force of the atmosphere on people. If so, why is it not evident? [Because its small compared to our weights.] How small? [By the ratio of the density of air to the density of a person (That is, buoyant force/weight = weight of air displaced/weight of person = density of air x volume/density of person x volume = density of air/density of person, since the volumes are the same.)] What is the density of a person? [Slightly less than the density of water, if the person can float in water.] Density of air/density of water = $(1.2 \text{ kg/m}^3)/(1000 \text{ kg/m}^3)$ = 0.0012, or 0.12%. This means we are buoyed up by about a tenth of one percent our weight — negligible. If our weights were reduced to a tenth of one percent our present weights, while keeping the same volume, then we'd float around like helium-filled balloons.

Bernoulli's Principle: Introduce Bernoulli's principle by blowing across the top surface of a sheet of paper, Figure 20.18. Blow extra large "Bernoulli bubbles" described earlier. Follow this up with any of the following variety of demonstrations:

DEMONSTRATIONS [20-7]: (1) Make a beach ball hover in a stream of air issuing from the reverse end of a vacuum cleaner. (2) Do the same with a Ping-Pong ball in the airstream of a hairdryer. (3) Line a cardboard tube with sandpaper and sling the ball sidearm. The sandpaper will produce the friction to make the ball roll down the tube and emerge spinning — you'll see that the ball breaks in the correct direction. Point out that paddles have a rough surface like the sandpaper for the same reason — to spin the ball when it is properly struck — that is, to apply "English" to the ball. (4) Swing a Ping-Pong ball taped to a string into a stream of water as shown in Figure 20.22. Follow this up with a discussion of the shower curtain in the last paragraph of the chapter.

[**Transparencies 38** and **39**, Figures 20.19, 20.20, and 20.21; applications of Bernoulli's principle]

A neat consequence of Bernoulli's principle involves the thickness of a firefighter's hose when water is moving and when it is at rest. When the hose is turned off, but under pressure, the hose is fatter than when it is turned on. The faster the water flows in the tube, the thinner it becomes. That's because the pressure in the hose drops as water increases in speed.

The curving of pitched balls can be more complicated than the text suggests, when different surface textures are taken into account. An excellent resource for more on this is Brancazio's informative book, *Sport Science*.

More Think-and-Explain Questions

1. How would the density of air at the bottom of a deep mine shaft compare to the density of the atmosphere at the surface of the ground?
   Answer: The density of air is greater at the bottom of a mine shaft. This is because air simply fills up the mine and by its own weight is more squashed at the bottom.

2. Why do your ears "pop" when you ascend to higher altitudes?
   Answer: Our bodies acclimate so as to push outward just as hard as the atmosphere pushes in against us. At higher altitudes where atmospheric pressure is less, this pushing outward is greater than the inward push of the atmosphere; hence our ears pop.

3. A balloon filled with air falls to the ground, but a balloon filled with helium rises. Why?
   Answer: The air-filled balloon weighs more than the buoyant force on it, so it falls. The weight of the helium-filled balloon is less than the buoyant force, so it rises.

4. Would a balloon rise in an atmosphere where the pressure was somehow the same at all altitudes? Would a balloon rise in the complete absence of

atmospheric pressure, like at the surface of the moon?

Answer: In both cases, the balloon would not rise, but would fall. This is because buoyant force is the result of greater pressure pushing up on an object than is pushing down on it. Without a pressure difference, there would be no buoyant force. It follows that without any pressure, there would likewise be no buoyant force.

5. What provides the lift to keep a Frisbee in flight?
Answer: Air moves faster over the spinning upper surface of the Frisbee and pressure there is reduced in accord with Bernoulli's principle. The bowl shape underneath carries along a relatively dead air space, that exerts near-normal pressure up against the bottom. The difference in pressures against the Frisbee produces an upward lift. Usually the lift nearly equals the weight, and the Frisbee remains airborne significantly longer than an ordinary projectile.

More Think and Solves

1. Suppose that air at normal pressure has a mass of 1.30 kg/m3, and hydrogen 0.09 kg/m3, how large must the gasbag of a balloon be if the total load has a mass of 300 kg and if the bag is to be filled with hydrogen at normal pressure and 0°C?
Answer: 248 m^3. By Archimedes' principle, the weight of (hydrogen + load) = weight of air displaced. Or in terms of mass, the mass of (hydrogen + load) = mass of air displaced. The mass of each gas is = density x volume. So we can say,
Density of hydrogen x vol + 300 kg = density of air x vol.
0.09 kg/m^3 x vol + 300 kg = 1/30 kg/m3 x vol.
Collect vol on one side of the equation and get
(1.3 - 0.09)kg/m^3 x vol = 300 kg.
vol = 300 kg / (1.3 - 0.09)kg/m^3 = 300/1.21 = 248 m^3.

[Another solution is knowing that the buoyant force will equal the difference in the weight of air and an equal volume of hydrogen, and must also be equal to the weight of 300 kg. Or in terms of mass, the difference in the masses of air and hydrogen must equal the mass of the load, 300 kg. That is, (1.3 - 0.09)kg/m^3 x vol = 300 kg; where vol = 300 kg / (1.3 - 0.09)kg/m^3 = 300/1.21 = 248 m^3.]

2. An automobile is supported by four tires inflated to a gauge pressure of 180 kPa. The area of contact of each of the tires is 190 cm^2 (which means the total area of tire contact is 0.076 m^2). Assume that the sidewalls of the tires do not contribute to holding the car up (that air pressure within the tires does the job). Find the mass of the car in kilograms.
Answer: 1396 kg. From the definition of pressure, 180 kPa pressure = weight of the car/area of tire contact. Or rearranging, weight of car = 180 kPa x area of tire contact = 180 x 103 N/m^2 x 0.076 m^2 = 13680 N. The mass is found from $W = mg$, where m = 13680 N/9.8 N/kg = 1396 kg. [Note that 1 kPa = 10^3 N/m^2, and g = 9.8 m/s^2 = 9.8 N/kg.]

3. Estimate the ratio of the atmospheric buoyant force per bodyweight for an average person.
Answer: 0.0012, or 0.12%. Buoyant force/weight = weight of air displaced/weight of person = density of air x volume/density of person x volume = density of air/density of person, since the volumes are the same. The density of air is about 1.2 kg/m^3. The density of an average person is about that of water, 1000 kg/m^3. So Buoyant force/weight = density of air/density of person = (1.2 kg/m^3)/ (1000 kg/m^3) = 0.0012, or 0.12%. This means we are buoyed up by about a tenth of one percent our weight — quite negligible.

CALCULATOR TIME!

21 Temperature, Heat, and Expansion

Objectives

- Define temperature, and explain how it is measured.
- Describe the relation between temperature and kinetic energy.
- Define heat, and explain why it is incorrect to think of matter as containing heat.
- Explain what determines whether heat will flow into or out of a substance.
- Distinguish between internal energy and heat.
- Describe how the quantity of heat that enters or leaves a substance is measured.
- Compare the specific heat capacities of different substances, given the relative amount of energy required to raise the temperature of a given mass by a given amount.
- Give examples of how the high specific heat capacity of water has an effect on climate.
- Give examples of the expansion of solids as they become warmer.
- Explain the operation of a bimetallic coil in a thermostat.
- Compare the thermal expansion of liquids to solids.
- Describe the unusual behavior of water as it is heated from $0°C$ to $15°C$.
- Explain why water at certain temperatures contracts as it becomes warmer.

Possible Misconceptions to Correct

- Heat and temperature are the same.
- Objects contain heat.
- *Everything* expands when heated.

Demonstration Equipment

- [21-1] Metal ball and ring apparatus.
- [21-2] Bimetallic strip and a flame source.

Introduction

Like the chapters on Properties of Matter, chapters on Heat place particular emphasis on water and the atmosphere. No attempt is made to familiarize the student with methods of temperature conversion from one scale to another. The effort saved can be better spent on physics.

In the text, temperature is treated in terms of the kinetic energy per molecule of substances. Although strictly speaking, temperature is directly proportional to the kinetic energy per molecule only in the case of ideal gases, we take the view that temperature is related to molecular translational kinetic energy in most common substances. Rotational kinetic energy, on the other hand, is only indirectly related to temperature, as is illustrated in a microwave oven. There the H_2O molecules are set oscillating with considerable rotational kinetic energy. But this doesn't cook the food. What does is the translational kinetic energy imparted to neighboring molecules that are bounced from the oscillating H_2Os like marbles that are set flying in all directions when they encounter the spinning blades of fans. If neighboring atoms did not interact with the oscillating H_2O molecules, the temperature of the food would be no different before and after the microwave oven was activated. Temperature has to do with the translational kinetic energy of molecules.

Quantity of heat is spoken of in terms of calories, a departure from the SI unit, joules. Learning about heat is simplified with the calorie, for the score counting is considerably easier. Life-science students will continue with the calorie in further study, while physical-science students will make the jump to joules in follow-up courses.

The definition of the calorie, page 311, implies that the same amount of heat will be required to change the temperature of water $1°C$ — whatever the temperature of the water. Although this relation holds approximately, it is not exact: a calorie is more precisely defined as the amount of heat required to raise a gram of water from $14°$ to $15°$ Celsius.

The concept of heat flow between temperature differences provides some background to the concept of electron flow (current) between electric potential differences in Chapter 34. Aside from this minor exception, the chapter serves as a prerequisite only for the three following chapters dealing with heat transfer, change of state, and thermodynamics.

Discussions of heat invariably include fire, not treated in the text. Fire depends on three things — heat, fuel, and oxygen. Technically, fire is a chemical reaction where a material unites with oxygen so rapidly that flames are produced. Remove any one of the three and the fire goes out. Heat can be taken away by cooling, oxygen can be taken away by excluding air, and fuel can be removed to a place where there is no flame.

In the lab, *Heat Mixes I & II* are essential activities that provide the hands-on experience students need for the sophisticated application experiment *Antifreeze in the Summer? The Bridge Connection* makes an excellent application experiment in which students must first calculate the coefficient of thermal expansion to estimate the expansion joints of the Golden Gate Bridge.

Suggested Lecture

Temperature: Begin by asking what the difference is between a hot cup of coffee and a cold cup of coffee [the molecules in the hot substance move faster]. And then discuss the measure of this energetic jostling and haphazard bumbling of molecules — temperature. Define temperature as the average KE of molecules or atoms in a substance.

CHECK QUESTIONS: Which has the higher temperature, a cup of boiling water, or a pot of boiling water? Which has the more energy? [Both have the same *average* KE per molecule, so the temperatures of both are the same. But there is more energy in the pot of boiling water, simply because there are more molecules. A pot of water will melt more ice than a cup of boiling water.]

Thermometers: Describe how the increased jostling of molecules in a substance result in expansion, the basis for the common thermometer. Draw a sketch of an uncalibrated thermometer on the board, with its mercury vessel at the bottom, and describe how the jostling of energy is transferred from the outer environment to the mercury within. If placed in boiling water, the jostling of the water molecules would be transferred to the mercury, which would expand up the tube. State that one could make a scratch on the glass at this level and label it 100. And then describe how, if placed in a container of ice water, the mercury would give energy to the cold water and slow down, contract, and fall to a lower level in the tube. One could again make a scratch and call this point zero. Then, if 100 equally-spaced scratches are made between the two reference points, one would have what used to be called a centigrade thermometer. Just as a cent is 1/100 of a dollar, the same prefix "centi" describes each grade as 1/100 the division between the freezing and boiling points of water. We now speak of the Celsius thermometer, in honor of the man who first suggested the scale (for laughs, Anders Thermometer!).

CHECK QUESTION: How would the calibration of the thermometer differ if the glass expanded more mercury? [The scale would be upside down, because the glass reservoir would expand and "open up" and allow more mercury to fill it. The mercury level above would fall with increases in temperature.]

If you're in the mood for humor, draw a second uncalibrated thermometer on the board and repeat your discussion (in abbreviated fashion) of placing it in boiling water. State that the upper level needn't be called 100, that any number would do so long as all thermometers were calibrated the same. Ask the class for any random number. Someone will say 212. Casually acknowledge the 212 response and write that on your diagram. Repeat the bit about placing the instrument in ice water and state that the position on the scale needn't be called zero, that any number would do. Ask for a random number. You'll have several students volunteer 32, which you graciously accept. The class should be in a good mood at this point, and you have acknowledged the essential conversions between the Celsius and Fahrenheit scales.

CHECK QUESTION: Which of the two temperature scales has the closest spaced degrees, and which is the more accurate when temperatures are expressed to the nearest whole number? [On the Fahrenheit scale there are 180 grades between the freezing and boiling points of

water, but there are only 100 on the Celsius scale. So degree marks are closer together on the Fahrenheit scale. The smaller degrees enables more accuracy when temperature readings are expressed to the nearest whole number.]

Acknowledge the Kelvin scale, and the absolute zero of temperature — the temperature at which molecules can give up no more energy. You'll return to the Kelvin scale in Chapter 24, Thermodynamics.

[**Next-Time Question 21-1** treats absolute temperature]

Difference between Heat and Temperature: Distinguish between temperature and heat. Define heat as the energy that flows by virtue of temperature differences. Temperature is measured in degrees (or kelvins), and heat is measured in units of energy — calories (or joules). Heat is the energy that flows from a higher to a lower temperature, and not the other way around — unless external work is done. When heat is added to a substance, the *internal energy* of the substance increases.

A neat case that illustrates the difference between heat and temperature is the familiar fireworks sparkler (illegal in some states). The temperature of the sparks from these things is well above 1000°C. Yet they strike your skin with no apparent harm. To say the sparks have a high temperature is to say the sparks have a high ratio of energy per molecule — very high, more than 1000°C worth. But how many molecules are in a spark? Relatively few, with the result that very little energy is transferred as heat when they touch the skin. This is a high temperature, low heat situation. By analogy, a tiny drop of boiling water touching your skin transfers very little energy to you, compared to a bucket of boiling water spilled on your skin. The energy per molecule and the total energy involved are different concepts.

CHECK QUESTION: When you strike a match, do you warm up the whole world? [Answer: Yes, but not noticeably; if the match were bigger or the world smaller, then maybe you would notice the warming that occurs.]

CHECK QUESTION: If you heat a half cup of tea and its temperature rises by 4 C$^\circ$, how much will the temperature rise if you added the same heat to a full cup of tea? [2 C$^\circ$] Does the internal energy in a cup of hot tea increase, decrease, or remain the same when it cools? [It decreases.] Where does the internal energy go when a cup of hot tea cools? [It goes into warming the surroundings. Soon the tea will be cooler and the surroundings warmer. They will achieve thermal equilibrium at a common temperature.]

Point out that heat or internal energy are the same form of energy, transferring or at rest, and obey the law of energy conservation. To say that a body cools is to say that something else warms. Energy may be spread around and diluted, becoming unavailable, but never disappearing if we know where to look!

CHECK QUESTION: A liter of 30°C water is mixed with a liter of 20°C water. What is the final temperature? [Answer: 25°C, the internal energy lost by the warmer water is gained by the cooler water.]

[**Practice Book 21-1** treats heat mixes and calorie-joule conversion]

Specific Heat Capacity: After distinguishing between calories and degrees, lead into the concept of specific heat capacity by asking your class to consider the difference in touching an empty iron frying pan that has been placed on a hot stove for one minute (ouch!) and doing the same except this time you have some water in it. You could safely place your hand in the water even if it were on the stove for several minutes. Ask which has the higher temperature, the empty pan or the one filled with water. Clearly, it is the empty pan. Ask which absorbed the greater amount of energy. The answer is the water-filled pan, if it was on the stove for a longer time. The water has absorbed more energy for less rise in temperature! Physics types have a name for this idea — *specific heat capacity*.

CHECK QUESTION: Which has the higher specific heat, water or land? [Water, as evidenced by how long it takes for it to heat up in the sunshine, as compared to land. This fact is a major contributor to weather.]

Water's High Specific Heat Capacity: Cite examples of water's high specific heat — hot water bottles on cold winter nights, cooling systems in cars, and the climate in places where there is much water. With the aid of a large world map, globe, or chalkboard sketch, show the sameness of the latitudes of England and the Hudson Bay, and the latitudes of the French and the Italian Riveria with Canada. State how the fact that water requires so long a time to heat and cool, enables the Gulf Stream to hold heat energy long enough to reach the North Atlantic. There it cools off. But if the water cools, then according to the conservation of energy, something else has to warm. What is that something? The air. The cooling water warms the air, and the winds at that latitude are westerly. So warmed air moves over the continent of Europe. Without this, Europe would have the same climate as regions of northern Canada. A similar situation occurs in the United States. The Atlantic Ocean off the coast of the eastern states is considerably warmer than the Pacific Ocean off the coast of Washington, Oregon and California, yet in winter months the east coast is considerably colder. This has to do with the high specific heat of water and the westerly winds. Air that is warmed by cooling water on the west coast moves landward and gives mild winters to Washington, Oregon, and California. But on the east coast, this warmed air moves seaward, leaving the east coast frigid in winter months. In summer months, when the air is warmer than the water, the air cools and the water warms. So summer months on the west coast states are relatively cool, while the east coast is relatively hot. The high specific heat of water serves to moderate climates. The climates on islands, for example, are fairly free of temperature variations. Even San Francisco, a peninsula that is close to being an island, has the most stable climate of any city in continental America.

(This is a good break place. Pose the following first:)

NEXT-TIME QUESTION: Preface the next section on thermal expansion with the ball and ring question. Consider a metal ball and metal ring [DEMO 21-1], where the ball barely fits in the hole in the ring when both have the same temperature. Ask your class if the ball would fit in the hole if the ball were heated? They'll quickly answer no, for the ball will expand upon being heated. Then ask the more serious question: If the ring is heated, will the ball fit though? In other words, will the hole in the ring get bigger, smaller, or stay the same size? Do not state the answer, but let this be a next-time question. At the beginning of your next class, discuss the surprising answer. [the size of the heated hole increases]. Many students will correctly reason that the thickness of the ring will increase, but they will then conclude that the hole becomes smaller. When you treat the answer, consider cutting the ring into 4 quadrants, and put the pieces into a hot oven. They all expand. Now bring them back together to form a ring. This should make it clear that the hole expands when the ring is heated. More simply, the circumference as well as the thickness and every other dimension increases. Support this by demonstration and by the examples of opening a stuck metal jar lid by placing it under hot water, and the fitting of iron wheel rims on wooden wagon wheels by first placing the slightly smaller iron rims into the blacksmith's fire. This provokes interest in thermal expansion.)

Thermal Expansion: Solids: State that steel lengths expand about 1 part in 100,000 for each Celsius degree increase in temperature. With this in mind, show a steel rod and ask if anybody would be afraid to stand with their stomach between the end of the rigidly held steel rod and a wall, while the temperature of the steel rod was increased a few degrees. This is a safe activity, for the slight expansion of the rod would be hardly noticeable. Now ask for volunteers for a steel rod a few kilometers in length. This is different, for although the rate of change is the same, the change in length of the rod could well impale you. Then discuss the expansion joints on large structures, as shown in Figure 21.9.

DEMONSTRATION [21-2]: Place the middle of a bimetallic strip in a flame to show the unequal expansions of different metals, and the subsequent bending.

Point out that different substances expand or contract (length, area, and volume) at their own characteristic rates (coefficients of expansion). Cite examples such as the need for the same expansion rate in teeth and teeth fillings; iron reinforcing rods and concrete; and the metal wires that are encased in glass light bulbs and the glass itself. Provision must be made when materials with different expansion rates interact; like the piston rings when aluminum pistons are enclosed in steel cylinders in a car, and the rockers on the supporting ends of bridges, and the overflow pipe for gasoline in a steel tank.

[**Practice Book 21-2** treats expansion of solids, liquids, and gases]

Expansion of Liquids: Elaborate on the overflow pipe on automobile gasoline tanks. Relate how mercury in a thermometer expands more than the solid glass, and how water overflows from a heated brim-filled pot.

CHECK QUESTION: How would a thermometer differ if glass expanded with increasing temperature more than mercury? [The scale would be upside down, because the reservoir would enlarge (like the hole enlarged in the heated metal ring) and mercury in the column would tend to fill it up with increasing temperature.]

Expansion of Water: To lead into the idea of water's low density at 4°C you can ask if anyone in class happens to know what the temperature at the bottom of Lake Michigan was on a particular date, New Year's eve in 1905, for example. Then for the bottom of Lake Tahoe in California for any other date. And for another, until many are responding "4°C".

CHECK QUESTION: Ask the same for the bottom of a rain puddle outside the building, and be prepared for some to say "4°C. [4°C was the correct answer for the deep lakes but the wrong answer for puddle. The temperature of a shallow puddle would be the same as the temperature of the surroundings.]

Then go into the explanation as given in the book — how the microscopic slush forms as the freezing temperature is approached, yielding a net expansion below 4°C. (I haven't done this, but I have thought of showing a Galileo-type thermometer in class — a small flask with a narrow glass tube filled with colored water, so changes in temperature would be clearly evident by different levels of water in the narrow tube. Then surround the flask with perhaps dry ice to rapidly chill the water. The water level drops as the temperature of the water decreases, but its rate slows as it nears 4°C, and then the direction reverses as cooling continues. This expansion of the water is due to the formation of "microscopic slush." The level of water observed, as a function of time, yields the graph of Figure 21.13.)

The exaggerated volume scale in Figure 21.23 should be emphasized, for it is easy for a student to erroneously conclude that a great change in the volume of water occurs over a relatively small temperature change. Despite the warning in the following page, some students will interpret the volume at 0°C to be that of ice rather than ice water.

CHECK QUESTIONS: Will a sample of 4°C water expand, contract, or remain unchanged in volume when it is heated? [Expand.] Will a sample of 4°C water expand, contract, or remain unchanged in volume when it is cooled? [Expand.] Why would water, instead of alcohol or mercury, be a poor liquid for a thermometer when near freezing temperatures are to be measured? [Because the column height would be ambiguous in the 0°C to

8°C range, as shown in Figure 21.13. You couldn't distinguish between temperatures to either side of 4°C.]

Discuss Figures 21.14 and 21.15, and the idea of "microscopic slush."

[**Transparencies** 40 and 41; Figures 21.13 and 21.14]

Ice Formation: Discuss the formation of ice, and why it forms at the surface and why it floats. And why deep bodies of water don't freeze over in winter because all the water in the lake has to be cooled to 4°C before colder water will remain at the surface to be cooled to the freezing temperature, 0°C. State that before one can cool a teaspoon full of water in the lake to 3°C, let alone 0°C, all the water beneath must be cooled to 4°C and that winters are neither cold or long enough for this to happen in the United States.

NEXT-TIME QUESTION: Ask your students to place an ice cube in a glass of ice water at home, and compare the water level at the side of the glass before and after the ice melts. Ask them to account for the volume of ice that extends above the water line after it melts. The answer to the original question is, of course, that the level remains unchanged. This can be explained from the principles learned in Chapter 19. The floating ice cube displaces its own weight of water, so if the cube weighs say a newton, then when placed in the glass, one newton of water is displaced and the water level rises. If it is first melted and then poured in the glass, again the water line would be higher, but by one newton, the same amount. More interesting is to account for the volume of floating ice that extends above the water line. The ice expanded upon freezing because of the hexagonal open structures of the crystals. Ask the class if they have any idea of how much volume all those billions and billions of open spaces constitute. That volume equals the volume of ice extending above the water line! When the ice melts, the part above the water line fills in the open structures as they collapse. Discuss this idea in terms of icebergs, and whether or not the coastline would change if all the floating icebergs in the world melted. The oceans would rise a bit, but only because icebergs are composed of fresh water. (They form above sea level and break off and then fall into sea.) The slight rise is more easily understood by exaggerating the circumstance — think of ice cubes floating in mercury. When they melt, the depth of fluid (water on mercury) is higher than before.

[**Next-Time Questions** 21-2 and 21-3 treat expansion]

More Think-and-Explain Questions

1. Which has the greater amount of internal energy, a giant iceberg or a hot cup of tea?
   Answer: Although the tea has a higher temperature, which is to say, its molecules move faster (higher average KE), the iceberg, because of the greater number of molecules, has more internal energy. Like 1000 people each with 10 cents in their pockets have more money than one person with 10 dollars.

2. Explain what is meant by saying a thermometer measures its own temperature?
Answer: Objects in the same locality will ultimately come to the same temperature when hot things cool and cool things warm. This is what a thermometer does. Thermometers come to thermal equilibrium with surroundings, and show this on the scale.

3. Why is a thick-bottomed glass inadvisable for hot drinks?
Answer: Expansion is greater in the hot part, which can fracture the glass.

4. An iron bar is welded across an iron hoop. When the temperature is increased, is the circular shape retained or does it warp? [sketch]
Answer: Retained, as all parts expand equally.

5. Which would be better to take to bed with you on a cold winter night? A hot brick wrapped with a towel, or a hot bottle of water wrapped in a towel? The purpose is to put your feet on the hot object to keep you warm.
Answer: The bottle of water, with its higher specific heat, will cool slower and keep your feet warm longer. The purpose of the towel is to keep you from initially burning your feet. When cooling occurs, it can be removed.

6. If water had a higher specific heat, would ponds and lakes be more likely or less likely to freeze?
Answer: Less likely. This is because the temperature would decrease less when water loses energy; water would less readily be cooled to the freezing point. (This is the opposite of T&E 15.)

More Think and Solves

1. What would be the final temperature of the mixture of 50 g of 20°C water and 50 g of 40°C water?
Answer: 100 g of 30°C water.

2. What would be the final temperature when 100 g of 25°C water is mixed with 75 g of 40°C water?
Answer: Heat gained by cool water = heat lost by warm water
$$m_1\, c\, \Delta T_1 = m_2\, c\, \Delta T_2$$
$$(100)\, c\, (T - 25) = (75)\, c\, (40 - T)$$
(Note that common sense dictates that ΔT_1 is final temperature T minus 25°, because T will be greater than 25°, and ΔT_2 is 40° minus T, because T will be less than 40°. ΔT_1 does not equal ΔT_2 as in problem 1 because of the different masses of cool and warm water.)
Solving the numberwork,
$$100T - 2500 = 3000 - 75T$$
$$175T = 5500$$
$$T = 5500/175 = 31.4^\circ C$$

3. What will be the final temperature of 100 g of 20°C water when 100 g of 40° iron nails are submerged in it? (The specific heat of iron is 0.12 cal/gC$^\circ$.)
Answer: Heat gained by water = heat lost by nails
$$(m\, c\, \Delta T)_{water} = (m\, c\, \Delta T)_{nails}$$
$$(100)(1)\, (T - 20) = (40)(0.12)(40 - T)$$
$$100T - 2000 = 192 - 4.8T$$
$$104.8T = 2192$$
$$T = 2192/104.8 = 20.9^\circ C$$

Objectives

- Explain why two materials at the same temperature may not *feel* like the same temperature when touched.
- Explain why porous materials with air spaces are better insulators than nonporous materials.
- Explain how heat can be transferred quickly through liquids and gases even though they are poor conductors.
- Distinguish, from an atomic point of view, between conduction and convection.
- Explain how heat can be transmitted through empty space.
- Given the color and shininess of two objects, predict which is likely to absorb radiant energy more easily.
- Compare the ability of an object to emit radiant energy with its ability to absorb it.
- Relate the temperature difference between an object and its surroundings to the rate at which it cools.
- Describe the processes of absorption and emission of radiant energy from the sun by the earth's atmosphere and surface.
- Describe global warming and the earth's greenhouse effect.

Possible Misconceptions to Correct

- Surfaces that feel cooler than others must have a lower temperature.
- A blanket is a source of heat energy.
- Walking barefoot without harm on red hot coals involves non-physics considerations.
- Only hot things radiate energy.
- The greenhouse effect on the planet earth is undesirable.

Demonstration Equipment

- [22-1] Metal bar, sheet of paper, and flame source.
- [22-2] Paper cup filled with water and flame source.
- [22-3] Test tube filled with water, wedged ice, and flame source.
- [22-4] Box with hole, painted white on inside (Figure 22.13).
- [22-5] Silvered and black container of hot or cold water, and thermometers.

Introduction

This chapter begins with conduction, convection, and radiation of heat with emphasis again on bodies of water and the atmosphere. The section on radiation serves as some background to electromagnetic waves that are covered in Chapter 37.

One of our tasks as physics teachers is to help students distinguish between science and psuedoscience. A misconception still popular is being exploited by people who claim to have special powers, and who for a fee, will teach people how to gain these special powers. The misconception is that one cannot harmlessly walk barefoot on red-hot coals of burning wood — that doing so is counter to scientific principles — that science is inadequate to explain this physical phenomenon. The fact is that many people have walked harmlessly on red-hot wooden coals with bare feet, without special powers. The explanation is an extension of my nephew Marcus Jones' statement on page 306, the Unit III opener. Conductivity, not only temperature, must be considered. For example you can momentarily put your hand in a very hot oven without harm, not because the temperature is low, but because air is a poor conductor of heat. And it is common knowledge that wood has low heat conductivity, which is why it is used for handles on cooking utensils. You'd burn yourself if you reached into a hot oven with your bare hand and grabbed a frying pan with an iron handle. But you'd be okay if you grabbed one with a wooden handle, and did so quickly. Wood is a poor conductor, even when its hot. And wood is still a poor conductor when it's red hot. After the surface of a red hot coal of low-conductivity wood gives up its heat, perhaps to a bare foot that has just stepped on it, more than a second passes before appreciable internal energy from the inside reheats the surface. So although the coal has a very high temperature, it gives up very little heat with brief contact to a cooler surface. For those who believe mind-over-matter rather than low conductivity is the predominant explanation, a trial on red-hot pieces of iron would be a horrible confrontation with physical reality.

Another popular misconception is that energy is saved if a heater is not completely turned off when leaving the house on a cold day. Whether or not to turn the thermostat down or off is the subject of Think and Explain #9. To illustrate its answer (turn it off!), make up the apparatus shown, which consists of a main reservoir that feeds "heat" into two identical "houses," that leak heat to the environment. The amount of leakage is caught by the bottom jars and can be compared at a glance. Arrange the input flow rates so that

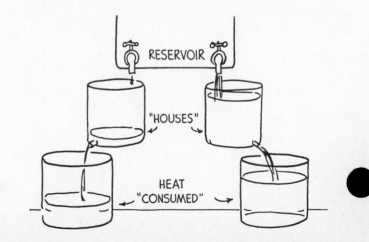

equilibrium is established when the "houses" are nearly full; then input = outflow. Turn one input off altogether. After some time, turn it back on until it fills to the level of the other "house." Now compare the differences in leaked water! Make comparisons of turning it down partway instead of off. This roughly approximates Newton's law of cooling. Leak rate is highest when ΔT, or in this case ΔP, is greatest.

Much of Unit 3 deals with heat as it relates to climate, so an optional lecture on the earth's seasons is included. This topic is not covered in the textbook, but may follow nicely from your treatment of radiation.

An interesting side point not in the text that has to do with changes in temperature is: It has long been known that a frog cannot discern small changes in temperature, and if sitting comfortably in a pan of water that is slowly heated on a stove will make no effort to jump out as the water temperature increases. It will just sit there and be cooked. This is not limited to frogs. According to accounts given by cannibals who cook their victims in large pots of water, the same is true of humans. More recent evidence took place a few years ago in Mill Valley, CA, where water in a hot tub gradually overheated (due to a faulty heater) and resulted in the death of the unsuspecting and drowsy occupants. You can compare this to other cases where adverse conditions are gradually increased. Humans will tolerate what otherwise would be completely unacceptable to them: smog, noise, pollution, crime, and so on.

I stress all through this manual the importance of the "check with your neighbor" technique of teaching. Please do not spend your lecture talking to yourself in front of your class! The procedure of the "check with your neighbor" routine keeps you and your class together. If nothing else, it gives you a chance to look over your notes on the spot, reflect on your presentation, and pace your delivery. I can't stress its importance to effective teaching enough!

Practice Book 22-1 can fit anywhere, and features seasons as the result of unequal solar radiation on the earth's surface.

In lab, students can use the computer to see the evidence of Newton's Law of Cooling in *Cooling Off*. With or without the software from *Laserpoint*, students will enjoy estimating the wattage of the sun in the experiment *Solar Equality*. With a little bit of luck on a sunny day, students can come up with an amazingly close value for the solar constant in the activity *Solar Energy*.

Suggested Lecture

Conduction: Begin by asking why pots and pans have wooden or plastic handles — then discuss conduction from an atomic point of view, citing the role of the electrons in both heat and electrical conduction. You might demonstrate the oldie of melting wax on different metal rods equidistant from a hot flame, and illustrate relative conductivities.

CHECK QUESTION: How is the tipping of a row of standing dominoes similar to heat conduction? [In both cases energy is transmitted from one place to another by the collisions of moving units.]

DEMONSTRATION: [23-1]: Do Activity # 3 of placing a metal bar wrapped in paper in the flame of a Bunsen burner. The paper doesn't catch fire. Why? [The metal conducts heat from the flame so efficiently that the paper cannot reach its ignition temperature of 233°C (recall this as 451 °F from Ray Bradbury's novel about book burning, *Fahrenheit 451*).

Other materials can be compared in their ability to conduct heat, like newspaper when having to sleep out-of-doors. Cite the case (not in the text) of Eskimos preferring their old bone and ivory saws to steel saws for cutting through blocks of snow in igloo construction. Because of the good thermal conductivity of steel, the saw freezes and sticks to the snow, whereas the bone or ivory saws with their low conductivities don't stick. Another tidbit not in the text: Do you know why wine glasses have long stems? It's because holding the wineglass by the stem doesn't warm the wine.

DEMONSTRATION [23-2]: Place a paper cup filled with water in the flame of a Bunsen burner. The paper will not reach its ignition temperature and burn because heat from the flame is conducted into the water. Water is not *that* poor a conductor — its high specific heat comes into play here also.

Discuss the poor conductivity of water, which ties to the previous lecture where you discussed the 4°C temperature of the bottom of deep lakes all year round.

DEMONSTRATION [23-3]: Do the activity in Figure 22.5, with ice wedged at the bottom of a test tube. Some steel wool will hold the ice at the bottom of the tube. It is impressive to see that the water at the top is brought to a boil while the ice below barely melts! (Convection, or better, the lack of convection is illustrated here as well. If heating was at the bottom and the ice cube at the top, it would quickly melt.)

Discuss the poor conductivity of air, and its role in insulating materials, e.g. down-filled sleeping bags and sportswear, spun glass and Styrofoam insulation, fluffy blankets, and even snow. Discuss thermal underwear, and how the fish-net open spaces actually trap air between the skin and the undergarment. This trapped air accounts for the insulating properties. The air trapped in animal fur similarly accounts for the insulation of fur. While the skin is warm, the temperature at the outer layer of the animal's pelt is about the same as the surroundings. Longer fur is therefore a better insulator. Of particular interest is the fur of the polar bear (discussed later in the optical fiber section of Chapter 29).

The fur of a polar bear is more than an excellent insulator. A polar bear's hairs are completely transparent, and appear white because visible light reflects from the rough inner surface of each hollow hair. Ultraviolet light, however, is absorbed and sent to the skin like light traveling in an optical fiber. The bear does not reradiate energy in the UV, so the hairs transmit energy primarily in only one direction — from the outside to the bear and not the other way around (sort of a thermal diode!). The high absorption by the skin is evidenced in its black color! So a polar bear is white on the outside, but black underneath its fur. The polar bear loses very little heat and is almost a perfect solar converter.

Discuss double-window thermopane. A misconception is that thermopane windows have a vacuum between the panes of glass. Not so, for they would be squashed together by atmospheric pressure. It is important that water vapor not be in the air space, for condensation can cloud the glass.

A dramatic demonstration of the poor conductivity of wood is the barefoot firewalk. Wood is a poor conductor whether it is hot or cold. It is even a poor conductor when red hot. Quick steps on red-hot wooden coals is taken by firewalker without harm (providing bits don't stick to their feet!). The slow conduction transfers safe amounts of energy with each step. So contrary to the "mind-over-matter" explanations of less-than-scientific people, it is straight physics. Some firewalkers prefer wet feet, and some dry. Wet feet absorb energy that the feet otherwise absorb, but wetness also means some greater likelihood of sticking. Similarly, one can quickly pick up red-hot pieces of charcoal with bare fingers — wet or dry. Wetness is preferred, for a chunk of charcoal won't stick just because your fingers are wet! I recommend this information NOT be communicated to students, for the chances of harm are high. Many people have been burned attempting these feats.

[**Next-Time Question 22-1** addresses firewalking]

[**Transparency 42**, Figure 22.7 on convection currents]

Convection: Illustrate convection by holding your fingers beside a flame as shown on page 330. Ask why you cannot do the same with your fingers above the flame.

Interestingly enough, the lack of convection in orbiting vehicles such as the space shuttle, has interesting consequences. In orbit, one cannot light a match without it snuffing out very quickly. One cannot exercise without overheating very quickly. This is because of the absence of convection in orbit. Much of the convection in fluids depends on buoyancy which in turn depends on gravity. In orbit the local effects of gravity are not there (because the shuttle and everything in the shuttle is freely falling around the earth). So with no convection, hot gases are not buoyed upward away from the flame, but remain around the flame preventing the entry of needed oxygen. The flame burns out. Without convection to carry heated air upward and away

from the body, the body overheats quickly. That's why astronauts use fans when exercising.

Why Warm Air Rises: When a portion of air is heated, it expands and is less dense than the surrounding air. Then the buoyancy is greater than its weight and it rises. Question: When it rises, what happens to the surrounding air pressure? [It decreases.] Question: When the surrounding pressure decreases, what happens to the volume of rising air? [It expands.] Question: What happens to its temperature when it expands? [It cools.] Question: Putting it all together, what happens to the temperature of rising warm air? [It cools!]

To see that expanding air cools, have your students blow on their hands: first with their mouths open so the air is warm, then with their lips puckered so that the air expands as it leaves their mouths. Noticeable cooling is the result (Doing Physics box on page 329).

CHECK QUESTION: We all know that warm air rises. So why are mountain tops cold and snow covered, and the valleys below relatively warm and green? Shouldn't it be the other way around? [No, nature is correct — as warm air rises, it cools. In fact, the cool tops of mountains are a consequence of rising warm air, not a contradiction!]

Discuss the role of convection in climates. Begin by calling attention to the shift in winds as shown in Figure 22.7. This leads you into radiation, the heat from the sun.

CHECK QUESTION: Why does the direction of coastal winds change from day to night? [Land warms faster than water, and in the day the land and air above it is warmer than the water and air above it. So it rises, and results in a seabreeze from water to land. At night, the reverse happens.]

Radiation: Make a distinction between radiation as it pertains to heat transmission and the radiation of radioactivity. This usage of the same word for two different phenomena is confusing.

Discuss the radiation one feels from red hot coals in a fireplace. And how the intensity of radiation decreases with distance. Consider the radiation one feels when stepping from the shade to the sunshine. Amazing! The heat is not so much because of the sun's temperature, because like temperatures are to be found in some welder's torches. One feels hot not because the sun is hot, but because it is big. Comfortably big!

You may want to discuss why the earth is warmer at the equator than at the poles, and get into the idea of solar energy per unit area (as contrasted to the notion that the equator is warmer because it is closer to the sun). A neat way to do this is to ask the class to compare the rays of sunlight striking the earth with vertically-falling rain that strikes two pieces of paper — one held horizontally and the other held at an angle in the

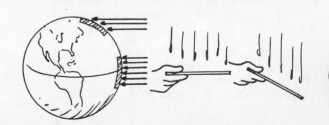

rain as shown. You can easily dispel the misconception that the paper held horizontally must get wetter than the paper held at an angle because it is closer to the clouds!

Seasons (optional): Depending on the time available, you might consider departing from the text, and continue with the solar energy per unit of area idea related to the seasons. The plane of the earth's equator is not parallel to the plane of the earth's orbit. Instead, the polar axis is inclined at 23 1/2 degrees (the ecliptic). Draw the sketch below on the board, first with only the two positions of the earth at the far left and far right. Ask which of these two positions represents winter months and which represents summer months. Encourage neighbor discussion.

Once it is clear that winter is at the left, show the position of the earth in autumn and in spring. Shift the position of the sun closer to the earth in winter, for this is the case. From your drawing, your class can see why northern hemisphere types enjoy an extra week of spring and summer! Southern hemisphere types are compensated by a somewhat milder climate year round due to the greater amount of ocean in the southern hemisphere (80% as compared to about 60% for the northern hemisphere).

Absorption and Emission of Radiation: There are various colors of eyes, but all have one thing in common. The pupils are black. Discuss why this is so.

DEMONSTRATION [22-4]: Make up and show the black hole in the white box, as shown by NTQ co-author Helen Yan in Figure 22.13.

Acknowledge that everything emits radiation — everything that has any temperature. But everything does not become progressively cooler because everything absorbs radiation. We live in a sea of radiation, everything emitting and everything absorbing. When emission rate equals absorption rate, temperature remains constant. Some materials, because of their molecular design, emit better than others. They also absorb better than others. They're easy to spot, because they absorb visible radiation as well and appear black. (Make the distinction that objects don't absorb *because* they're black, but that because they absorb so well, they are black. Cause precedes effect.)

DEMONSTRATION [22-5]: If your students did not do Lab Manual Activity 55 *Cooling Off*, check the temperatures of two pairs of black and silvered containers as your class period progresses. Have one pair filled with hot water, and the other pair filled with cold water. (This is much more instructive with two sets than one set, for you demonstrate both emission and absorption.)

Newton's Law of Cooling: Relate the rate of cooling to the black and silver containers that are cooling and warming. We see the difference between a proportionality sign and an equals sign for the formula here, for the rate of cooling or warming is not only proportional to the difference in temperatures, but in the "emissivities" of the surfaces. Relate Newton's law of cooling to Think and Explain questions #7 (cream in the coffee), #8 (cooling a beverage in the frig), and #9 (thermostat on a cold day). These questions make excellent discussion topics.

CHECK QUESTION: Does Newton's Law of Cooling apply to the warming of a cold object in a warm environment? [Yes.]

[**Transparency 43**, Figures 22.18 and 22.19, on global warming and the greenhouse effect]

Global Warming and the Greenhouse Effect: Discuss the greenhouse effect, first for florist's greenhouses, and then for the earth's atmosphere. The key idea is that the medium, glass for the greenhouse, atmosphere for the earth, is transparent to high-frequency (visible) electromagnetic waves but opaque to low-frequency (infrared) electromagnetic waves.

If you wish to go deeper than the text coverage of the greenhouse effect, briefly discuss the idea of wave frequency. Figure 22.11 shows the relationship of wave frequency and wavelength. A vigorous shaking of a stretched rope produces high-frequency waves (or short wavelengths). The origin of electromagnetic waves is vibrating electrons in matter. The more frequently they vibrate, the higher the frequency of waves they emit. This relates to temperature. In equation form, $f \sim T$, which reads, the frequency of electromagnetic radiation emitted by a source is proportional to the temperature of the source. Electrons vibrate at greater frequencies in hot matter than in cold matter. The sun is so hot that the frequency of electromagnetic waves it emits are high — high enough to activate our visible receptors. Write $f \sim T$ in big letters to indicate large values of both frequency and temperature. This radiation is visible light. It is absorbed by the earth, which in turn emits its own radiation. Write $f \sim T$ in small letters to indicate low values of both frequency and temperature. Interesting point: The atmosphere of the earth is primarily warmed by terrestrial radiation, not solar radiation. That's why air near the ground is warmer than air above. The opposite would be the case if the sun were the primary warmer of air!

Before linking these ideas to the greenhouse effect of the earth, first consider what happens to the interior temperature of a car on a hot sunny day. Window glass is transparent to the high frequencies of sunlight, so visible light and the energy it carries comes through the windshield and is absorbed by the car interior. The car interior in turn radiates its own electromagnetic waves, but in accord with $f \sim T$, at a substantially lower frequency than sunlight. These are infrared waves, to which the window glass is opaque. These waves can't get through the glass. Hence the glass acts as a one-way valve; high-frequency waves can come in, but low-frequency waves can't get out. Internal energy of the car interior increases. (A way to diminish this is to put a reflecting surface inside — reflected light doesn't change frequency, and goes back through the windshield!).

With the car model of the greenhouse understood, go on the greenhouse effect of the earth. Like the car window, our atmosphere is transparent to visible light but opaque to infrared. Opacity is primarily due to water vapor and carbon dioxide in the atmosphere. The greenhouse effect increases the internal energy of the earth. This is a quite desirable effect, it turns out. Without the greenhouse effect, we wouldn't be here, for the average temperature of the earth would be a chilling -18°C! So the controversy over the increased CO_2 in the atmosphere and its effect on the greenhouse effect has to do with the degree of the effect, not the effect itself. Interestingly enough, the carbon that is spewed by burning is the same carbon that is absorbed by tree growth. So a realistic step in the solution to the increased greenhouse effect is to simply grow more trees (while decreasing the rate at which they are cut down)! Johnny-Appleseed types — to the task! This would not be an end-all to the problem, however, because the carbon returns to the biosphere when the trees ultimately decay.

Interesting point: The earth is always "in equilibrium" whether it is overheating or not. At a higher temperature, as the increased greenhouse effect tends to produce, the earth simply radiates more terrestrial radiation. Income and outgo match in any case; the important consideration is the temperature at which this income and outgo match.

Solar power has been with humans from the beginning. We see its application whenever we see clothes hung on a line (do you see that much anymore?) and we see it as a power source on the roofs of new buildings under construction. If you have up-to-date information on this technology, share it with your class here.

More Think-and-Explain Questions

1. Wood is a better insulator than glass. Yet fiberglass is commonly used as an insulator in wooden buildings. Why?
   Answer: Air is an excellent insulator. The reason that fiberglass is a good insulator is principally because of the vast amount of air spaces trapped in it.

2. You can bring water in a paper cup to a boil by placing it over a flame. Why doesn't the paper cup burn?
   Answer: Much of the energy of the flame is readily conducted through the paper to the water. The paper cup and water comprise a thermal system that as a whole will increase in temperature. The

relatively large amount of water, compared to paper, absorbs the energy that would otherwise heat the paper. This keeps the temperature of both the cup and the water well below the ignition temperature of paper.

3. Place a thermometer in a fur coat. Will the temperature rise?
   Answer: No, the coat is not a source of heat, but merely keeps the thermal energy of the wearer from leaving rapidly.

4. A bowl of soup may be too hot for comfortable consumption. If the top surface is removed, it will likely then be consumable. Why?
   Answer: The hottest part of the soup is the least dense and floats at the surface.

5. On sunny days, why do hot-air balloons suddenly rise when they drift over a wide road or parking lot made of black asphalt?
   Answer: The air is warmed over the black surface, and rises.

6. Turn on a incandescent lamp and you feel its heat immediately. Quickly turn it off and touch it. It isn't hot. Explain why you felt heat from it.
   Answer: The heat you received was from radiation.

7. Why does a good emitter of heat radiation appear black at room temperature?
   Answer: The reason that a good *absorber* appears black is discussed at the footnoted answers on page 333. A good absorber by its design is also a good emitter of radiation. This is evident when a good absorber is not generally any warmer than poor absorbers in the same environment. Balance is called thermal equilibrium. A good emitter appears black at room temperatures because the radiation it is emitting is too low in frequency to be seen. The rest is logic: since a good absorber appears black, and since a good absorber is also a good emitter, it follows that a good emitter appears black. (Heat a normally black body to incandescence and you'll find it a better emitter than a non-black body of the same temperature.)

8. Why are space shuttle heat insulating tiles black?
   Answer: They are excellent absorbers of heat, as evidenced by their blackness.

9. A number of objects at different temperatures placed in a closed room will ultimately come to the same temperature. Would this thermal equilibrium be possible if good absorbers were poor emitters and if poor absorbers were good emitters? Explain.
   Answer: If good absorbers were not good emitters, then thermal equilibrium would not be possible. If a good absorber only absorbed then its temperature would climb above that of poorer absorbers in the vicinity. And if poor absorbers were good emitters their temperatures would fall below that of better absorbers.

23 Change of Phase

Objectives

- Explain why evaporation of water is a cooling process.
- Explain why condensation is a warming process.
- Explain why a person with wet skin feels chillier in dry air than in moist air at the same temperature.
- Distinguish between evaporation and boiling.
- Explain why food cooked in boiling water takes longer to cook at high altitude than at sea level.
- Explain why water with substances dissolved in it freezes at a lower temperature than pure water.
- Describe the circumstances under which something can boil and freeze at the same time.
- Give examples of the tendency of ice to melt under pressure and refreeze when the pressure is removed.
- Describe the conditions for a substance to absorb or release energy with no resulting change in temperature.

Possible Misconceptions to Correct

- Constant temperature of something indicates all the molecules have the same energy.
- Boiling is a warming process.
- Ice melts only when heat is added.

Demonstration Equipment

- [23-1] Aluminum soda pop cans, hot plate, pan of water.
- [23-2] Flask of water with enough air pumped out so water boils by heat of hand.
- [23-3] Triple-point apparatus (Figure 23.10).
- [23-4] Ice, copper wire, and weights to hand from water (Figure 23.11).

Introduction

Again the emphasis is on bodies of water and the atmosphere. Material from this chapter is not a prerequisite for chapters that follow.

Note that the unit calorie is used to express the heat of fusion and vaporization of water. SI units have their merits, and they have their drawbacks too. I have a strong bias to saying 1 calorie will raise the temperature of 1 g of water by 1 C , rather than 4 186 J will raise the temperature of 1 kg of water by 1 C , and that 80 calories will melt 1 gram of ice and 540 calories will vaporize 1 gram of boiling water, rather than the SI figures 334.88 kJ/kg and 2260 kJ/kg. I find the SI values somewhat more conceptually difficult. If you're a 100% SI type, the footnotes on page 347 give the SI units, and you can lecture with SI units and point out the few places where the unit calorie occurs.

If you wish to introduce the idea of distribution curves in your course, this is a good place to do it. Treat the cooling produced by evaporation with

plots of numbers of molecules in a liquid versus their speeds, and show how the distribution shifts as the faster-moving molecules evaporate. You may wish to point to the bell-shaped distribution curves that represent the distributions of many things, from molecular speeds to examination scores to people's IQ scores. Regrettably, many people tend to regard such distributions not as bell-shaped, but as spikes. This makes a difference in attitudes. For example, suppose you compare the grade distributions for two sections of your course, Group 1 and Group 2, and that the average score for Group 1 is somewhat greater than that for Group 2. For whatever reason, Group 1 outperforms Group 2. With this information can we make any judgment about an individual from either group? One who looks at these distributions as spiked shaped behaves as if he can - and say (or not say but think) that all individuals from Group 1 do better than any individual from Group 2. On the other hand, one who thinks in terms of the broad shape of the bell shaped distribution will not make any assumptions about each individual. So be aware of the region of overlap in two distribution curves. Attitudes toward individuals from either group should be unbiased by unwarranted prejudice. Hence the difference between narrow-mindedness and broad-mindedness!

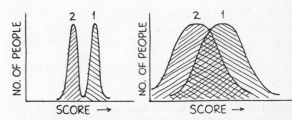

NARROW-MINDED PERCEPTION   BROAD-MINDED PERCEPTION

In the lab *Boiling is a Cooling Process*, students will be surprised when they pour cool water over a flask and cause the water inside to boil. In the lab *Melting Away*, students calculate the latent heat of fusion and in *Getting Steamed Up* the latent heat of vaporization for water. In *Going Through Another Phase* students see that the temperature remains constant during a phase change. Although *Work for Your Ice Cream* is not only an excellent experiment in thermodynamics, but makes tasty activity the day before vacation. *The Drinking Bird* makes an excellent summation activity for your heat unit.

Suggested Lecture

Evaporation: Begin by citing the familiar experience of leaving the water when bathing and feeling chilly in the air, especially when it is windy. Explain the cooling of a liquid from an atomic point of view, and reinforce the idea of temperature being a measure of the average molecular kinetic energy, which means there are molecules that move faster and slower than the average.

CHECK QUESTION: Why does a canvas bag of water cool when the bag is slung over the bumper of a car driven in hot weather? [Water seeps through the canvas. The faster-moving molecules vaporize, leaving less energy per molecules behind.]

CHECK QUESTION: Name at least two ways to cool a hot cup of coffee. [Increase evaporation by (1) blowing on it, and (2) pouring it into the saucer to increase the evaporating area. Or cool it by conduction by (3) pouring it into the cooler saucer. Or cool it by putting silverware in it, to (4) absorb heat by conduction and (5) provide a radiating antenna.]

Condensation: Evaporation is a cooling process. What kind of process is the opposite of evaporation? This is condensation, which is a warming process. After explanation, ask why many people taking a shower will begin drying in the shower stall before getting outside. (While still in the shower region, appreciable warming by condensation offsets the cooling by evaporation.)

Make the point that a change of phase from liquid to gas or the opposite is not entirely one or the other. Condensation and evaporation occur together. The net effect is usually what is spoken about. Make clear just what is cooling when evaporation occurs, and what is warming when condensation occurs. To say that one thing cools is to say that another warms. When a hot cup of coffee cools by evaporation, the surrounding air is warmed. Conservation of energy reigns!

CHECK QUESTION: When alcohol is applied to your skin, why do you feel a chilly sensation? [You are chilled by the rapid evaporation of the alcohol.] Why do you feel extra warm on a muggy day? [Answer: You are warmed by the condensation of vapor on you.]

If you haven't shown the collapsing can demo in your atmospheric pressure lecture, now is a good time:

DEMONSTRATION [23-1]: Heat some aluminum soda pop cans on a burner, empty except for a small amount of water that is brought to a boil to make steam. With a pot holder or tongs, pick up a can and quickly invert it into a basin of water. Crunch! The atmospheric pressure immediately crushes the can with a resounding WHOP! Very impressive. Do this first by inverting cans into a cold basin of water. It is evident that condensation of the steam and vapor on the inside takes place, pressure is correspondingly reduced, and the atmospheric pressure on the outside crunches the can. Then repeat but this time invert cans into a basin of very hot water, just short of the boiling temperature. Crunch again, but less forceful than before. Steam molecules stick to the water surface, hot or cool, like flies sticking to fly paper (al la Figure 23.5). Then repeat, but this time invert cans into *boiling* water. No crunch. Lead your class into the explanation wherein the *net* effect is no change, as condensation of steam is met with just as much vaporization from the boiling water.

Make clear just what is cooling when evaporation occurs. To say that one thing cools is to say that another warms. When a hot cup of coffee cools by evaporation, the surrounding air is warmed. Conservation of energy reigns!

[**Transparency** 44, Figure 23.5 or colliding water molecules]

Figure 23.5: An interesting way to present the condensation of water vapor to droplets is the following: Ask why a glass containing an iced drink becomes wet on the outside, and why a ring of moisture is left on the table. I inject a bit of humor here and state that the reason is... and then write a big 23.5 on the board. Then ask why the walls of the classroom would become wet if the temperature of the room were suddenly reduced. State that the answer is...then underline your 23.5. Ask why dew forms on the morning grass, and state the answer is...another underline for 23.5. Ask why fog forms, and how the clouds form, and back to your 23.5. By now your class is wondering about the significance of 23.5. Announce you're discussing *Figure* 23.5, and with class attention and interest go on to discuss the formation of fog and clouds.

Boiling: Discuss boiling and the roles of applying heat and pressure in the boiling process. A tactic I use throughout my teaching is to ask students to pretend they are having a one to one conversation with a friend about the ideas of physics. Suppose a friend is skeptical about the idea of boiling being a cooling process. I tell my class just what to say to convince the friend of what is going on. I tell them to first point out the distinction between heating and boiling. If the friend knows that the temperature of boiling water remains at 100°C regardless of the heat applied, point out that this is so because the water is cooling by boiling as fast as it is being warmed by heating. Then if this still is not convincing, ask the friend to hold her hands above a pot of boiling water — in the steam. She knows she'll be burned. But burned by what? By the steam. And where did the steam get its energy? From the boiling water; so energy is leaving the water — that's what is meant by cooling!

Bring in the role of pressure on boiling, and illustrate this with the pressure cooker.

Explain how a geyser is like a pressure cooker. Interesting tidbit: The average depth of the ocean is about 2 miles, and the boiling point at this depth of seawater is about 370°C (700°F). Discuss the operation of a coffee percolator.

CHECK QUESTIONS: In bringing water to a boil in the high mountains, is the time required to bring the water to a boil longer or shorter than at sea level? [Shorter.] Is the time required for cooking longer or shorter? [Longer. (Preface this second question with the statement that you are posing a different question, for any confusion about this is most likely due to failing to distinguish between the two questions.)]

DEMONSTRATION [23-2]: Evacuate air from a flask of water that is at room temperature, enough so that the water in the flask will boil from the heat of the students' hands as it is passed around the classroom. (Do this only for a thick-walled flask that won't implode.)

DEMONSTRATION [23-3]: The triple-point demonstration, Figure 24.10.

Freezing: Recall the open structure of ice crystals discussed in Chapter 21. This model makes credible why introducing foreign molecules that do not fit into the structure lower the freezing point. It also explains why pressure causes regelation.

DEMONSTRATION [23-4]: Regelation of an ice cube with a copper wire, Figure 15.8. (The wire must be a good heat conductor for this to work.)

[**Transparency 45** and **46**, Figure 23.12 on energy changes, and graph of same in Figure 23.13]

[**Practice Book 23-1** and **23-2** are on change of phase energy changes]

[**Next-Time Questions 23-1** and **23-2** are on change of phase and energy changes]

Energy and Changes of Phase: Ask if it is possible to add heat to a substance without raising its temperature, and why a steam burn is more damaging than a burn from boiling water at the same temperature. In answering these, discuss the change of phase graph of Figure 23.13, and tie this to Figure 23.12. After citing examples of changes of phase where energy is absorbed, cite examples where energy is released — like raining and snowing. People sometimes say that it is too cold to snow. Explain that this statement arises from the fact that when it is snowing, the temperature of the air is higher than would otherwise be the case — that it is really never too cold to snow, but that whenever it is snowing the air is relatively warm.

Ask about cooling a room by leaving the refrigerator door open, and compare it to putting an air conditioner in the middle of a room instead of mounting it in a window. Ask what the result would be of mounting an air conditioner backwards in a window.

The last check question in this chapter, and its answer on page 350 may need further explanation. To do so, consider a pair of molecules before and after collision. Make a representation of them on the board as shown, each with say the same KE. Suppose they bounce from each other with the same speed. Then they each have the same KE after. KE before and after is the same. But now ask if they might collide such that one gains speed, which you show with a larger size KE. This is okay if the other has a correspondingly small KE, which you write with smaller letters. Again, KE before and after is the same. Now consider what happens if the molecule that loses KE is a water molecule. If its hit by a fast-moving molecule of any kind, it will be brought up to high speed and high KE again. But if it instead

encounters another slow-moving water molecule, one that has similarly given its energy to another molecule in collision, what happens? The answer is, the two probably stick together. Suppose this happens for not a pair of molecules, but for many water molecules in a sample of gas. Then the KE/molecule of remaining gas should increase as water condenses. Viola!

An interesting example of energy absorbed in change of phase is the heat shields on spacecraft for reentry into the atmosphere. The KE of a spacecraft in orbit is many times greater than the amount of energy needed to vaporize the craft. The shield is made of a synthetic resin or plastic ablative material that dissipates heat by melting and vaporizing. At altitudes between about 40 and 25 km, almost the entire KE is dissipated within about a period of 1 minute, heating the shield to several thousand degrees Celsius. Because of its very low conductivity, only a few percent of the heat evolved on reentry is absorbed by the craft. A centimeter or two of the ablative material is consumed by ablation, radiating about 80% of the heat to the surrounding air. Interesting extension: if the reentry trajectory is too steep, heating will be too sever to deal with by ablative cooling. If the trajectory is too flat, the spacecraft will be in danger of being "bounced off" the earth's atmosphere and overshooting forever into space. Spacecraft usually enter the atmosphere at angles between about 5 and 10 degrees to the earth's surface.

Another interesting application of change of phase not in the text is the fine spray of water that firefighters use in combating fires. Rather than douse the burning materials with water that may be in short supply, a fine spray that easily vaporizes is often effective in lowering the temperature to below ignition temperature. This is accomplished by the energy absorbed by the tiny drops (more surface area per volume) in changing phase.

More Think-and-Explain Questions

1. Would evaporation be a cooling process if all the molecules in a liquid had the same speed?
   Answer: No, because the energy of molecules leaving the liquid would be no different than the energy of molecules left behind. Although the internal energy of the liquid would decrease with evaporation, the energy per molecule would be unaffected. No change in temperature would take place.

2. Your teacher hands you a closed flask of water (that has been checked for strength so it doesn't implode). When you hold it in your bare hands, the water begins to boil. You're impressed. Now impress your teacher and explain it.
   Answer: The air in the flask is very low in pressure, so that the heat from your hand will produce boiling at this reduced pressure.

3. Suppose an inventor proposes a design of cookware that will allow boiling to occur at temperatures lower than 100 °C so that food will cook with less energy. Comment on this idea.
   Answer: It is a very poor idea, because it is the high temperature that cooks food, not the bubbles that may or may not be present in the water. When

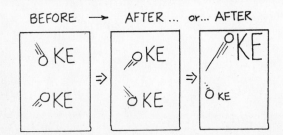

BEFORE → AFTER ... or... AFTER

food cooks in boiling water, it cooks because the water has a temperature of 100°C, not because it is boiling.

4. Why will spraying fruit trees with water before a frost help to protect the fruit from freezing?
Answer: Every gram of water that undergoes freezing releases 80 calories of energy, much of it to the fruit. So while freezing is occurring, the fruit is being warmed to the freezing temperature of water (which is not as low as the freezing temperature of the fruit). We can say in a way that the cold weather freezes the water instead of the fruit. Very importantly, the thin coating of ice then acts as an insulating blanket against further coldness.

5. What is the relationship of Figure 24.5 to the moisture that forms on the inside of car windows when you're parking on a cool night?
Answer: Aside from the connotation of kissing molecules and parking on a cool night, the warm air generated in the car's interior meets the cold glass. The resulting decrease in molecular speed results in condensation of water on the inside of the windows.

6. Why do clouds often form above mountain peaks? (Hint: Consider the updrafts.)
Answer: Air swept upward expands in regions of less atmospheric pressure. The expansion causes cooling, which means molecules are moving at speeds low enough to result in sticking when colliding, so the moisture forms a cloud.

7. Air conditioning units contain no water. Yet it is common to see water dripping from them when they're running on a hot day. Explain.
Answer: Condensation of moisture in the surrounding air occurs on the cool surface of these devices.

8. Why will clouds tend to form above either a flat or a mountainous island in the middle of the ocean? (Hint: Compare the specific heat of the land with that of the water and the subsequent convection currents in the air.)
Answer: Because land has a lower specific heat than water, the land is warmed faster than the surrounding water. This causes updrafts above the warmed land; the rising air laden with H_2O expands, cools, and condenses (Figure 24.5).

9. Why does a hot dog pant?
Answer: Dogs have no sweat glands (except between the toes for most dogs) and therefore cool by the evaporation of moisture from the mouth and the respiratory track. So dogs literally cool from the inside out when they pant.

10. Place a jar of water in a saucepan of water so the bottom is suspended. Put both on a stove. The water in the pan will boil, but not in the jar. Why?
Answer: When the jar reaches the boiling temperature, further heat cannot enter it because it is in thermal equilibrium with the surrounding 100°C water.

11. Why should you not pick up a hot skillet with a wet dish cloth? [steam will burn]
Answer: Moisture in the cloth will convert to steam and burn you.

More Think and Solves

1. How many calories are given off by 1 gram of 100°C steam that changes phase to 1 gram of ice at 0°C.
Answer: 540 + 100 + 80 = 720 calories.

2. Compare the heat given off by 1 gram of steam that condenses to boiling water, to 1 gram of boiling water that cools to form ice, and then continues giving off energy all the way to absolute zero. (The specific heat of ice is 0.5 cal/gram°C.)
Answer: 540 calories for 1 gram of 100°C steam to 100°C boiling water: For the same boiling water to absolute zero; 100 cal to cool to 0°C water, 80 cal to change to ice; 273 x 0.5 = 136.5 cal from 0°C to -273°C. In total, 100 + 80 + 136.5 = 316.5 cal, appreciably less than the heat given off for simply a change of phase from steam to boiling water!

Here are Think and Solves with answers in joules

1. How much energy does is take to melt 5 kg of ice at 0° C?
Answer: 1.66 x 10⁶ J

2. How much energy is given to your body when 0.5 kg of steam condenses on your skin?
Answer: 1.13 x 10⁶ J

3. If that same amount of energy(answer to #2) were used to warm 4 kg of water (8 times as much!) initially at 0° C, what would be the final temperature of the water?
Answer: 67.5° C

4. The heat of vaporization of ethyl alcohol is 8.5 x 10⁵ J/kg. If 2 kg of it were allowed to vaporize in a refrigerator, how much energy would be drawn from the air molecules?
Answer: 1.7 x 10⁶ J

5. How much energy does it take to warm 1 kg of ice at -10° C to steam at 120° C?
Answer: 3.072 x 10⁶ J

24 Thermodynamics

Objectives

- Describe the concept of absolute zero.
- State the first law of thermodynamics and relate it to energy conservation.
- Describe adiabatic processes and cite examples.
- State the second law of thermodynamics and relate it to heat engines.
- Define the ideal efficiency of a heat engine in terms of input and output temperatures.
- Define entropy and give examples.

Possible Misconceptions to Correct

- There is no lower or upper limit of temperature.
- The vast internal energy of bodies like the ocean can be converted to useful energy.
- A friction-free heat engine would be a 100% efficient engine.

Demonstration Equipment

- [24-1] Pressure cooker, heat source, and pot-holder type glove.

Introduction

In keeping with the preceding chapters on heat, this chapter focuses on the environment. Particular emphasis is given to the atmosphere. What do most people talk about in casual conversations? The weather, of course. This chapter provides some physics insights that underlie the weather.

The topics absolute zero and internal energy were introduced in Chapter 21 and are treated in more detail in this chapter. This chapter concludes Part III and is not prerequisite to chapters that follow. It may be skipped if a brief treatment of heat is required.

In lab, in addition to estimating absolute zero, *The Uncommon Cold* also is a good lesson on the pit-falls of two-point graphing.

Suggested Lecture

Absolute Zero and the Kelvin Scale: Follow your discussion of the C and F scales with the idea of a lowest temperature — absolute zero and the Kelvin (K) scale. (Named after "Lord Scale?")

A treatment of absolute zero is in the experiment *Uncommon Cold.* Simply state that the Kelvin scale is "nature's scale" and begins at the coldest possible value for its zero point. (Note the degree symbol ( ) is not used with K to reinforce the concept that its zero point was not chosen by human convention.)

[**Transparency 47**, Figure 24.1 with selected absolute temperatures]

[**Practice Book 24-1** treats the volume versus temperature graph to establish absolute zero]

CHECK QUESTION: Suppose you order a piece of hot apple pie at your friendly restaurant. The waitress brings cold pie, at 0° C, straight from the fridge. You tell her you'd like hotter pie, in fact, twice as hot. What will be the temperature of the pie? (After encouraging neighbor discussion, state that "zero degrees" is a wrong answer.) Do not give the answer yet. Then ask what the new temperature would be if the pie were initially 10°C, and acknowledge that the answer is *not* 20°C! Now you're ready for the "Celsius — the Village Tailor" story.

Celsius, the Village Tailor: Hold a measuring stick against the wall of the lecture room (so that the bottom of the vertically-oriented stick is about 1 meter above the floor) and state that that you are Celsius, the village tailor, and that you measure the heights of your customers against the stick, which is firmly fastened to the wall. You state that there is no need for the stick to extend to the floor, nor to the ceiling, for your shortest and tallest customers fall within the extremities of the stick. Mention that all tailors using the same method could communicate meaningfully with each other about the relative heights of their customers providing the measuring sticks in each shop were fastened the same distance above the "absolute zero" of height. It just so happens that the distance to the floor, the "absolute zero," is 273 notches — the same size notches on the stick itself. Then one day, a very short lady enters your shop and stands against the wall, the top of her head coinciding with the zero mark on the measuring stick. As you take her zero reading, she comments that she has a brother who is twice her height. Ask the class for the height of her brother. Then ask for the temperature of the twice-as-hot apple pie. When this is understood, ask why the pie will not *really* be 273° C. Or that for the initially 10°C pie, the temperature will not really be 293°C. (Considerable heat has gone into changing the state of the water in the pie, which accounts for it being "dried out." If you wish to avoid the change of state factor, begin your discussion with the temperature of something such as a piece of metal that will not change state for the temperature range in question.)

Or use the "Hotel Elevator" analogy that Charlie Spiegel uses, where Kelvin Hall is at the basement level, Celsius Hall is on the first floor, and Fahrenheit Hall is on the third floor. Occupants of each hall measure zero height from their own respective floors.

First Law of Thermodynamics: Introduce the first law of thermodynamics by citing the findings of Count Rumford: that when cannon barrels were being drilled and became very hot, that it was the friction of the drills that produced the heating. Recall the definition of work, *force x distance*, and cite how the metal is heated by the frictional force x distance that the various parts of the drill bit move. Have your students rub their hands together and feel them warm up. Or warm part of the chair they sit on by rubbing.

Follow this up with the account of Joule with his paddle wheel apparatus and his measuring the mechanical equivalent of heat. Of interest is Joule's attempt to extend this experiment to a larger scale while on his honeymoon in Switzerland. Joule and his bride honeymooned near the Chamonix waterfall. According to Joule's conception of heat, the gravitational potential energy of the water at the top should go into increasing the internal energy of the water when at the bottom. Joule made a rough estimate of the increased difference in water temperature at the bottom of the waterfall. His measurements did not substantiate his predictions, however, because considerable cooling occurred due to evaporation as the water fell through the air. Without this added complication, however, his predictions would have been supported. What happens to the temperature of a penny, after all, when you slam it with a hammer? Similarly with water. Emphasize that the first law is simply the law of energy conservation for thermal systems.

Adiabatic Processes: Cite the opposite processes of compression and expansion of air and how each affects the temperature of the air. It's easy to see that compressing air into a tire warms the air; and also that when the same air expands through the nozzle in escaping, it cools. Have your students blow on their hands, as Figure 24.5 suggests.

DEMONSTRATION [24-1]: Bring water to a boil in a regular pressure cooker. Then remove the weighted cap so that steam expands violently from the nozzle. For drama, put your gloved hand in the path of the "steam" about 20 cm above the nozzle. Ask if you dare do the same with a bare hand. Then remove the glove and hold your hand in the stream. Amazing! Actually the "steam" is quite cool. Acknowledge that your hand is not in the steam, which is invisible and in the first 1 to 3 cm above the nozzle. Your hand is in condensed vapor, considerably cooled by expansion (and mixing with air).

Discuss cloud formation as moist air rises, expands, and cools.

If you have a model of an internal combustion engine, such as is shown in Figure 24.4, strongly consider showing and explaining it in class. Many of your students likely have little idea of the process. (It still amazes me that automobile engines are as quiet as they are!)

[**Transparency 48**, Figure 24.4 of the 4-cycle engine]

Meteorology and the First Law: Discuss the adiabatic expansion of rising air in our atmosphere. Ask if it would be a good idea on a hot day when going for a balloon ride to only wear a T-shirt. Or would it be a good idea to bring warm clothing? A glance at Figure 24.6 will be instructive.

Discuss the check question on page 359, about yanking down a giant dry-cleaner's garment bag

from a high altitude and the changes in temperature it undergoes. Interesting stuff.

There is more to Chinook winds than is cited in the text. As Figure 24.7 suggests, warm moist air that rises over a mountain cools as it expands, and then undergoes precipitation where it is gains latent heat energy as vapor changes state to liquid (rain) or solid (snow). Then when the energetic dry air is compressed as it descends on the other side of the mountain, it is appreciably warmer than if precipitation hadn't occurred. Without the heat given to the air by precipitation, it would cool a certain amount in adiabatically expanding and warm the same amount in adiabatically compressing, with have no net increase in temperature.

Discuss temperature inversion and the role it plays in air pollution; or at least in confining air pollution. On the matter of pollution, we find now that even rain is polluted. Acid rain has wrecked havoc with the environment in many parts of the world. Interestingly enough, it isn't the destruction of vast forests or poisoning of wildlife that has evoked the loudest public outcry — acid rain dulls the high-tech finishes on automobiles, and for many people *that* is going too far!

[**Transparency 49**, Figure 24.10 of the steam turbine]

Second Law: Introduce the second law by discussing Think-and-Explain 5 on page 369, about immersing a hot tea cup in a large container of cold water. Stress that if the cup were to become even warmer at the expense of the cold water becoming cooler, the first law would not be violated. You're on your way with the second law.

According to my friend Dave Wall who worked for a couple of years in the patent office in Washington DC, the greatest shortcoming of would-be inventors was their lack of understanding the first and second laws of thermodynamics. The patent office has long been besieged with schemes that promise to circumvent these laws. This point is worth discussion, which you can direct to Carnot's efficiency equation and its consequences, like why better fuel economy is achieved when driving on cold days. (Remember in pre-SI days we talked of "mileage" — now it's fuel economy, because "kilometerage" just doesn't have the right ring yet.)

CHECK QUESTION: Temperatures must be expressed in kelvins when using the formula for ideal efficiency, but may be expressed in either Celsius of kelvins for Newton's law of cooling. Why?[In Carnot's equation, ratios are used; in Newton's law of cooling, only differences.]

CHECK QUESTION: Incandescent lamps are typically rated only 5% efficient, and fluorescent lamps are only 20% efficient. Now we say they are 100% efficient.
Isn't this contradictory? [5% and 20% efficient as light sources, but 100% efficient as heat sources. All the energy input, even that that becomes light, very quickly becomes heat.]

[**Next-Time Question 24-1** on lamp efficiency]

Entropy: Conclude your treatment of this chapter with your best ideas on entropy — the measure of messiness.

More Think-and-Explain Questions

1. On a cold 10°C day, your friend who likes cold weather says she wishes it were twice as cold. Taking this to mean she wishes the air had half the internal energy, what temperature would this be?

   Answer: The air will be at half its absolute temperature, or (1/2)(273 +10) = 141.5K. To find how many Celsius degrees below 0°C this is, we first subtract 141.5K from 273K; this is 273 - 141.5 = 131.5K below the freezing point of ice, or -131.5°C. (Or simply, 141.5 - 273 = -131.5 C.) Quite nippy!

2. Why is "thermal pollution" a relative term?

   Answer: The term pollution refers to an undesirable by-product of some process. The desirability or undesirability of a particular by-product is relative, and depends on the circumstances. For example, ejecting hot water into cooler water can be quite desirable from one point of view and undesirable from another point of view.

3. Is it possible to construct a heat engine that produces no thermal pollution? Defend your answer.

   Answer: According to the 2nd law, it is not possible to construct a heat engine that is without exhaust. If the exhausted heat is undesirable then the engine is a polluter. If the exhausted heat is desirable, heating a swimming pool for example, then in this sense the heat engine produces no thermal pollution.

4. What happens to the efficiency of a heat engine when the temperature of the reservoir into which heat energy is rejected is lowered?

   Answer: When the temperature is lowered in the reservoir into which heat is rejected, efficiency increases; substitution of a smaller value of T_{hot} into $(T_{hot} - T_{cold})/T_{hot}$ will confirm this. (Reexpress the equation as $1 - T_{cold}/T_{hot}$ to better see this.)

More Think and Solves

1. To increase the efficiency of a heat engine, would it be better to increase the temperature of the reservoir while holding the temperature of the sink constant or to decrease the temperature of the sink while holding the temperature constant. Show your work.

   Answer: As in the Think-and-Explain Question #4 above, inspection shows that decreasing T_{cold} will contribute to a greater increase in efficiency than by increasing T_{hot} by the same amount. For example, let T_{hot} be 600K and T_{cold} be 300K. Then efficiency = (600 - 300)/600 = 1/2. Now let T_{hot} be increased by 200K. Now efficiency = (800 - 300)/800 = 5/8. Compare this with T_{cold} decreased by 200K, in which case efficiency = (600 - 100)/600 = 5/6, which is clearly greater.

2. What is the ideal efficiency of an automobile engine wherein fuel is heated to 2700K and the outdoor air is 300K?

   Answer: Ideal efficiency is (2700 - 300)/2700 = 24/27 = 88.8%.

25 Vibrations and Waves

Objectives

- Relate a drawing of a sine curve to the crest, trough, amplitude, and length of a wave.
- Describe the relation between frequency and period of a wave.
- Describe what it is that travels when a wave moves outward from a vibrating source.
- Describe what affects the speed of a wave.
- Distinguish between a transverse wave and a longitudinal wave.
- Distinguish between constructive and destructive interference.
- Define a standing wave and explain how it occurs.
- Describe the Doppler effect for sound and relate it to the blue and red shifts for light.
- Describe the conditions for a bow wave to occur.
- Describe the conditions for a sonic boom to be heard.

Possible Misconceptions to Correct

- Wave speed and wave frequency are synonymous.
- When a wave travels in a medium, the medium moves with the wave.
- Wave amplitude and wave displacement are synonymous.
- Combinations of waves can be added, but not canceled.
- Changes in wave speed (rather than wave frequency) constitutes the Doppler effect.
- A sonic boom is a momentary burst of high pressure produced when something exceeds the speed of sound (rather than a continuous front of high pressure generated by faster-than-sound sources).

Demonstration Equipment

- [25-1] Simple pendulum, and meter stick.
- [25-2] Thin ruler or meter stick.
- [25-3] Slinky and/or rope to shake.
- [25-4] Bell Telephone torsion-type wave machine (distributed about 25 years ago by Bell Telephone Company).

Introduction

This chapter serves as a necessary background for the following chapter, and a useful background for all chapters in Unit IV.

As the chapter stands, it is heavily weighted with a multitude of terms and different ideas, so to avoid information overload you'll note that torsional waves, although important, are not discussed.

A note of caution: When toying with a pendulum it is easy to forget the distinction between a simple pendulum and a physical pendulum. A simple pendulum is one where the mass of the bob is very small compared to the length of string. Its rotational inertia is simply ML^2, where M is the mass and L the length of the pendulum. But if the mass is not concentrated at the end of a string, but makes up part of a stick, for example, we no longer have a simple pendulum. Such is a physical pendulum, where rotational inertia is less. The rotational inertia of a meter stick swung from one end, for example, is $1/3\ ML^2$ (Figure 11.14 back on page 157) and pivoted about its midpoint, $1/12\ ML^2$. Many good teachers forget this distinction when making lab calculations of pendulum-bob speed at the bottom of its swing. For a simple pendulum, $v = \sqrt{2gh}$, but for a physical pendulum (a bob at the end of a stick, for example) the speed is greater. A physical pendulum is less lazy for its mass than a simple pendulum. Recall that rotational inertia is greatest when all the mass involved is at maximum distance from the rotational axis.

This idea is nicely illustrated by comparing the falls of a pair of upright meter sticks with their lower ends against a book on your lecture table — one meter stick bare and the other with a ball of clay or some other mass attached to its upper end. Because of the greater rotational inertia per mass for the clayed stick, it is slower to rotate to the table. And while we're on falling sticks, consider the falling times of a meter stick that rotates with its lower end against a book and a stick that is allowed to slide across the table as it falls. Careful investigation will show the sliding stick reaches the table first — it's center of mass falls nearly vertically, while the stick with its lower end against the book must rotate and travel a longer distance. This is similar to comparing times for a mass sliding down an incline and a mass dropping the same vertical distance. Nice stuff.

Waves and wave motion can be introduced using *Good Stuff* software (Laserpoint) in the lab *Catch a Wave*. If you don't do it as a lab, show the simulations as demonstrations. In the simulation *Longitudinal Waves*, it is easily seen that the wave moves while the medium is not transported. The simulation *Doppler Effect* shows the decreasing pitch of sound when a plane or car passes an observer or vice versa. Moved faster, a shock wave is produced. Measurement of the half-angle of the cone off the screen enables an estimation of speed (see Practice Book 25-2).

In lab, *Tick-Tock* and *Grandfather's Clock* beautifully demonstrate the effectiveness of the learning cycle. Introduce waves and wave motion using Laserpoint *Good Stuff* software in the lab *Catch a Wave*. If you enjoy setting up and having students use ripple tanks, then *Ripple While You Work* is just the lab for you!

Suggested Lecture

Vibrations: Begin by tapping your lecture table or the chalkboard. Call attention to how frequently you tap and relate this to the term *frequency*. Call attention to the time intervals between taps and relate this to the term *period*. Establish the reciprocal relationship between frequency and period — before you get into vibrations and waves.

DEMONSTRATION [25-1]: Attach a small massive weight to the end of a piece of string, about 1 m, and swing it to and fro: this is a simple pendulum. Identify frequency. Then identify period. Time how long it takes to swing to and fro 10 times. Repeat to show that the result does not change from trial to trial. (Galileo is credited as the first to report this.) Divide the time by 10 to get the period (or skip the division and use the total time for the comparisons).

Now ask the class if changing the weight at the end of the pendulum will change the period. After they have given various answers, add more mass to the end of the string without changing the overall length of the pendulum. Repeat and show the same result as before. Weight does not affect the period of the pendulum. (As Figure 25.1 suggests, weight does not affect the rate of free fall. Neither does it affect the rate of sliding down a frictionless surface. Likewise, pendula of the same length will have the same period.)

CHECK QUESTION: What principle of mechanics accounts for the different periods of pendulums of different length? [Rotational inertia (Chapter 11).]

DEMONSTRATION [25-2]: Show an upside-down pendulum by holding up a long thin ruler or meter stick and swing it to and fro. Show that its period depends on length.

Interestingly enough, buildings behave the same way. Each building has its own period. Each of the two towers of the World Trade Center in New York City has a period of 10 seconds. On a windy day the towers sway to and fro in 10-second cycles, swinging as much as 1 meter on a side in a strong wind, and twice this amount for hurricane winds. If the gusts come in rhythm with the vibrations of the building, resonance occurs. (We'll return to this idea in the next chapter.) Shorter buildings have shorter periods. The period of a 20-story building may be 1.5 seconds.

[**Transparency 50**, Figure 25.3, a sine curve]

[**Practice Book 25-1** treats a general wave description]

Wave Description: Vertically move a piece of chalk up and down on the board, tracing and retracing a vertical straight line. Call attention to how "frequently" you oscillate the chalk, again tying this to the definition of frequency. Also discuss the idea of displacement and amplitude (maximum displacement). With appropriate motions, show different frequencies and different amplitudes. Then do the same while walking across the front of the board tracing out a sine wave. Show waves of different wavelengths.

DEMONSTRATION [25-3]: You and a student hold the ends of a stretched spring or a slinky and send transverse pulses along it, stressing the idea that only the disturbance rather than the medium moves along the spring. Shake it and produce a

sine wave. Then send a stretch and squeeze (elongation and compression) down the spring, showing a longitudinal pulse. Send a sequence of pulses and you have a wave. After some discussion, produce standing waves.

CHECK QUESTION: With respect to the direction of the wave's motion, how do the directions of vibrations differ for transverse and longitudinal waves? [Sideways (perpendicular) for transverse; along (parallel) for longitudinal.]

DEMONSTRATION [25-4]: Show waves on a Bell Telephone torsion-type wave machine.

[**Transparency 51**, Figure 25.9 on longitudinal and transverse waves]

Cite the sameness of the frequency of a vibrating source and the frequency of the wave it produces. Explain or derive wave velocity = frequency x wavelength. Support this with examples, first the freight car question on page 377, and then the waves as in the Think-and-Solve problems. Calculate the wavelength of one of your local popular radio stations. (For example, 1000 kHz on the dial has a wavelength = speed/frequency = $(3 \times 10^8 \text{m/s})/10^6 \text{Hz} = 300$ meters — surprisingly long!) If you discuss electromagnetic waves, be sure to contrast them with longitudinal sound waves and distinguish between them.

[**Transparency 52**, Figure 25.13, standing waves]
[**Next-Time Question 25-1** is about a standing wave]

Electromagnetic Waves (Optional): Depending on your course design, consider discussing Chapter-27 and Chapter-37 material and get into the family of electromagnetic waves and how they group according to wavelength and frequency. Refer ahead to Figure 27.4 on page 408. You can use local radio stations as examples and discuss such things as assigned frequency, clear channel, wattage, and directional signals. You can bring in well-known waves such as microwaves, CB's, black light, x-rays, gamma rays, etc. Or wait until later to discuss such waves.

Interference: Describe interference by drawing Figure 25.10 on the board. If you have a ripple tank, show the overlapping of water waves and interference. Produce standing waves.

CHECK QUESTION: Can waves overlap in such a way as to produce a zero amplitude? [Yes, that is the destructive interference characteristic of all waves.]

Make a pair of transparencies of concentric circles. Superimpose them on your overhead projector and show the variety of interference patterns that result when their centers are displaced. One example is shown in the text (Figure 25.12).

You'll return to interference of sound in the next chapter when you show the unforgettable demonstration [26-10]; bringing a pair of out-of-phase radio speakers face to face to show sound cancellation. Or you could do this here.

Doppler Effect: Introduce the Doppler Effect by throwing a ball, perhaps sponge rubber or

Styrofoam, around the room. In the ball you first place an electronic whistle that emits a sound of about 3000 Hz. Or swing a sound source in a horizontal circle at the end of a string. Relate this to the siren of a fire engine and radar of the highway patrol (Figures 25.17 and 25.18). (Note that sound requires a medium; radar doesn't.)

Treat the Doppler effect as done in the chapter (Figure 25.15). Draw circles to show the top view of circular ripples made by a bug bobbing in the water. Wave speed is the same in all directions, as evident by the circular shape. Wave frequency is the same in all directions also, since wavelength and speed is the same in all directions. Now consider a moving bug and the pattern it makes (Figure 25.16). Explain how the frequency of waves is increased in front of the bug; waves would be encountered more often (more frequently) by your hand placed in the water in front of the bug. Similarly waves would be encountered less often (less frequently) in back of the bug. Likewise with the waves from the moving sources of Figure 25.17, and 25.18.

CHECK QUESTION: The waves are more crowded in front of the swimming bug and more dragged out behind. Is the wave *speed* greater in front of the bug (and less behind the bug)? [No, no, no! Frequency, not speed, is greater in front of the bug and less in back. Emphasize the distinction between wave speed and wave frequency.]

[**Practice Book 25-2** treats shock wave construction]
[**Next-Time Question** is about a shock wave]

Bow Waves and Shock Waves: Ask the class to consider the waves made by two stones thrown in the water. Sketch the overlapping waves as shown in the sketch. Ask where the water is highest above the water level, then indicate the two places where the waves overlap with X's. This is constructive interference. From this and your swimming bug, you can extend the bug to speeds greater than wave speeds and show the regions of overlap that produce the bow wave (sketching Figures 25.15, 25.16, and 25.19). Then show that this is what happens with a bow wave, that a series of overlaps make up the V-shaped envelope. Then discuss the shock waves produces by supersonic aircraft.

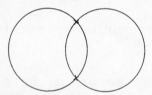

The analogy between bow waves in water and shock waves in air is useful. Questions raised by students about shock waves and the sonic boom can be effectively answered by translating the question from one of an aircraft in the air to one of a speedboat knifing through the water, a situation much easier to visualize. For example, if you're enjoying a picnic lunch at the edge of a river and a speedboat comes by and douses you, you're not apt to attribute the dousing to the idea that the speedboat just exceeded the speed of the water waves. You know the boat is generating a continuous bow wave so long as it travels faster than waves in water. Likewise for aircraft.

CHECK QUESTION: Why is it that a subsonic aircraft, no matter how loud it may be, cannot produce a shock wave or sonic boom? [There will be no overlapping of spherical waves to form a cone unless the craft moves faster than the waves it generates.]

The treatment of shock waves is simplified in the text. There are actually two parts of a shock wave, the outer cone that is the superposition of condensations, and an inner low-pressure cone that is the superposition of rarefactions. A graph of pressure versus time forms an "N", as shown. Sonic boom damage is intensified with the incidence of low pressure rapidly following the high-pressure front.

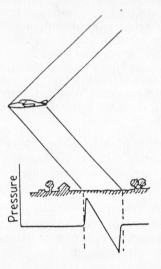

If you wish to go further with shock waves than in the text, but featured in the Chapter 25 material in the *Conceptual Physics Practice Book*, consider explaining how the speed of an aircraft can be estimated by the angle of its shock wave (shock waves are visible, for light is refracted in passing through the denser air — you might show any of the popular photographs of shock waves made by speeding bullets). Construct a shock wave on the board by the following sequence: first place your chalk on the board anywhere to signify time zero. Draw a meter-long horizontal line, say to the right, to represent how far an aircraft has moved in a certain time. Suppose it moves at twice the speed of sound (Mach 2).

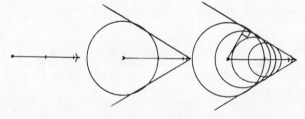

Then during the time it moves your one meter, the sound it made initially has moved half this distance, which you mark on the midpoint of your line. State that the initial sound has expanded spherically, which you represent two-dimensionally by drawing a circle as shown. Explain that this circle represents only one of the nearly infinite circles that make up the shock wave, which you draw by making tangents from the end point to the circle. The shock wave should be a 60 degree wedge (30 degrees above your horizontal line, and 30 degrees below). (Now here's the tricky part.) Move the center 10 cm at a time in the direction of travel and draw circles, (reduce the radius each time), within the two tangents. Explain how the speed of the craft is simply the ratio of the horizontal line (1 m) to the radial distance (1/2 m) of the big circle (and likewise the respective horizontal lines to radii of smaller circles). (If your students are science students, at this point and not before, introduce the sine function). Now your test of all this: Distribute pages from the Practice Book and have your students construct shock waves of different angles, and find the speeds of craft by investigating the generated angles. Or construct on the board a shock wave of different angle and ask your class to estimate the speed of the craft that generated it. (This is featured on NTQ 25-2.) In making constructions, working backwards now, the most common student error is constructing the right angle from the horizontal line rather than from the shock wave line that is tangent to the circle. Have your students draw circles for other Mach numbers. Be sure to practice all this several times. Making these geometrical constructions is an enjoyable activity!

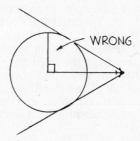

More Think-and-Explain Questions

1. What is the source of wave motion?
 Answer: Something that vibrates.

2. If you triple the frequency of a vibrating object, what happens to its period?
 Answer: The period decreases to 1/3 its former value.

3. How far, in terms of wavelength, does a wave move in one period?
 Answer: One wavelength.

4. What kind of motion would you apply to a slinky to produce a transverse wave? A longitudinal wave?
 Answers: To and fro at right angles (90 and 270 degrees) to the slinky axis; to and fro (0 and 180 degrees) along the axis of the slinky.

5. A stone is tossed into a quiet pond, and waves spread over its surface. What becomes of the energy when they die out?
 Answer: The energy is transformed into thermal motion of the water molecules (internal energy).

6. Toss a stone in still water and concentric circles are formed. What form will waves have if a stone is tossed into smoothly flowing water?
 Answer: The same. The circles formed are relative to the water, and both will travel downstream together.

7. Whenever you watch a high-flying aircraft overhead, its sound seems to come from behind the craft rather than from where you see it. Why?
 Answer: It takes a noticeable time for the sound to travel between the aircraft and you. The sound that reaches you was generated when the aircraft was farther back.

More Think and Solves

1. What is the frequency, in hertz, that corresponds to each of the following periods: (a) 0.10 s, (b) 5 s, (c) 1/60 s, (d) 24 hours?
 Answers: (a) $f = 1/T = 1/0.10$ s $= 10$ Hz; (b) $f = 1/5 = 0.2$ Hz; (c) $f = 1/(1/60)$ s $= 60$ Hz; (d) f $= 1/24$ h x 1 h/3600 s $= 1.15$ x 10^{-5} Hz.

2. What is the period, in seconds, that corresponds to each of the following frequencies: (a) 10 Hz, (b) 0.2 Hz, (c) 60 Hz, (d) 1.15 x 10-5 Hz?
 Answers : (a) 0.10 s, (b) 5 s, (c) 1/60 s, (d) 86400 s (24 hours)

3. The crests on a long surface water wave are 20 m apart, and in 1 minute 10 crests pass by. What is the speed of this wave?
 Answer: $v = f\lambda = 10/\text{min}$ x 20 m $= 200$ m/min. (or 3.3 m/s).

4. If the speed of a longitudinal wave is 340 m/s, and the frequency is 1000 Hz, what is the wavelength of the wave?
 Answer: $\lambda = v/f = (340$ m/s$)/1000$ Hz $= 0.34$ m.

5. At one place in a groove of a phonograph record the "wave" is 0.01 cm long. This travels past the stylus with a speed of 40 cm/s. (*a*) What is the frequency of vibration in the stylus? (*b*) In an inner groove where the speed is 20 cm/s, what will be the wavelength to give the same frequency as in *a*?
 Answers: (a) 4000 Hz; (b) 0.005 cm; (a) $f = v/\lambda = (40$ cm/s$)/0.01$ cm $= 4000$ Hz. (b) $\lambda = v/f = (20$ cm/s$)/4000$ Hz $= 0.005$ cm; half as much.

Objectives

- Relate the pitch of a sound to frequency.
- Describe what happens to air when sound moves through it.
- Compare the transmission of sound through air with transmission through solids, liquids, and a vacuum.
- Describe factors that affect the speed of sound.
- Give examples of forced vibration.
- Describe the conditions for resonance.
- Describe the conditions for beats.

Possible Misconceptions to Correct

- The speed of sound is the same in all media.
- Sound cannot cancel sound.
- Resonance and forced vibrations are the same thing.

Demonstration Equipment

- [26-1] Large tuning fork and container of water to stick it in.
- [26-2] Large bare loudspeaker and audio oscillator (or other source to drive speaker).
- [26-3] Aluminum rod (about a meter long).
- [26-4] Rosin or pitch to put on fingers for stroking aluminum rod (see your gym colleague for rosin used by gymnasts; or your biology colleague for some Canada Balsam, refined pine pitch used for cell fixing).
- [26-5] Vacuum jar with ringing doorbell inside, and vacuum pump.
- [26-6] Container of helium gas, and container of SF_6 gas (for breathing).
- [26-7] Pair of matched tuning forks mounted on sounding boxes, for resonance.
- [26-8] Small bare loudspeaker and music source (tape cassette player) and a baffle board (nearly a square meter of cardboard of the equivalent) with hole somewhat smaller than the speaker cut in middle.
- [26-9] Speaker box in which to place the bare speaker.
- [26-10] Stereo tape player with mono mode, matching speakers, and a means (switch or jacks) to reverse the polarity of either of the speakers.
- [26-11] Laser and pair of mounted tuning forks of [26-7].

Introduction

This chapter lends itself to many interesting lecture demonstrations: a ringing doorbell inside a vacuum jar being evacuated; the easily seen vibrations of a tuning fork illuminated with a strobe lamp; interference with a pair of radio speakers out of phase with each other; resonance and beats with a pair of tuning forks mounted on sound boxes; and the

8-mm film loop of the *Tacoma Narrows Bridge Collapse*. This footage is also on the videotape *Conceptual physics Alive, Part 2*, and on the videodisk from the same series.

Forced vibrations, resonance, and interference provide a useful background for the same concepts applied to light in following chapters.

An impressive demonstration of vibrations and sound is the stroking of an aluminum rod with your fingers. It's necessary to put some pine pitch or violin bow rosin on the rod and/or your fingers. If you use pitch, acetone dilutes it so you can get a light layer on the rod and your thumb and finger. Hold the rod by its end for the fundamental tone, then by its midpoint for the first harmonic. Practice is highly recommended.

Another neat demo is resonance in a long stovepipe. Put three layers of wire window screen on crossed wires 1/4 of the way up from the bottom of the stovepipe. Heat over a Bunsen burner, but not so hot as to melt the screen! The screen is a white noise generator, while the tube is the frequency selector that resonates at the fundamental frequency of the tube. When it is removed from the flame, it continues to sound as the wire screen cools. Turn the pipe sideways till the sound subsides for a few seconds, then turn it back to vertical — the sound returns. Very impressive!

Do as Tom Rossing does and be sure to play music via stereo speakers in your class. Tom plays monophonic music from a tape cassette recorder (a radio will do). First he plays one speaker, then both in phase. The result is only slightly louder sound. This illustrates the logarithmic nature of our response to changes in sound level, for doubling the intensity of the sound results only in a small perceived increase in loudness. It takes about eight times the intensity to perceive twice loudness.

Speaker systems for stereos have polarity indications on their terminals, which is essential for optimum sound. The speakers must operate with the same relative phase for a given input signal; that is, both diaphragms must move in the same direction for a given direction of current from the amplifier. If they move in opposite directions, as happens when they are out of phase, destructive interference results. The sound is clearly lower in volume when the speakers are out of phase. Tom Rossing goes the spectacular step further and faces the speakers against each other. Near silence! Then he pulls the speakers farther apart and the sound returns. This demo is a must.

The diminishing of sound by destructive interference may suggest a cancellation of energy. Not so. A radio loudspeaker is in effect a microphone if the input is a vibration and the output is induced voltage. This is electromagnetic induction, and is analogous to how a motor is a generator and vice versa depending on input and output. When the speakers face each other they "drive" each other, inducing back voltages in each other that cut the currents in each down. So energy is diminished, but not canceled.

Interestingly enough, electronic synthesizers are so sophisticated now that human voices are often done electronically in recording studios, replacing backup singers. The voices of some recording artists are so electronically altered that they have great difficulty in live performances. Their recording performances are hard acts to follow. Your students will likely have more information about this in class discussion.

There are three programs on the computer disk *Good Stuff!* that compliment this chapter. *Sum of Two Waves* nicely illustrates interference, wave superposition, and beats. *Frequency Analyzer* treats the different sounds of instruments. To see the overtones that give sounds their character, you will need an analog-to-digital converter, a microphone, and an audio amplifier. Sing or play a steady note and adjust the pitch to obtain the clearest display. *Music* turns the keyboard of the Apple into a piano keyboard. Although you can only play one note at a time, you see the note you're playing on the staff.

If your students do it right, you won't be able to stand the lab activity *Chalk Talk* for long! In lab, *Mach One* produces quite accurate results, and is interesting when done with carbon dioxide.

Practice Book 26-1 can fit anywhere in this chapter. Likewise for **Next-Time Question 26-1**.

Suggested Lecture

Sound: Begin on a light note and state with mocked profoundness that sound is the only thing that the ear can hear. Then more seriously, state that the source of sound or all wave motion is a vibrating object.

DEMONSTRATION [26-1]: Tap a large tuning fork and show that it is vibrating by dipping the vibrating prongs in a cup of water. The splashing water shows that the prongs are moving. (Small forks do not work well.)

DEMONSTRATION [26-2]: Show a large radio speaker without its cover. Play low frequencies with an audio oscillator (or other source) so students gathered around can actually see the diaphragm vibrating. (This is most impressive the first time it is seen!)

DEMONSTRATION [26-3]: Hold a long aluminum rod (a meter or so) horizontally at its midpoint and strike its end with a hammer. You excite vibrations that travel and reflect back and forth along the length of the rod. The sustained sound heard is the due to energy "leaking" from the ends, about 1% with each reflection. So at any time the sound inside is about 100 times as intense as that heard at the ends. (This is similar to the behavior of light waves in a laser.) Shake it to and fro and illustrate the Doppler effect.

DEMONSTRATION [26-4]: Rub some pine pitch or rosin on your fingers and stroke the same aluminum rod. If you do it properly, it will "sing" quite loudly. Do this while holding the rod at its midpoint, then at different places to show harmonics. (Of course you have practiced this first!)

DEMONSTRATION [26-5]: Show the ringing doorbell suspended in a bell jar that is being evacuated of air (Figure 26.6).

Media that Transmit Sound: While the loudness of sound diminishes from the ringing doorbell, discuss the movement of sound through different media — gases, liquids, and solids (vibrating Ping-Pong balls analogy). Ask why sound moves faster in warm air [faster-moving balls take less time to bump into one another].

Speed of Sound: Discuss the speed of sound through different media — four times as fast in water than in air — about eleven times as fast in steel. The elasticity of these materials rather than their densities accounts for the different speeds. Cite how the American Indians used to place their ears to the ground to hear distant hoofbeats. And how one can put the ear to a track to listen for distant trains.

Sound travels faster in moist air than in dry air. Why? [Because H_2O molecules move faster than N_2 or O_2. This shortens the time between collisions that transmit the sound energy.] But why do H_2O molecules move faster? Use the "check-your-neighbor routine" and see if you can prod your students into applying some good physics here. [H_2O molecules have less mass (18 amu) than O_2 (32 amu) and N_2 (28 amu). At the same temperature, molecules would have the same KE, and the less massive would move faster. That is because less m means more v for same KE in KE = $1/2$ mv^2. Or by the principle of exaggeration: If an elephant and a mouse run with the same KE (so they would do equal work in colliding into a barn door), which of the two must be running with the greater speed?]

Discuss the speed of sound and how we can estimate the distance from a thunder storm. [$d = vt$ = 340 m/s x t].

DEMONSTRATION [26-6]: Show the effect of different speeds of sound through different gases by singing and talking after inhaling a light gas (He), and then a heavy gas (SF_6). Be sure to conclude your demonstration with the heavier SF_6 by tipping your body head down so all the gas will pour out of your lungs. This should impress your students.

Forced Vibration, Natural Frequency, and Resonance: Introduce the phenomenon of forced vibration by striking an unmounted tuning fork and then holding it firmly with its base against your lecture table or the chalkboard. Then follow this up by doing the same with the mechanical part of a music box. Turning the handle when it is held in air and then placed on your table or chalkboard is impressive.

Acknowledge the natural frequencies of the prongs of the music box "comb," and of different tuning forks — and of objects around the room. Compare the sounds of a couple of pennies dropped on a hard surface — one dated before 1981 and one after. The old penny is made of 95% copper and 5% zinc, which sounds noticeably different than the new pure zinc core pennies plated with copper.

The ear can discriminate among more than 300 000 tones!

DEMONSTRATION [26-7]: Show resonance with a pair of tuning forks, explaining how each set of compressions from the first fork push the prongs of the second fork in rhythm with its natural motion. Compare this to pushing somebody on a playground swing. Illuminate the forks with a strobe light for best effect!

When you are adjusting the frequency of one of your tuning fork boxes, by moving the weights up or down the prongs, call attention to the similarity of this with tuning a radio receiver. When one turns the knob to select a station, one is adjusting the frequency of the radio set to resonate with the frequency of incoming station signals.

Cite other examples of resonance; the chattering vibration of a glass shelf when a radio placed on it plays a certain note; the loose front end of a car that vibrates at only certain speeds; crystal wine glass shattering by a singer's voice; troops marching in step in bridge crossing.

Conclude your treatment of resonance with the exciting film loop *The Tacoma Narrows Bridge Collapse*.

(This is a good break place.)

[**Transparency 54**, Figure 26.13 on wave interference]

Interference: Review interference by sketching overlapping sine curves on the board (as in Figure 26.13, or more simply like Figure 25.10 of the previous chapter). Now you're ready for a series of fantastic demonstrations — perhaps the most unforgettable of your course!

DEMONSTRATION [26-8]: Play music via a very small naked speaker, a few centimeters in diameter, connected to the auxiliary output of a portable cassette recorder. The music will sound tinny. Then produce a baffle (large flat piece of cardboard or whatever) with a hole slightly smaller than the size of the speaker cut in its middle. Place the speaker behind the hole and note the much improved sound quality. The baffle reduces the interference between the back and front waves.

Explain that a radio loudspeaker produces waves from both its front and its rear that are 180° out of phase. When it producing a compression in front, it is producing a rarefaction in back, and vice versa. When sound reaches your ears from both the front and back of a speaker, destructive interference occurs. This is most pronounced for long waves where the different distances traveled from speaker to you are relatively small. (Sound will both diffract around the speaker and reflect from surfaces behind the speaker. Diffraction is enhanced for long waves.) The result is that a naked loudspeaker tends to sound tinny because it produces little sound energy for wavelengths much longer than its diameter. The long-wavelength base notes are canceled. This cancellation is notably reduced when the baffle is introduced.

DEMONSTRATION [26-9]: Now place the same naked speaker behind the hole in a small closed box to show even better quality. The speaker enclosure is a so-called "infinite baffle", which prevents rear waves from interfering with front waves.

Most popular speaker enclosures are more complex than simple boxes. Whatever their features, your class now knows why speakers are mounted in enclosures!

DEMONSTRATION [26-10]: Play mono music from a cassette recorder (or any monophonic amplifier) via a pair of common enclosed stereo speakers side by side facing the class. (1) Play one speaker. (2) Then play both in phase. The resulting sound is slightly louder than with one speaker. (3) With a switch or otherwise, reverse the leads to one of the speakers to reverse its phase. The sound is much less intense than from the single speaker. (4) With speakers still facing forward, try different separation distances and illustrate the wavelength dependence of the interference. You'll increase the loudness of sound heard by increasing the distance between the speakers. Sound with wavelengths greater than the distance between speakers is canceled; waves shorter than the separation distance are not totally canceled. Note the variations in the quality of the sound heard. (5) Now for the grand finale, face the speakers toward each other with only a small gap between them. Play one, then both in phase. No big deal. Now reverse the polarity of one of the speakers. The result is almost total silence. Sound at virtually all wavelengths is being canceled by destructive interference. As you pull them apart and increase the distance between them, shorter wavelengths avoid total destructive interference, and the sound level increases. Spectacular!

[**Transparency 55**, Figure 26.16 on beats]

Beats: Interference and beats are nicely shown with an oscilloscope trace of a pair of sound sources slightly out of sync.

DEMONSTRATION [26-11]: Show beats as Paul Robinson does by bouncing laser light off a pair of vibrating tuning forks. Quite lively!

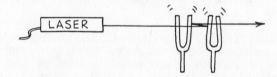

More Think-and-Explain Questions

1. Why do flying bees buzz?
 Answer: Bees buzz when in flight because they flap their wings at audio frequencies.

2. Why is an echo weaker than the original sound?
 Answer: An echo is weaker than the original sound because sound spreads and is therefore less intense with distance. If you are at the source, the echo will sound as if it originated on the other side of the wall from which it reflects (just as your image in a mirror appears to come from behind the glass). It is weaker still because the wall is not perfectly reflecting.

3. Your neighbor whispers in your ear. To sound just as loud, how much louder does your friend's voice have to be to be if she is ten times farther away?
Answer: Ten times farther means one-hundredth the intensity for the same whisper, in accord with the inverse-square law, so she'll have to speak 100 times louder.

More Think and Solves

1. What is the wavelength of a 680-Hz tone in air? What is the wavelength of a 68,000 Hz ultrasound wave in air?
Answer: Wavelength = speed/frequency = (340 m/s)/680 Hz = 1/2 m. For a 68,000-hertz wave; wavelength = (340m/s)/68,000 Hz = 0.005 m = 1/2 cm.

2. A bat flying in a cave emits a sound pulse and receives its echo in 1 second. How far away is the cave wall?
Answer: 15. Assuming the speed of sound to be 340 m/s, the cave is 170 meters away. This is because the sound took 1/2 second to reach the wall (and 1/2 second to return). Distance = speed x time = 340 m/s x 1/2 s = 170 m.

3. An sea vessel surveys the ocean bottom with ultrasonic sound that goes at 1530 m/s in seawater. How deep is the water if the time delay of the echo from the ocean floor is 4 seconds?
Answer: The ocean floor is 3060 meters deep. The 4-second time delay means that the sound reached the bottom in 2 seconds. Distance = speed x time = 1530 m/s x 2 s = 3060 m. (Note similarity with T&S 3 in the text)

4. A rule for estimating the distance in kilometers between an observer and a lightning stroke is to divide the number of seconds in the interval between the flash and the thunder by 3. Is this rule correct?
Answer: The rule is correct: this is because the speed of sound in air (340 m/s) can be rounded off to 1/3 km/s. Then, from distance = speed x time = (1/3) km/s x (number of seconds). Note that the time in seconds divided by 3 yields the same value.

Objectives

- Describe the dual nature of light.
- Explain why it is much more difficult to measure the speed of light than to measure the speed of sound.
- Describe the relation between light, radio waves, microwaves, and X rays.
- Explain what happens to light when it enters a substance and how the frequency of the light affects what happens.
- Describe the conditions for a) solar and b) lunar eclipses.
- Cite evidence that light waves are transverse.
- Explain why Polaroid sunglasses are helpful in cutting sun glare from horizontal surfaces such as water and roads.

Possible Misconceptions to Correct

- Light and sound have the same wave nature but have different frequencies.
- Light is fundamentally different than radio waves, microwaves, and X rays.
- Light passes through transparent materials in a way similar to bullets passing through materials.
- Polarized light is a different form of light.

Demonstration Equipment

- [27-1] Swinging balls apparatus.
- [27-2] Rubber tubing and a grating (from an oven or refrigerator) to pass it through.
- [27-3] Three sheets of poloraid (the larger the better — like a square foot each).
- [27-4] Slide projector and 2 x 2-inch slides made of poloroids; crumpled cellophane, and/or shiny Scotch tape (both of which discern polarized light).

Introduction

Some teachers begin their physics course with light, a topic that has a greater appeal than mechanics to many students. Your course could begin with this chapter and continue through the following chapters of Unit IV, or you could pick up Chapters 25 and 26 before finishing the sequence of this unit. Be flexible. The reason for jumping in at this chapter is to avoid the more technical nature of Chapter 25. This sequence, Chapter 27, 25, 26, 28 - 31, is a gradual entrance to the study of physics. If this chapter is used as a launch point, only the definitions of speed and frequency need to be introduced. In addition, give a demonstration of resonance with a pair of tuning forks. Your students will then experience resonance, which will be a jumping off place to understand explanations of the interaction of light and matter. Note the "depth of the plow" in the treatment of light transmission, reflection, and absorption. The aim is not to separate and name these categories, but to get into the physics. Your students will get into some rather deep physics in this chapter — a deepness they can understand. Understanding more than one may expect, and discovering more than one thought there was, is a real joy of learning. So this should be an enjoyable chapter — the reason some teachers may opt to begin their course here.

In reference to the visual illusions of Figure 27.23 on page 418 (also on Transparency 59): The vertical lines are parallel, and the tiles are not crooked. This can be seen by looking at the page at a grazing angle. The width of the hat is the same as its height, the "fork" and "rectangular" piece could not be made in the shop, and there are two THEs in the PARIS IN THE THE SPRING.

There is more to say about the equally bright rectangles.

The equally bright rectangles illustrate a phenomenon called *lateral inhibition*, wherein gradual differences in the intensity of light aren't perceived very well. The human eye can perceive brightness that ranges about 500 million to 1. The difference in brightness between the sun and the moon, for example, is about 1 million to 1. Lateral inhibition prevents the brightest places in the visual field from outshining the rest. Whenever a receptor cell on your retina sends a brightness signal to your brain, it also signals neighboring cells to dim their responses. In this way, you even

out your visual field, and you can discern detail in very bright areas and in dark areas as well. Lateral inhibition exaggerates the difference in brightness at the *edges* of places in your visual field. Edges, by definition, separate one thing from another. So we accentuate differences rather than similarities. The gray rectangle on the left in Figure 27.23 appears dimmer than the gray one on the right when the edge that separates them is in our view. But cover the edge with your pencil or your finger and they look equally bright. That's because both rectangles *are* equally bright; each rectangle is shaded lighter to darker, moving from left to right. Your eye concentrates on the boundary where the dark edge of the left rectangle joins the light edge of the right rectangle, and your eye-brain system assumes that the rest of the square is the same.

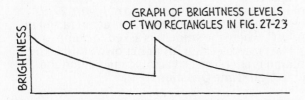

GRAPH OF BRIGHTNESS LEVELS OF TWO RECTANGLES IN FIG. 27-23

Is the way the eye picks out edges and makes assumptions about what lies beyond similar to the way we sometimes make judgements about other cultures and other people? Don't we in the same way tend to exaggerate the differences on the surface while ignoring the similarities and subtle differences within?

In lab, extend the simple hands-on activity *Shady Business* to the cause of eclipses. *Absolutely Relative* is a lab in which students use the computer to discover the inverse square law for light. In the lab *Shades* students will learn how polarized sunglasses work.

Suggested Lecture

Begin by stating that, strictly speaking, light is the only thing we see. And to understand what light is, we will first try to understand how it behaves. Call attention to the rainbow of colors that are dispersed by a prism or by raindrops in the sunlight. We know white light can be spread into a spectrum of colors. Ask your students to consider the world view of little creatures who could only see a tiny portion of the spectrum, creatures who would be color blind to all the other parts. Their world view would be very limited. Then state that we are like those little creatures, in that the spectrum of colors we can see are a tiny portion of the electromagnetic spectrum — less than a tenth of one percent! We are color blind to the other parts. The instruments of science have extended our view of the other parts. These instruments are not microscopes and telescopes, for they enable closer viewing of the part of the spectrum we are familiar with. It is the infrared detecting devices, microwave and radio receivers, that allow us to explore the lower-frequency end of the spectrum, and ultraviolet, X-ray, and gamma-ray detectors that let us "see" the higher-frequency end. What we see without unaided eyes is a tiny part of what's out there in the world around us.

Electromagnetic Spectrum: Depart from the order in the book and call attention to Figure 27.4, the electromagnetic spectrum, and the tiny part that is light.

[**Transparency 57**, Figure 27.4]

[**Next-Time Question 27-1** treats EM radiation]

CHECK QUESTION: Where does sound fit in the electromagnetic spectrum? [It doesn't! Sound is a mechanical wave, a vibration of material particles. It too has a spectrum, only a small part of which is heard! Electromagnetic waves are not vibrations of material stuff, but are vibrations of pure energy (we will see in Chapter 37 that the energy is in the form of electric and magnetic fields — hence the name *electromagnetic waves*.)]

Speed of Light: Light is fast — too fast to measure over short distances with everyday devices. But over long distances, it can be measured without sophisticated equipment. Discuss Roemer's calculation (page 406).

[**Transparency 56**, Figure 27.3, Michelson's measurement of light speed]

[**Practice Book 27-1** on general light properties]

CHECK QUESTION: What would be the consequences of using a four-sided rotating mirror rather than the octagonal mirror? [It would have had to spin twice as fast because it would need to rotate 1/4 turn rather than 1/8 turn to direct the returning light into the eyepiece.]

Light and Transparent Materials: Recall your demonstration of sound resonance earlier (or if you haven't done this, demonstrate now the resonance of a pair of tuning forks). Sound resonance, which is experienced by your students, becomes the basis for understanding the interaction of light with matter. In some cases light strikes a material and rebounds, a phenomenon called *reflection* (Chapter 29). In other cases where light continues through the material, we call the material *transparent*.

Point out the value of scientific models in understanding physical phenomena. Hence the discussion of tuning forks, and imaginary springs that hold electrons to the nuclei of atoms. A model is not correct or incorrect, but useful or nonuseful. Models must be refined or abandoned as they fail to account for various aspects of a phenomenon.

Go over the explanations on page 410, and Figure 27.7.

DEMONSTRATION: Show the swinging balls apparatus that is usually used to ilustrate momentum and energy conservation. Here you are showing that the energy that cascades through the system of balls is analogous to light energy cascading through transparent matter. Just as the incident ball is not the same ball that emerges, the incident "photon" of light upon glass is not the same photon that emerges through the other side. Although too difficult to sense, slight interaction times between balls produces a slight time delay between incidence and emergence of balls. Likewise for light.

CHECK QUESTION: Why is light slow while in transparent materials such as water or glass? [According to the model treated in the text, there is a time delay between the absorption of light and its re-emission. This time delay serves to decrease the average speed of light in a transparent material. Similarly, the average speed of a basketball moving down a court depends on the holding time of each player.]

Opaque Materials: State that light generally has three fates when it is incident upon a material: (1) bounces off (reflects), (2) is transmitted through the material, and (3) is absorbed by the material. Usually a combination of all three fates occurs. When absorption occurs, the vibrations given to electrons by incident light are often great enough to last for a relatively long time, during which the vibratory energy is shared by collisions with neighboring atoms. The absorbed energy warms the material.

CHECK QUESTION: Why is a black tar road hotter to the touch than a pane of window glass in the sunlight? [Sunlight is absorbed and turned into internal energy in the road surface, but transmitted through the glass to somewhere else.]

Shadows: Illustrate the different shadows cast by small and large sources of light. Ask why there appears no definite shadow of students' hands when held above their desks, and relate this to the multiple sources and and diffused light in the room.
Discuss solar and lunar eclipses after the lab *Shady Business.*

CHECK QUESTION: Does the earth cast a shadow in space whenever a lunar or solar eclipse occurs? [Yes, but not only when these events occur — the earth, like all objects illuminated by light from a concentrated source, casts a shadow. Evidence of this perpetual shadow is seen at these special times.]

[**Transparency 58** Polarization]

Polarization: Distinguish between polarized and nonpolarized light.

DEMONSTRATION [27-2]: Tie a rubber tube to a distant firm support and pass it through a grating (as from a refrigerator or oven shelf). Have a student hold the grating while you shake the free end and produce transverse waves. Show that when the grating *axis* and the plane of *polarization* are aligned, the wave passes. And when they are at right angles to each other, the wave is blocked.

DEMONSTRATION [27-3]: Cross a pair of Polaroids in front of a light source as shown in the left and center photos of Ludmila in Figure 27.19. Show this schematically with vectors on the chalkboard.

The explanation for the sandwiching of a third polaroid as shown in the right photo of Figure 27.19 is not given in the text. The question is again raised in Appendix C, where the student is asked to come to you as a last resort — after his or her own efforts. The explanation is as shown by vectors here (and in the answer to **Next-Time Question 27-2**).

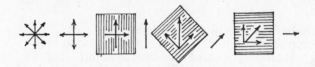

[**Practice Book 27-2** on polarization]

[**Next-Time Question 27-2** treats polarization]

[For an ideal polarizer, 50% of the incident light (electric) vectors are transmitted. That is why a Polaroid passes so little light compared to a sheet of window pane. The transmitted vectors are aligned and the light is polarized. So in the above diagram, 50% of the incident light vectors are transmitted by the first sheet, 50% cos θ gets through the second sheet, where θ is the angle between the polarization axes of both sheets, and (50% cos θ) cos φ gets through the third sheet, where φ is the angle between the polarization axes of the second and third sheet. The emerging vector represents the amplitude of the emerging light. For a value of 45° for both angles, the amplitude that emerges is 25% of the incident amplitude. Since the intensity of any wave is proportional to the square of the amplitude, the intensity emerging would be 25^2% or 6.25% the incident intensity. This and the fact that polarizers are less than ideal, is why the lovely smile of Ludmila is barely seen through the three-sheet system.]
An important goal of this course is to help students make distinctions between things. The practice of making distinctions need not be confined to physics, as is indicated in my statement about life success in Figure 27.20. I hope this helps to prompt students to make the important distinction between life success and financial success. The two are sometimes closely related, but seldom synomonous. We can all cite cases of despondent millionaires and cheery poor people (and vice versa!).

Reflected Polarized Light: Explain how the light that reflects from nonmetallic surfaces is polarized parallel to the plane of the surface. Do this by making an analogy of skipping flat rocks off a water surface only when the plane of the rock is parallel to the water surface. Then draw on the chalkboard the sets of sunglasses shown in the boxed question on page 417, and ask which are the best for reducing road glare. If you want to discuss the viewing of three-dimensional slides and movies, you'll have a transition to such by way of sunglasses C.

The following demonstration can be presented now as a follow up to polarization, or saved until you treat interference in Chapter 31. Either way, it can be one of the most memorable demonstrations of your course.

DEMONSTRATION [27-4]: The vivid colors that emerge from cellophane between crossed Polaroids makes a spectacular demonstration. Have students make up some 2 x 2 inch slides of cut and crinkled cellophane mounted on Polaroid material (which can be obtained inexpensively from suppliers such as Edmund Scientific Co.). Place the same in a slide projector and rotate a sheet of Polaroid in front of the projecting lens so that a changing montage of colors is displayed on the screen. Also include a showing of color slides of the interference colors seen in the everyday environment, as well as of microscopic crystals. This is more effective with two projectors with hand dissolving from image to image on the screen. Do this in rhythm to some music and you'll have an unforgettable lecture demonstration! [My students report that this is the best part of my course — to which, of course, I have mixed feelings. I would prefer that some of my explanations were the highlight of my course!]

DEMONSTRATION [27-5] While you have the lights out and the screen in view, shine a laser on a a small mirror glued to a rubber membrane stretched over a radio speaker. You'll produce fascinating lissajous-type patterns. Very impressive!

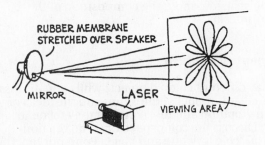

These demonstrations neatly usher you into the next chapter, the study of color.

More Think-and-Explain Questions

1. If a one-side-silvered plane mirror were used in the Michelson apparatus, how much faster would it have had to spin so reflected light would be seen in the telescope?
   Answer: Only twice as fast! When light incident at 45 degrees on it makes a round trip, the mirror must rotate 90 degrees in order to be at 45 degrees to the telescope. Unless the back side of the mirror

also reflects, the next pulse of light would not occur until the back side of the mirror turns through 270 degrees.

2. Pretend a person can walk only at a certain pace — no faster, no slower. If you time her uninterrupted walk across a room of known length, you can calculate her walking speed. If, however, she stops momentarily along the way to greet others in the room, the extra time spent in her brief interactions gives an *average* speed across the room that is less than her walking speed. How is this like light passing through glass? In what way is it not?
   Answer: The person walking across the room and pausing to greet others is analogous to the transmission-of-light model in that there is a pause with each interaction. But the same person that begins the walk ends the walk, but in light transmission there is a "death-birth" sequence of events as light is absorbed and "new light" is emitted in its place. The light to first strike the glass is not the same light that finally emerges. [Another analogy is a relay race, or mail going to San Francisco from Kansas City by Pony Express — a change of horse at each station.]

3. Lunar eclipses are always eclipses of a full moon. That is, the moon is always seen full just before and after the earth's shadow passes over it. Would it be possible to have a lunar eclipse when the moon is in its crescent or half-moon phase? Explain.
   Answer: No, a full moon occurs every 28 days when sun, earth, and moon are lined up. It is when the alignment is exact that eclipses occur — solar when the moon is between the sun and earth, and lunar when the earth is between the sun and moon. Then the moon is located in the earth's shadow. When the moon is in a half-moon stage, it is one-quarter of a month away from being in the earth shadow, and is even farther from the shadow when it is in its crescent stage.

4. What astronomical event would observers on the moon see at the time the earth was seeing a lunar eclipse?
   Answer: Moon observers would see the earth in the path of the sunlight and see a solar eclipse.

5. What astronomical event would observers on the moon see at the time the earth was seeing a solar eclipse?
   Answer: Moon observers would see a small shadow of the moon slowly move across the full earth. The shadow would consist of a dark spot (the umbra) surrounded by a not-as-dark circle (the penumbra).

6. Why do Polaroid sunglasses reduce glare, whereas unpolarized sunglasses simply cut down on the total amount of light reaching our eyes?
   Answer: Glare is composed largely of light polarized in the plane of the reflecting surface. Most glaring surfaces are horizontal (roadways, water, etc.,) so sunglasses with vertical polarization axesfilter the glare of horizontally polarized light. Conventional non-polarizing sunglasses simply cut down on overall light transmission by reflection and/or absorption.

28 Color

Objectives

- Explain why white and black are not colors in the sense that red and green are.
- Describe why the interaction of light with atoms or molecules of a material differs for different frequencies.
- Describe what factors determine whether a material will reflect, transmit, or absorb light of a particular color.
- Explain how color television screens are able to display pictures in full color even though the television tube produces only spots of red, green, or blue light.
- Define complementary colors and give examples of pairs.
- Distinguish between color mixing by subtraction and color mixing by addition.
- Explain why the sky is blue and why it changes color when the sun is low in the sky.
- Explain why water is greenish blue.
- Explain what the lines in a line spectrum represent and how such a spectrum can be used to identify the presence of an element.

Possible Misconceptions to Correct

- White and black are colors.
- Red, yellow, and blue light make white light.
- Red and green light make brown.

Demonstration Equipment

- [28-1] Singerman Color Apparatus (A box that casts three circles of light on a translucent screen, with an assortment of colored filters), or its equivalent.
- [28-2] Three lamps, red, green, and blue, that can be clamped to lecture table.
- [28-3] Two trays of tuning forks (for simulating light sources).
- [28-4] Transparent container of water, powdered milk, light source to provide a strong beam.
- [28-5] Either a single lecture-size diffraction grating, or enough small ones to pass out to the class, and an assortment of gas discharge tubes with an appropriate lamp to display them (atomic spectra).
- [28-6] Ultraviolet lamp and an assortment of objects that will both fluoresce and phosphoresce when so illuminated.

Introduction

The model chosen to explain color is the *oscillator* where electrons of an atom are forced to vibrate by the oscillations of light waves. (There is a vague difference between *oscillate* and *vibrate*. Vibrate usually refers to motion of matter (mechanical); oscillate usually refers to motion of electrons and the electromagnetic field. The source of a wave vibrates, and the wave oscillates.)

Be sure your students have seen and heard a demonstration of resonance with tuning forks. Resonance is a central idea in this chapter; the tuning fork model accounts for selective light reflection and transmission.

If you have not already done it, show a box with a white interior that has a hole in it, as shown back in Figure 22.13 on page 332.

A must-do demo: Mount three floodlights on your lecture table, red, green, and blue, of shades such that all three overlapping produce white on a white screen. Party lights, 75-watt colored bulbs, work fine. Subdue the room lighting and stand in front of the lamps, illuminated one at a time and show the interesting colors of the shadows. Impressive!

The chapter ends with a very brief treatment of atomic spectra — sort of tagged on the end as an extention of color. Be sure to do the lab *Flaming Out* with it. If you wish to continue further and cover fluorescence and phosphorescence, an optional lecture follows. Atomic spectra leads quite nicely to Unit VI, Atomic and Nuclear Physics. Jumping from this chapter directly to Chapter 37 has some merit if a short course is desired.

This interesting chapter can be taught very rigorously or it can be a plateau where physics is fun — I recommend the latter. Except for atomic spectra, it is not a prerequisite to chapters that follow.

In lab, *Flaming Out* will become familiar with atomic spectra, and see why astronomers know more about the composition of distant stars than geologists know about the composition of the earth's interior.

Suggested Lecture

Display different colored objects while you discuss the oscillator model of the atom, and the ideas of forced vibration and resonance as they relate to color. Discuss the color spectrum, and the non-spectral "colors" white and black. Point out that the color of nonluminous objects are the color of the light they reflect or the light they transmit. Discuss Figures 28.5 and 28.6.

Sunlight: The source of all light is accelerating electrons. The internal energy of the sun shakes its electrons so violently that waves of energy bathe the solar system and extend beyond. This is sunlight, which has a wide frequency range. Draw the radiation curve for sunlight on the board (Figure 28.7). Go further than the text, and divide the visible portion into thirds — a low frequency section that averages to red, a middle section that averages to green, and a higher frequency section that averages to blue. These three regions correspond to the three regions of color to which our retina is sensitive.

Hence we see that red, green, and blue are the three primary colors of white light.

The eye is most sensitive to yellow green, the peak frequency of sunlight. That is why today's fire engines are yellow-green in color. Our eyes are also most sensitive to the yellow-green light of sodium lamps. This means for a given wattage, we see more under sodium light than under the white light of an incandescant source.

Mixing Colored Lights: The primary colors are shown in Figure 28.8.

DEMONSTRATION [28-1]: Show the overlapping of the primary colors with the Singerman Color Apparatus (or its equivalent). Show complementary colors.

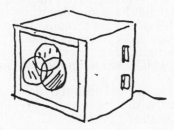

CHECK QUESTIONS: Ask several questions such as those at the top of page 425.

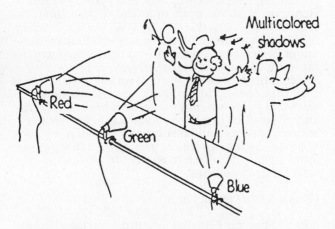

DEMONSTRATION [28-2]: With the room dark, stand between a white surface and three lamps, red, green, and blue, that are at least a meter apart. Better understanding results if you turn the lamps on one at a time, discussing what is seen at each stage. Turn on the red lamp and view your black shadow. Then turn on the green lamp and show that the black shadow cast by the red light is now illuminated by green light (as if the red light were casting a green shadow — strange at first). Note the shadow cast by the green light is not black like the room with lights off, but red like the red that was there before the green light was switched on! Most interesting, note the yellow everywhere where red and green overlap. Then turn on the blue light and the yellow background becomes white. Now you have a third shadow. Can your students account for the colors of your shadow?

[**Transparencies 60 through 66**, Figures 28.8, 28.9, 28.10, 28.11, Table 28.1 and color overlays of Figure 28.12 — good stuff]

[**Next-Time Question 28-1** colored shadows]

[**Practice Book 28-1** colored shadows]

Mixing Colored Pigments: Now we address color mixing as it relates to early finger painting experience (blue + yellow = green; red + yellow = orange; red + blue = purple). This was probably the only color mixing information previously given to your students. Distinguish between the colors that we see as a result of absorption (color mixing by subtraction), and the effect of superposing colored lights (color mixing by addition).

Discuss Figure 28.11.

Pass a magnifying glass around and look at the cyan, magenta, and yellow dots that make up the colors on the color plates in the chapter, and of magazines and the like.

Not mentioned in the text, the eye can distinguish nearly 8 million differences in color.

There are no blue pigments in the feather of a blue jay. Instead there are tiny alveolar cells in the barbs of its feathers that scatter light — mainly high-frequency light. So a blue jay is blue for the same reason the sky is blue — scattering. Interestingly enough, although brown eyes in people are due to pigments, the blue in blue eyes is similarly due to scattering from tiny spheres in the iris.

Blue-Sky Lecture Skit (Demo [28-3]): Here's where your showmanship comes in handy. Place a variety of six tuning forks at one end of your lecture table — call them "red," "orange," "yellow," etc., to "violet." Ask your class what "color" sound they would hear if you struck all the tuning forks in unison. Your class should answer, "White." Then suppose you have a mirror device around the forks so that when you "light" (strike) them again, a beam of sound travels down the length of your lecture table. Ask what "color" they will hear. Several might say "White" again, but state that if there is no medium to scatter the beam that they will hear nothing (unless, of course, the beam is directed toward them). Now place a tray of tuning forks at the opposite end of your lecture table (the tray I use is simply a 2 x 4 piece of wood, about a third meter long, with about a dozen holes drilled in it to hold a dozen tuning forks of various sizes). Ask your class to pretend that the ends of your lecture table are 150 million km apart, the distance between the earth and the sun. State that your tray of assorted tuning forks represents the earth's atmosphere — point to the tuning forks, calling out their "colors;" "blue," "violet," "blue," "blue," "red," "blue," "violet," "blue," "green," "blue," "violet," and so forth emphasizing the

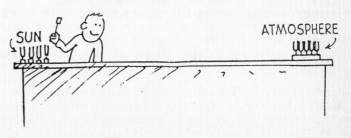

preponderance of blue and violet forks. Your tray of forks is perpendicular to the imaginary beam from the sun (representing the "thin" atmosphere seen by the sun at midday). Walk to the sun end of the table and again pretend to strike the forks and show how the beam travels down the table and intercepts and scatters from the atmospheric tuning forks in all directions. Ask what "color" the class hears. And you have a blue sky: especially if they're a bit deficient in hearing violet.

FORKS LIKE THIS FOR "THIN" ATMOSPHERE

[**Transparency 67**, Figure 28.16, red sunsets]

Red Sunset: Sketch a rendition of Figure 28.16 on the board, and show that at sunset the sunlight must go through many kilometers of air to reach an observer — that blue light is scattered all along these kilometers. What frequencies survive, you ponder. Then back to your sun and earth forks on the lecture table. Select a student (a cooperative one, of course) from the class to sit in back of the tray of earth forks. State to the class that your volunteer represents an earth observer at sunset. Go back to the sun forks which you pretend to strike. Down the table comes the beam, which you follow. Whap, into the earth's atmosphere where most of it scatters throughout the classroom. Again, ask the class what "color" they "hear." "Blue," is the answer, correct. Now you ask your volunteer what color he or she heard. "White," is the correct answer! The thin noon-time atmosphere did little to the white beam from the sun. Fine! Now rotate the tray of forks that represent the earth's atmosphere 90 degrees to simulate a thicker atmosphere. Go back to your sun and repeat the process. When your light reaches the earth tuning forks, ask your class what color they hear. (Although blue is still the correct answer, many will say orange. But not so from their vantage point.) Emphasize that blue is still the color they see because of the preponderance of blue forks, seen from any angle except straight on. Now ask your volunteer what color he or she hears. "Orange," is the answer! Your demonstration has been a success. By "experiment" you have proved your point. Your student volunteer has simply heard a composite of the lower-frequency left-over colors after the class received most all the higher-frequency blues. So the pretty colors at sunset are what? Left-over colors!

DEMONSTRATION [28-4]: Shine a beam of white light through a colloidal suspension of a very small quantity of instant nonfat dry milk in water, to show the scattering of blue and transmission of orange. Students will see the beam in the water turn blue as they see the spot of light cast on the wall turn orange. Impressive.

Point out that the sky looks blue only when viewed against the blackness of space (or the darkness of distant mountains, in which case the mountains appear blue). The blue is really not very bright, as is reported by astronauts who see no blue when looking straight downward from orbit. Then the brightness of reflected earth light overwhelms the weak blue.

The Violet Sky: Compare the molecules in the atmosphere to tiny bells; when "struck," they "ring" with high frequencies. They "ring" most at violet, and next at blue. We're better at "hearing" blue, so we "hear" a blue sky. On the other hand, bumble bees and other creatures with good vision in violet see a violet sky. So if we were better at seeing violet, our sky would be violet.

White Clouds: Larger molecules and particles, like larger bells, ring at lower frequencies. Very large ones ring in the reds. In a cloud there are a wide assortment of particles — all sizes. They ring with all colors. Ask your class if they have any idea why clouds are white! (Cumulus clouds are composed of droplets and are white because of the multitude of particle sizes, but higher-altitude cirrus clouds are composed of ice crystals, which like snow reflect all frequencies.)

Discuss the blueness of distant dark mountains and the yellowness of distant snow-covered mountains (Boxed questions, page 435).

Greenish-Blue Water: Water absorbs infrared. It also absorbs some visible light, nearer the red end of the color spectrum. Take away red from white light and you are left with the complementary color — cyan. Hence the sea looks cyan, or greenish-blue. Interestingly enough, deep down there is no red left in white light, so things that look red in sunlight look black under deep water. A red crab and black crab have the same appearance on the ocean floor.

Interestingly enough, tropical waters have a deeper cyan than cooler waters. That's because warmer water is a purer water in the sense it has less oxygen and disolved air in it than cooler water. The greater amount of oxygen and disolved air in cooler waters not only changes its optical properties, but supports more organisms, which makes cooler water ecologically richer in nutrients.

(This is a good break point.)

Atomic Spectra: Cite that a century ago the chemical composition of the stars were thought to be forever beyond our knowledge — and now today we know as much about their composition as we do earth's. This is because the light emitted by all things are atomic fingerprints, and reveal their atomic sources. These fingerprints are atomic spectral lines (Figure 28.21).

Make an analogy of light emission with the emission of sound by tiny bells. If the bells are made to ring all at once while they are crammed together in a box, the sound will be discordant. The same is true of light emitted by atoms that are crammed together in a solid (or liquid) state. There is a spread of frequencies, so we get a wide radiation curve, such as that from the sun in Figure 28.7. The light is "smudged," and appears white. (Likewise, the sounding of a wide range of sound frequencies is called *white noise.*) When bells are far apart from one another, however, the sound they emit is pure and unmuffled. So it is with atoms in the gaseous state that emit light. The light emitted by glowing atoms in the gaseous state can be separated into discrete pure colors with a spectroscope.

DEMONSTRATION [28-5]: Show the spectra of gas discharge tubes with a large diffraction grating (I use an 8 1/2 x 11 inch sheet of plastic grating from Edmund Scientific Company in New Jersey). Or pass small gratings among the class. Follow this up with individual student viewing of spectral lines of discharge tubes seen with a spectroscope. The spectrum of helium gas is impressive.

Atomic Excitation (Optional): The text doesn't get into the details of the atomic excitation that produces the light analyzed by the spectroscope. You can present a simplified Bohr model of the atom, and explain how impact by particles can boost electrons to higher shells. Lift your book above the table and state the higher it is raised, the more PE it has. When released, the book slams onto the table and makes a sound. In an analogous way, when electrons in an atom return to lower PEs, they give off energy — but not as sound. They emit light.

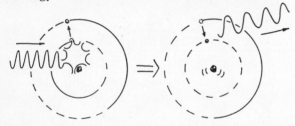

The different energy levels in the atom are like different steps. When a ball bounces down a stairway, it gives off different sounds for different steps. Likewise for an electron making transistions in the atom. Every transition corresponds to a different color — a different spectral line. Light analyzed with a spectroscope truly gives us the fingerprint of atoms!

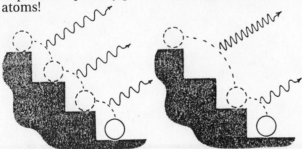

Cite examples of spectroscope use — how very minute quantities of materials are needed for chemical analysis — how tiny samples of ores are sparked in carbon arcs and the light directed through prisms or diffraction gratings to yield precise chemical composition — and note their use in fields as diverse as chemistry and criminology.

Fluorescence (Optional): Consider extending the textbook material and consider the stimulation of light by higher-frequency and therefore more energetic light — fluorescence. Show some fluores-cent materials in the room light. Explain the role of light from overhead lamps — shaking the electrons in the molecules in the material that produces not only reflection, but emission — hence the term *day-glow* that sometimes describes fluorescent paints. (As the footnote on page 438 states, there is more going on here than forced vibration of electrons in the molecules. Electrons are being dislodged from their stable orbits and being kicked to higher-energy orbits. We say they are *excited*. It is when they de-excite and return to lower-energy levels that they emit light. The frequency of the emitted light is directly proportional to the difference in the energy states the electron traverses in the atom.)

CHECK QUESTION: Would higher-frequency light produce more glowing, and why? [Yes, higher-frequency light is more energetic light (this idea will be treated in detail in Chapter 38).]

DEMONSTRATION [28-6]: Show fluorescent materials illuminated with an ultraviolet lamp (black light). Discuss the observations with the black light still on, and then extinguish the light so the room is totally dark. Ask what is happening. [High-energy ultraviolet light incident upon the fluorescent materials knocks electrons in the material up to higher energy states. When the electrons return to lower states, light is emitted that has a frequency directly proportional to the difference in energy between the upper and lower states]. Illuminate some phosphorescent materials.

Discuss phosphorescence and cite common examples — watch and clock faces, light switches, and nite-lites, etc. In the case of phosphorescent materials, there is a time delay between excitation and de-excitation, that produces the familiar afterglow of these materials when excited. Some watch faces, not common however, are activated by radioactive minerals. (Such watches are not recommended, and are harmful — especially when sleeping with your eyes near your wrist! Eyes are very prone to radiation damage.)

"Oral Borealis": This must be done with a mirror in the complete dark, so perhaps it will be a home project. Buy a roll of wintergreen-flavored Life Savers (in the green roll). After your eyes have adapted to the dark, bite down on a candy while looking in the mirror. The Life Saver will spark and glitter as you chew! (You can't get a shock — only cavities.)

This form of atomic excitation is called "tribolu-minescence," (Greek *tribein* meaning "to rub" and Latin *lumin* meaning "light.") This is light created by friction. When the candy crystals are crushed, nitrogen atoms give off ultraviolet light, as well as violet and blue. The wintergreen oil (methyl salicylate) is fluorescent and converts the ultraviolet light (invisible) into visible blue light, adding to the effect. The excitation of nitrogen in the upper atmosphere near the earth's poles is what makes the glowing aurora borealis, so, in a sense, you have a mini-aurora in your mouth.

The same blue glow can be seen if you unroll masking tape in the dark. The blue glow occurs where the tape is unsticking from itself. This does not work with all masking tapes, however, and particularly not "Magic Mending Tape."

More Think-and-Explain Questions

1. Why are black and white not listed as colors?
   Answer: Because they are not parts of the color spectrum. Black is the absence of light, and white is a composite of all colors.

2. On a TV screen, red, green and blue spots of fluorescent materials are illuminated at a variety of relative intensities to produce a full spectrum of colors. What dots are activated to produce yellow? Magenta? White?
   Answers: Red and green produce yellow; red and blue produce magenta; red, blue, and green produce white.

3. If the sky on a certain planet in the solar system were normally orange, what color would sunsets be?
   Answer: An orange sky indicates preferred scattering of low frequencies. At sunset when the scattering path is longer, very little low-frequency light would get to an observer. The less-scattered high frequencies would produce a bluish sunset.

4. When white light is shone on red ink dried on a glass plate, the color that is transmitted is red. But the color that is reflected is not red. What is it?
   Answer: The reflected color is white minus red, or cyan.

5. What causes the beautiful colors sometimes seen in the burning of various materials in a fireplace?
   Answer: Atoms of the material are heated to glowing, wherein different kinds of atoms give off their own characteristic colors.

6. What is the evidence for the claim that iron exists in the atmosphere of the sun?
   Answer: Iron spectral lines are found in the solar spectrum.

29 Reflection and Refraction

Objectives

- Distinguish between what happens to light when it strikes a metal surface and when it strikes glass or water.
- Given the direction of light striking a reflective surface, predict the path of the reflected light.
- Explain why the image formed by a mirror is virtual.
- Describe the conditions for diffuse reflection.
- Give examples of ways to control reflected sound.
- Explain the change in direction of a water wave when it crosses a boundary between deep and shallow water.
- Give examples of refraction of sound waves and its effects.
- Give examples of refraction of light and its effects.
- Explain how a prism separates white light into colors.
- Describe the conditions for a rainbow.
- Describe the process of total internal reflection.

Possible Misconceptions to Correct

- The (average) speed of light is constant in all materials.
- The average speed of light and instantaneous speed of light in a material is the same.
- The law of reflection is restricted to plane surfaces.
- Both sound and light travel only in straight lines.
- A prism changes (rather than separates) white light into colors.
- A rainbow is a physical thing that can be approached and grasped if you're lucky.

Demonstration Equipment

- [29-1] Glass tank of water with dye added, prism, mirror, and light source (laser).
- [29-2] Root beer mug filled with root beer (or any dark liquid), and glass tank of water.
- [29-3] "Magic Elixir" that consists of 590 ml carbon tetrachloride and 410 ml benzene (approximately 10:7 by volume), which has the same index of refraction as pyrex, in a 1 or 2-liter beaker. Three or four small pyrex test tubes. Hamer and napkins. (Caution: both carbon tet and benzine are hazardous.)
- [29-4] Rainbow sticks (shown to the right).

Introduction

The treatment of reflection in this chapter is brief, with scant applications to convex and concave mirrors. The treatment of refraction is supported by many examples of both sound and light. The oscillator model of the atom is used to explain refractive index. If you haven't demonstrated resonance with a pair of tuning forks on sound boxes, consider doing so now.

As a brief treatment on light, this chapter can stand on its own. In this case the behavior, rather than the nature of light, is emphasized.

Assign Activities 2 and 3 on page 461 as home projects. These ask for the minimum size mirror needed to view ones full-length image. I regret to report, that seldom do I find half of my class answering these two questions correctly — even when I first emphasize that the results will be surprising, and that if they are careful they will learn something about their image in a mirror that all their lives has likely escaped their notice (that the size of the mirror is independent of their distance from it). I ask them to mark the mirror where they see the top of their head and bottom of their chin, and then compare the distance between the marks with the height of their face. And then to step back and see what effect there is (if any) with increased distance from the mirror. Still, most students miss it. The fact that distance doesn't change the answer is simply not believed by some students — in spite of the evidence to the contrary. Perhaps like many visual illusions, their belief in their uninvestigated explanations are so strong that they will not see what is there even when it is explicitly pointed out to them. This has somewhat disturbing connotations. Are your students more perceptive than mine? Would doing this in 8th or 6th grade class help? In any event, when you discuss the answer, bring into class a full-length mirror or pass a few small mirrors among your students. It's worth the extra effort.

If you're into ripple-tank demos, do as Connecticut physics teachers Jon Wallace and Jim Harper do and use a K-Mart "Prism Frame" (less than six bucks). The frame is clear plastic a little more than an inch deep. Put water in it and mount on an overhead projector. Put strips of screen mesh around the edges to reduce unwanted reflected waves. Use a large-diameter wooden dowel to generate waves. A gentle roll forward followed by a quick roll backward produces a nice single pulse. You control the frequency of additional pulses. If you wish to make custom-designed plexiglass shapes to show diffraction, Jon and Jim suggest a material called Lenax (Plexiglass often doesn't respond well to drilling or cutting).

An explanation of why a rainbow is bow-shaped is aided with this simple apparatus that is easily constructed: Stick three colored dowels into a sphere of clay, strofoam, wood, or whatever that represents a raindrop. One dowel is white, one violet, and the other red, to represent incident white light and refracted red and violet. The angles between dowels

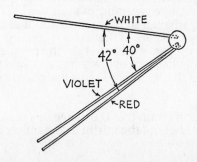

is shown in the sketch. A student volunteer crouching in front of your chalkboard shows the class how the only drops that cast light to him or her originate in drops along a bow-shaped region. (More on this in the lecture below.)

More information on rainbows: The different sizes of raindrops affect the proportions of color seen in a rainbow. Drops between 0.5 and 1 mm diameter create the most brilliant colors. Drops of 1-2 mm diameter show very bright violet and green with scarcely any blue. Larger drops are poor rainbow producers because they depart from a truly spherical shape due to flattening by air pressure and the oscillations they undergo. In drops smaller than 0.5 mm, red is weak. In the 0.02-0.3-mm range, red is not seen. At 0.08-0.10 mm, the bow is pale with only violet vivid. Smaller drops produce weak bows with a distinct white stripe. And as a sheet of Polaroid will show, rainbows are polarized.

An interesting reference on rainbows is *Light and Colour*, by M. Minnaert, Dover 1954 ISBN 0-486-20196-1. An excellent set of 35-mm slides of rainbows, halos, and glories, is available from Blue Sky Associates, PO Box 429, Reading, MA 01867. You can preview these in Bob Greenler's book, *Rainbows, Halos, and Glories* (Cambridge University Press, 1980).

Lab activity *Images* treats the formation of virtual images, *Pepper's Ghost* deals with multiple reflections, and *Funland* investigates the properties of a circular spherical mirror (scarcely treated in the text). An application of multiple reflections is *The Kaleidoscope*, and *Satellite TV* treats the focusing properties of a spherical reflector.

If you are crimped for time, lab omissions for this chapter have less drawbacks than for other chapters.

Suggested Lecture

Reflection: Cite a ball bouncing on a street, or on the bank of a pool table. The angle of incidence equals the angle of rebound (reflection); same same for light (Figure 29.3).

[**Transparency 68**, Figures 29.1 and 29.2, reflection of waves]

Discuss panes of glass both transmitting and reflecting light. Reflection is more noticeable when its dark on the other side of the glass, and less noticeable when its light on the other side. Stress that the percentage reflected (about 4%) is the same in both cases, but in the first case the 4% is noticeable, and in the second it isn't — like stars that are really in the sky both day and night.

CHECK QUESTION: How do the one-way mirrors used in places like gambling casinos work? [They are partially silvered so they reflect about as much light as they transmit. If there is no light source behind the mirror, you cannot see the people there because reflected light overwhelms any light you might see of them. If they light a match, you can see them.]

Show by ray diagram that the image in a plane mirror is as far behind the mirror as the object is in front.

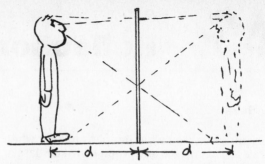

CHECK QUESTION: Why will a camera with a sonar or infrared range finder give poor results for taking a picture of yourself in a mirror? [The camera will focus on the mirror surface, where the sonar or infrared beam is reflected, to set the automatic focus. But your image is as far behind the mirror as you are in front.]

Investigate Figure 29.6 and point out the law of reflection along every facet of curved surfaces is the same as for flat surfaces. A single ray of light does not distinguish between a large area and the tiny part with which it interacts (similarly the world appears flat to a single observer on its surface).

[**Transparency 69**, Figure 29.4 and 29.6 mirror reflections]

[**Next-Time Questions 29-1—29-2** Reflection]

Cite the role of reflection for ghost signals on TV pictures. The signal from the broadcasting station can take more than one path to reach the antenna. If it bounces off buildings and other surfaces, it may not reach the antenna in phase with the direct signal — hence the multiple image.

Interesting thought: Because of the finite speed of light, your image in the mirror is always younger than you.

Diffuse Reflection: Show by a ray diagram that reflection from a rough surface is diffused. Point out that for every facet of the surface, the law of reflection holds (Figure 29.7). We see most of our environment by diffuse reflection. Cite the different appearance of a highly waxed floor and the same floor when the wax has worn off.

Ask if students have ever noticed while driving in a car on a rainy night that it is difficult to see the road ahead. The explanation involves diffuse reflection, and is a neat one. When the road is dry, it is rough, and light from the car headlights is diffused — some of it returning to the driver. But on a rainy night, the road has a water surface that acts as a mirror. The light is not diffusely reflected back to the driver, but is reflected ahead by the mirror-like surface. This has an added disadvantage to approaching drivers, and to yourself. Instead of the light from headlights being diffused in many directions, it is reflected into the eyes of oncoming motorists.

CHECK QUESTION: Would your book be easier to read if the pages were shinier? Why or why not? [No. There would be more glare and less softly diffusely reflected light.]

Reflection of Sound: The law of reflection also applies to sound. Walls that diffusely reflect sound are preferred in concert halls. Point out the interesting interplay between sound and light in the disks shown in Figure 29.12. Since both light and sound obey the same law of reflection, where its seen is where its heard.

Discuss echos, and multilple echos — reverberations.

CHECK QUESTION: Why does your voice sound fuller when singing in the shower? [Each note lasts slightly longer as your voice reverberates between the walls.]

[**Practice Book 29-1** Reflection]

Refraction of Sound: Refraction of any wave depends on changing its speed. Note the sound of a bugle being refracted both upward and downward in Figure 29.15. In the figure the reason for refraction is the change in speed through different air densities. It could also be because of different wind speeds. The upper illustration could represent faster ground winds, and the lower illustration faster upper winds. Listing all variables helps.

A useful application of sound refraction, ultrasound imaging, is replacing x-rays in probing the internal organs. This technique is useful in examining unborn children in pregnant women. This method seems to be relatively free of dangerous side effects.

Another interesting example of sound refraction is sonar in water which makes submarine detection very difficult. Thermal gradients in the ocean and the resulting refractions of sonar waves leaves gaps or "blind spots" in the water, which are used to advantage by submarines. But for this submarines would easily be detected by sonar.

CHECK QUESTION: What is the key factor for refraction (of any kind of wave)? [A change in wave speed.]

[**Transparency 70**, Figure 29.13 and 29.17 general refraction]

[**Practice Book 29-2, 29-3** Refraction]

[**Next-Time Questions 29-3—29-6** Refraction]

Refraction of Light: The change in (average) speed for light was established in Chapter 27, highlighted by Figure 27.7 back on page 410. Another way to treat this is: If a bullet is fired through a thick board, it will emerge with a speed that is less than its incident speed. This is clear enough — it loses energy in the board, as evidenced by the warm wood around the hole and the warm bullet. State that if light did the same thing, one could direct a beam of light into a bank of glass plates, it would slow with successive encounters, and a weak bit of light might gleem from the last plate. Ask why this doesn't happen. Recall the model of light passing thought the glass plate back in Figure 27.7 (or the additional Think and Explain Question #2, and answer, back on pages 126 and 127 of this manual). Be sure to stress that different frequencies of light travel at different speeds in a transparent material — red slowest, and blue and violet fastest (which is important information in the explanation of dispersion in a prism)

Cite the role of refraction in the atmosphere, and in a prism. Note that all this applies also to sound.

DEMONSTRATION [29-1]: Show examples of reflection, refraction, and total internal reflection with the usual apparatus — light source (laser), prisms, and a tank of water with a bit of fluorescene dye added.

DEMONSTRATION [29-2]: Show a thick root beer mug filled with root beer (or cola). Because of significant refraction of light from the glass mug to the air, the mug appears to contain more root beer than it actually does (Figure 29.19 right). You can betray this by immersing it in a tank of water. Because the light doesn't change speed as much in traveling through the glass mug to the water, you can better see the glass thick-ness. (This is similar to the bottles of Coke in T&E 10.) Fascinating!

DEMONSTRATION [29-3]: Prepare a "Magic Elixir" that consists of 590 ml carbon tetrachloride (caution!) and 410 ml benzene (approximately 10:7 by volume), which has the same index of refraction as pyrex. Prior to the students entering the classroom, the solution is poured into a beaker (1 or 2 liter) and three small pyrex test tubes are placed in the solution. They cannot be seen from a distance. You might do as Herb Ringel does and tell the class the liquid has a memory, because if a test tube is broken and the pieces placed in the liquid, the atoms will separate and within seconds rearrange themselves to reform the test tube! Napkins and hammers are available. Invariably, someone asks for a repetition, therefore the extra test tubes!

Total Internal Refraction: Depart from the order of the text and get into total internal refraction, as shown in your first tank-of-water demonstration. Ask your class to imagine how the sky would look from a lakebottom. For humor, above water we must turn our heads through 180 degrees to see from horizon to horizon, but a fish need only scan twice the 48 degree critical angle to see from horizon to horizon — which is why fish have no necks!

Fibre optics: Show some examples of light pipes, as shown in Figure 29.34. Discuss some of the many applications of these fibres, or "light pipes," particularly in telephone communications. Information not in the text: because of the higher frequencies of light compared to electric currents, a pair of glass fibers as thin as a human hair can carry 1300 simultaneous telephone conversations, but only 24 can be carried by a conventional copper cable. Signals in copper cables must be boosted every 4 to 6 kilometers, whereas re-amplification in lightwave systems occurs in 10 to 50-kilometer segments. For infrared optical fibers, the distance between regenerators may be hundreds or perhaps thousands of kilometers. Very transparent! Hooray for fibre optics!

Call attention to the fiber-optic nature of polar bear hairs, Link to Biology, page 459. What's white and black and warm all under? A polar bear under the Artic sun.

[**Transparency 71**, Figure 29.26 and 29.27, the rainbow]

The Rainbow: State that all rainbows are complete circles, but the ground gets in the way. I have seen complete circles of both primary and secondary bows from a helicopter over Kauai. Spectacular!

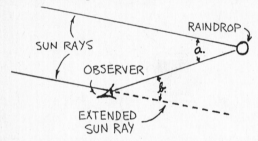

Point out that there are not distinct layers of color in the rainbow, but rather the colors merge from one hue to another. We separate the rainbow into the colors we have learned to identify.

A rainbow has depth. Rather than a segment of a disk in the sky, we look "through" it, as looking through the glass in a glass cone. The thicker it is, the move...

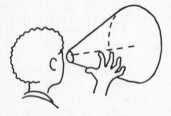

DEMONSTRATION [29-4]: Show the rainbow-sticks apparatus described earlier and compare it to the rainbow schematic drawing of Figure 29.26. The white stick represents incoming white light, and the red and violet sticks the refracted rays. Have a student volunteer crouch in front of the board as shown in the sketch. Place the ball near the chalkboard so the white dowel is perpendicular to the board (from the sun at the horizon for simplicity). Position the free end of the violet dowel so that it nearly meets the volunteer's eye.

State that a drop at this location refracts violet light to the eye. The question follows: are there other locations that will also refract violet light to the eye? Move the "drop" to other locations along the board while keeping the white dowel perpendicular to the board. It is easy to see that refracted violet from drops farther away miss the eye altogether. The only locations that send violet light to the eye are along a bow — which you trace with violet or blue chalk. This is easy to do if the students holds the end of the violet dowel near the eye while you scribe the arc in compass fashion.

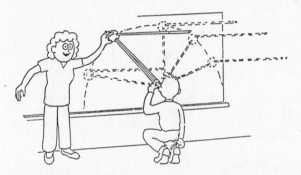

CHECK QUESTION: With the ball and dowels positioned at the top of the bow, ask where the volunteer must look to see red — above the violet, or below? [Above (2° to be exact).] Show this by moving the "drop" up, whereupon the red dowel lines up with the eye. Complete your demo by sweeping this wider bow with red chalk.

Enlist a second volunteer to crouch in front of the board at a different position. Show how this volunteer must look to different drops in the sky to see a rainbow. Ask the class if the two volunteers see the same rainbow. [No, each sees his or her own personal rainbow!] Do as Marshall Ellenstein does and quip that when one person says to another, "Look at the beautiful rainbow," an appropriate response is, "Move over and let me see!"

Rainbows cannot be seen when the sun is more than 42 degrees in the sky because the bow is below the horizon where no water drops are to be seen. Hence rainbows are normally seen early and late in the day. So we don't see rainbows in midday in summer in most parts of the world (except from an airplane, where they are seen in full circles).

Point out a significant yet commonly unnoticed feature about the rainbow — that the segment bounded by the bow is appreciably brighter than the rest of the sky. The rainbow is similar to the chromatic aberration around a bright spot of projected white light.

Extend rainbows to the similar phenomenon of the halo around the moon. Explain how the halo is produced by refraction of moonlight through ice crystals in the atmosphere. Note the important difference: whereas both refraction and internal reflection produce rainbows, only refraction produces halos. And whereas the observer is between the sun and the drops for seeing a rainbow, the ice crystals that produce halos are between the observer and the moon. Moonlight is refracted through ice crystals high in the atmosphere — evidence of the coldness up there even on a hot summer night.

More Think-and-Explain Questions

1. What kind of wind conditons would make sound more easily heard at long distances?
   Answer: When the wind traveling toward the listener is faster above the ground than at ground level. Then the waves are refracted downward, as shown in Figure 29.16.

2. Does light travel faster through the lower atmosphere or the upper atmosphere?
   Answer: Light travels faster through the upper atmosphere where there are less interactions with air.

3. When a fish looks upward at an angle of 45 degrees does it see the sky or does it see the reflection of the bottom underneath? Defend your answer.

Answer: 45° is less than the critical angle in water (48°), so the fish sees out into the air above. The view seen by the fish of the upper environment is bounded by the edge of a large circle — part of a 96° cone. A photographer's "fisheye lens" is so named because it similarly compresses a wide angle view.

4. Place a glass test tube in water and you can see the tube. Place it in transparent liquid benzene, and you can't see it. What does this tell you about the speed of light in the benzene and in the glass?
   Answer: The speeds are the same, so there is no refraction between the glass and benzene.

5. Does refraction appear to bend the pencil, or does it *really* bend it, as the cartoon suggests?
   Answer: Humor aside, the pencil appears bent only in the water!

30 Lenses

Objectives

- Distinguish between a converging and diverging lens.
- Distinguish between a real image and a virtual image formed by a lens.
- Given the focal length of a converging or diverging lens and the position of an object, construct a ray diagram that shows the position of the image.
- Give examples of how some optical instruments use lenses.
- Explain how the human eye focuses light.
- Explain the causes of nearsightedness, farsightedness, and astigmatism.
- Give examples of aberration in lenses.

Possible Misconceptions to Correct

- A lens can produce (rather than simply concentrate) energy.
- A lens is necessary for image formation.
- If part of a lens is covered, only part of an image can be seen.

Classroom Equipment

Several converging (and diverging) lenses to pass around the class

Demonstration Equipment

- [30-1] Prism and light source.
- [30-2] Model of eye (see sketch on next page).
- [30-3] Brightly-colored card sheets (3 or 4 colors).

Introduction

This chapter is an extension of the previous chapter and applies refraction to lenses, and introduces the ideas of ray optics. It may be omitted without consequence to the chapters that follow.

Just as it would be fruitless for a swimming coach to discuss the techniques of swimming away from the activity of swimming, it is fruitless to show the techniques of ray diagram construction without students constructing their own. And just as swimming motions are best made in water, your students should have a lens in hand, and an object and image to witness when they make their constructions. Ray diagrams are abstractions. Unless they are tied to experience, they are of questionable value. Let your treatment of this chapter be a class activity.

The class activity of calculating the sun's diameter by measurements taken of the sun's image through a pinhole is one of the most impressive of this course. Be sure to do it. It is a striking example of how the richness in life is not only looking at the world with wide-open eyes, but knowing what to look for. You are the guide to that richness, for you are their physics teacher. And how nice that your students can go home after class and announce to their parents that they calculated the sun's diameter with the use of a meterstick! Another example of the most profound concepts in physics being the simplest.

Begin your study of lenses with *Camera Obscura* followed by *Lensless Lens. Camera Obscura* will help your students understand the formation of images in both the eye and a single lens reflex (SLR) camera. *Air Lens* will reinforce the concept that light bends away from the normal when going from a more (optically) dense medium to a less dense medium — do this one only if you have ample time. If you introduce the workings of a lens with the computer program *Thin Lens*, your students should have a lens in their hand. *Bifocals* is a conceptual mirror image of *Funland* If time is short, have your students do one or the other or alternatively have half the class do one lab while the other half of the class does the other. Students will know how to find the focal length of a convex (positive) lens after doing the lab *Bifocals* and how to find the focal lens of a concave lens (negative) lens after doing*Where's the Point?* Interesting point: There is a Pinhole Journal (see the list of vendors listed in the TE of the lab manual). After doing the lab *Lensless Lens*, your students may want to consider joining!

Suggested Lecture

Begin with a demo.

> DEMONSTRATION [30-1]: Show how a prism refracts a ray of light. Do this with an actual prism, and then introduce ray tracing on the board.

Contrast the deviation of light by a prism with the absence of deviation by a pane of glass. Show that a pane only *displaces* light rays, and show how thicker panes produce greater displacements — evident with thick panes of glass in aquariums. Show how a lens behaves as a smooth curved prism (Figure 30.1).

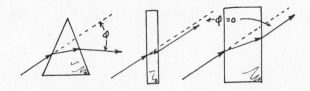

Image Formation: Confine the first part of your presentation to converging lenses. Pass some converging lenses around class and have students cast images of the windows on the wall, or ceiling lights on their desks. (Most find this fascinating.) Have them cast images of closer brightly illuminated objects (bright enough to cast a clearly seen image).

CHECK QUESTION: Is there a relationship between the image distance (distance from lens to place where sharp image appears) and the object distance (from object to lens)? [Yes, the farther the object, the nearer the image. Your students will learn that when an object is sufficiently far away, the image appears in the focal plane.]

Point to any part of a blank wall. Ask if there is an image on the wall of some particular bright object (that you identify on the other side of the room). It so happens there is — over *every* part of the wall. We don't see the image only because it is over-lapped by an infinite number of images of every-thing else in sight. The fascinating thing is that if the overlapping images were blocked, the image of the object in question would be seen. A light-tight barrier with a pin hole does just that. That is because the pin hole by virtue of its tiny size, prevents the passage of light rays that overlap.

Pass around the class a box with a pin hole and transluscent viewing screen on opposite ends. Describe with a simple ray diagram how images are formed, and why they are inverted. Discuss the pinhole camera activity at the back of the chapter. Note that the size of the hole compared to the distance to the viewing screen affects two things: the amount of light that makes the image, and how sharp it is. A larger hole will admit more light, but overlapping images through different parts of the hole reduce sharpness. Of course a large hole covered by a lens solves both problems. When this was discovered and cameras utilized lenses instead of pinholes (as they first did), the greater amount of light meant pictures could be taken faster — hence the name "snap shots."

Call attention to the round spots of light that are found beneath trees on a sunny day. This is worth bringing your class outside — really! Just as the cultivated ear appreciates music not really heard by others, and just as the trained touch of a physician feels irregularities beneath the skin that others miss, and just as the cultivated pallet tastes food that others are insensitive to, we see here that the trained eye sees what others miss. The spots of light beneath the tree brances are indeed circles if the sun is overhead, or stretched out circles (el-lipses) if the sun is low in the sky — literally images of the sun. This is more convincing at the time of a partial solar eclipse, in which case the images are crescents. What is happening is that openings between leaves in the trees behave as pinholes when the openings are small compared to their distances from the ground. As such, they cast images of the sun on the ground. Class interest at this point should be in high gear.

Poke a hole in a piece of cardboard and hold it in the sunlight. Note the circle of light on an area beneath. To convince your students that the cirlce is not merely the image of the hole itself, cut different shape circles — squares, stars, whatever. Held an appropriate distance away, the image remains circular. That the spot of light is truly an image of the sun is nicely seen when a partial solar eclipse occurs. Then the image is a crescent. At the time of a partial solar eclipse an array of crescents rather than ellipses fall on the ground beneath trees in the sunlight!

Now for a fantastic quantitative exercise. Hold up a meter stick and announce that measurements of the elliptical images and their distance from their pinholes, together with the knowledge that the sun is 150,000,000 km distant, provides a calcula-tion of the sun's diameter. To simplify this task, place a coin beneath the pinhole and adjust the distance of the pinhole from the coin to where it is exactly eclipsed by the sun's image (the short diameter of the ellipse should equal the diameter of the coin). This affords an accurate method of measuring the diameter of the solar image, for the diameter of the coin is easily measured. Here's the neat part: The ratio of image diameter to pinhole distance is the same as the ratio of the sun's diameter to 150,000,000 kilometers. We have one equation, one unknown. [Careful measurements will show the ratio of coin size to distance from the pinhole is about 1/108. It is then easy to show that the diameter of the sun is 1/108 of 150,000,000 km. The answer of approximately 14,000 km agrees with the accepted value (shown in Table B-1 in Appendix B).]

CLASS PROJECT: Have your class calculate the sun's diameter as described.

I think it is quite profound that a student of average ability armed only with a meter stick can calculate the diameter of the sun! Likewise for the moon, where the ratio is the same. The only difference is the moon-earth distance, 3.8×10^5 km.

[**Practice Book 30-1** is an exercise in the above — pinhole image of the sun and measurement of the sun's diameter]

Image Formation Through a Lens: Investigate what happens with more than one pinhole. You can do this by poking an extra hole in your pin-hole "camera," or poking an extra hole in a piece of cardboard that you hold between a bright region (window or overhead light) and a dark viewing area. Two holes will produce two images. Poke a third hole and you have three images. Many holes, like a piece of pegboard, produce many images — one for each hole. Here's the neat part: Place a convex lens behind (or in front of) the holes and show how all the images are focused in one place. At the proper distance they neatly overlap to produce a clear and brighter image. So an appropriately-placed lens simply directs a multitude of images atop one another!

You can go further. Choose a bright scene with noticable depth, so perspective plays a role when viewed from close positions (for example, from each eye). Then due to perspective the images through far-apart holes are noticably different. When these somewhat-different images are combined by a lens, parts of the composite image are fuzzy. A composite image through closely-spaced holes, however, is sharp. This is why photographers take pictures through a small aperture for "depth of field" in their photographs. All parts of an image seen through a small appature are sharper. When a fuzzy background is desirable, a flower closeup for example, the aperture of the camera is opened wide. The focal plane is set for sharpness of the flower, and things closer or farther appear fuzzy.

CHECK QUESTION: When the aperture setting of a camera is small, should the exposure time be correspondingly longer or shorter? [The smaller aperture means less light per time, so the film should be exposed to light for a longer time.]

[**Transparencies 72**, and 73; Figure 30.11, converging lens ray diagrams, and Figure 30.12 of diverging ray diagram]

Ray Diagrams: At the board, discuss the key features of a converging lens (Figure 30.3) and sketch a ray diagram for the case of parallel light along the principle axis. This defines the focal point. Then sketch a diagram for a nearer object, such as Figure 30.9. Discuss the rules for ray-diagram construction, page 467, and go over the various cases of Figure 30.11.

Learning takes place not in seeing diagrams made, but in making them. Take time to have students make diagrams, preferatably for lenses they have in their hands and the objects and images they are witnessesing.

After progress has been made with converging lenses consider diverging lenses. They're trickier. I suggest avoiding too much emphasis on diverging lenses.

[**Practice Book 30-2** treats ray diagrams for convex and concave lenses]

Optical Instruments: As much as possible, show taken-apart samples of the variety of optical instruments treated briefly in the text. Note the simplicity of the diagrams of these instruments in the text, compared to their actual construction. A valueable lesson is learned looking for the simplicity that underlies the seemingly complex.

The Eye: Here you'll be overlapping what students learn about the eye in their life science courses. If they haven't done it before, they'll be fascinated with the blind spot experiment. Do it in class, and cite the case of the old king who used to delight in closing one eye and "chopping off" the heads of the people he scanned in his court.

DEMONSTRATION [30-2]: Simulate the human eye with a spherical flask filled with a bit of fluorescene dye. Paint an "iris" on the flask and position appropriate lenses in back of the iris for normal, farsighted and nearsighted vision. Then show how corrective lenses placed in front of the eye focus the light on the retina.

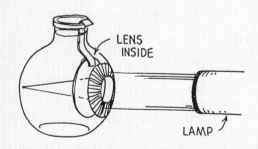

LENS INSIDE

LAMP

You have probably already discussed why the pupil of the eye looks black. Flashbulb photos often show it to be pink. This is largely because the light from the flash reflects directly back from the assemblage of blood vessels on the retina. Of interest (not in the text) is the particularly bright reflection from the eye pupils of many animals when illuminated at nighttime — so bright as to look luminous. This results from refection from a thin membrane located in back of the rods in the animal's eyes, which provides a "second chance" for the animal to perceive light that initially misses the rods. This arrangement, common in owls, cats, and other night predators, gives excellent night vision.

[**Next-Time Question 30-1** treats vision under water]

Color Vision (Optional): Discuss the function of the rods and cones in the retina of the eye, and how color cannot be perceived in dim light, and how the colored stars appear white to us whereas they show up clearly colored with camera time exposures. (I show a colored slide that I took of the stars, and discuss the curved lines encircling the north star, and get into a discussion of how long the camera shutter was held open.)

In discussing color vision, point out that in a bullfight, the bull is angry not at the redness of the cape that is flaunted before him, but because of the darts that have been stuck into him! A frog is "wired" to see *only* motion, and so it is also on the *periphery* of our vision. Discuss the fact that we see only motion and no color at the periphery of our vision.

DEMONSTRATION [30-3]: Stand at a corner of the room and shake brightly colored cards, first turned backward so the color is hidden and students can adjust the position of their heads (looking toward the other corner of the room). When they can just barely see the moving cards at the corners of their eyes, turn them over and display the color. Try with different colors. Your students will see the cards as they move, but not their color. This surprising circumstance goes over well.

Pupilometrics (Optional): The study of the size of the pupil as a function of attitudes is called *pupilometrics* (See Scientific American, April 1965). A lot of brain functioning occurs in the eye itself — the eye does some of our "thinking." This thinking is betrayed by the iris, that contracts and expands to regulate the size of the pupil for admitting more or less light as intensity changes. Its changing size is also related to our emotions. If we see, smell, taste, or hear something that is pleasing to us, our pupils automatically increase in size. If we sense something repugnant, they automicaly contract. Many a card player has betrayed the value of a hand by the size of his pupils. This topic is very interesting. CAUTION: If you treat it, it is important that you dispel misconceptions your students may associate with pupil sizes. It would not be well for people who normally have small pupils to feel self-conscious about this, and mistakenly feel that small pupils display a negativity of some sort. Also, pupil size decreases with age. It would not be well for young people to mistakenly feel that their older peers were "emotionally down" in general. It is the CHANGE in pupil size, not the pupil size itself, that pupilometrics is about.

More Think-and-Explain Questions

1. If you've ever watched a water strider or other insect upon the surface of water, you may have noticed a large shadow cast by the contact point where the thin legs touch the water surface. Then around the shadow is a bright ring. What accounts for this?
   Answer: The "nonwettable" leg of the water strider depresses and curves the surface of the water. This effectively produces a lens that directs light away from its course to form a bright ring around a darker region that then appears as a shadow. [Interestingly enough, the overall brightness of the shadow and bright ring averaged together is the same whether or not the water is depressed — "conservation of light."]

2. It is often stated that you look at the image of an image when you look through a telescope. What is meant by this?
   Answer: The eyepiece looks at the image of the object cast by the objective lens.

Think and Solve

No glass is prefectly transparent. Mainly because of reflections, about 92% of light passes through an average sheet of clear windowpane. The 8% loss is not noticed through a single sheet, but through several sheets it is apparent. How much light is transmitted by two sheets?
Answer: The amount of light transmitted through two sheets of glass is 84.6%. To see this, consider an incident intensity of 100 units. Then 92 units are transmitted through the first pane. 92% of this amount are transmitted through the second pane (0.92 of 92 = 84.6).

31 Diffraction and Interference

Objectives

• Explain why water waves after passing through a narrow opening have curved wave fronts.
• Describe the conditions for visible diffraction of waves.
• Describe the conditions for visible bright and dark fringes of light caused by interference.
• Explain causes of the bright and dark bands that appear when monochromatic light is reflected from a thin material.
• Explain the causes of colors that shine from soap bubbles, or gasoline slicks on a wet surface.
• Distinguish between light from a laser and light from a lamp.
• Distinguish between a hologram and a photograph.

Possible Misconceptions to Correct

• Light travels only in straight lines.
• Light cannot cancel light.
• A laser is an energy source that can put out more energy than it consumes.
• A laser is a high-efficiency device that emits more than just light.
• A hologram is a mystery of science.

Demonstration Equipment

• [31-1] Water-filled ripple tank with wave barriers and dowel to generate plane waves.
• [31-2] Index cards with slit cut in them for entire class. Vertical show-case lamp or fluorescent lamp separated into three segments by red, clear, and blue plastic.
• [32-3] Laser and piece of glass with irregular surface (showerdoor glass, crystal glassware, etc.), and (optional) music.
• [32-4] Polaroid 2 x 2 "slides" with crumpled cellophane or shiny Scotch-type tape and slide projector.
• [32-5] Laser and a means to show laser lissajous patterns.

Introduction

This chapter is best taught with a ripple tank of some sort — if not a commercial tank that shows detail on a screen, a large pan can serve your purposes. As already suggested in Chapter 29, do as Connecticut physics teachers Jon Wallace and Jim Harper do and use an inexpensive (less than six bucks) K-Mart "Prism Frame." The frame is clear plastic a little more than an inch deep. Put water in it and mount on an overhead projector. Put strips of screen mesh around the edges to reduce unwanted reflected waves. Use a large-diameter wooden dowel to generate waves. A gentle roll forward followed by

a quick roll backward produces a nice single pulse. You control the frequency of additional pulses. If you wish to make custom-designed plexiglass shapes to show diffraction, Jon and Jim suggest a material called Lenax (Plexiglass often doesn't respond well to drilling or cutting).

If you put some care into the three "light shows" with music suggested here, you'll impress your students with the beauty of physics that can be among the high points of your course. Do not show all three in a single lecture.

If you view interference colors in soap bubbles, you might mention that the thin film of the bubble is about the thinnest thing seen with the unaided eye.

In lab, *Rainbows Without Rain* will challenge your students to understand the phenomenon of interference.

Suggested Lecture

Start by acknowledging Huygen's principle: not only can waves combine to form bigger waves, but also waves can be considered to be made up of smaller waves.

Diffraction: Introduce this topic by way of demonstrations.

DEMONSTRATION [31-1]: Show the diffraction of water waves in a ripple tank. Arrange objects in the tank to diffract waves through a variety of slit sizes. Water waves are your example, but these wave properties apply also to sound waves, light waves, and ALL kinds of waves.

DEMONSTRATION [31-2]: After discussing diffraction, pass some index cards with razor slits in them throughout the class. Show a vertical show-case lamp or fluorescent lamp separated into three segments by colored plastic; red, clear, and blue. Have your students view the diffraction of these three segments through the slit, or through a slit provided by their own fingers. Note the different fringe spacings of different colors.

[**Transparency 74**, Figure 31.9, wave diffraction]

Interference: This topic was introduced in Chapter 25 and applied to sound in Chapter 26.

DEMONSTRATION [31-3]: This is a great one! With the lights out, shine laser light through an irregular piece of glass (showerdoor glass, sugar bowl cover, crystal glassware, etc.) and display beautiful interference patterns on the wall. This is especially effective if you make slight movements of the glass in rhythm with music. (I do it to Bach's Suite Three in D.) Your students will not forget this demonstration!

Thin-Film Interference: After your students do the lab activity *Rainbows Without Rain*, shine light from a sodium lamp, or laser light diffused through a diverging lens onto a pair of glass plates as shown in Figure 31.20. Relate the interference fringes to those explained in Figure 31.16. It is important that Figure 31.16 be understood, so spend some time discussing it.

[**Practice Book 31-1**, in addition to interference pattern construction, treats Figure 31.16 in detail]

CHECK QUESTION: What is the similarity between Figure 31.16 on page 489 and Figure 26.13 back on page 397? [They both illustrate the same phenomenon of interference, one of sound and the other of light. A big difference is the wavelengths involved, light being much smaller — hence the narrower fringes.]

Iridescence from Thin Films: Cite the iridescent colors that appear to change with position in the feathers of some birds — peacock, pigeon, starling, and so on. And also the spectrum of colors seen in soap bubbles, and in certain seashells. State that these colors are produced by interference. Illustrate the colors reflected from gasoline on a wet street via Figure 31.21 sketched on the board.

CHECK QUESTION: Why are interference colors not seen from gasoline spilled on a dry surface? [Two smooth reflective surfaces are necessary for interference. Without the smooth water beneath the film of gasoline, the lower surface of the gasoline would not be a smooth reflector.]

Emphasize the need for two surfaces for interference colors, and why the film should be thin. (Recombination of "split" waves cannot occur when the reflected rays are widely displaced.)
A nice example of interference not given in the text is that of the bluish tint of coated lenses. Lenses are coated to destroy doubly-reflected light in a lens. Light that doubly reflects in a lens arrives at the film out of focus. All the wavelengths of light that are doubly reflected can't be destroyed by interference — not with a single thin film. But a film thickness of one-quarter the wavelength of yellow light will cancel the most predominant color in sunlight — yellow. So the sunlight you see reflected from a coated lens is deficient in yellow. Hence its bluish appearance.

DEMONSTRATION [31-4]: The vivid colors that emerge from cellophane between crossed Polaroids makes a spectacular demonstration. Have students make up some 2 x 2 inch slides of cut and crinkled cellophane mounted on Polaroid material (which can be obtained inexpensively from Edmund Scientific Co.). Place in a slide projector and rotate a sheet of Polaroid in front of the projecting lens so that a changing montage of colors is displayed on the screen. Also include a showing of color slides of the interference colors seen in the everyday environment, as well as of microscopic crystals. This is more effective with two projectors with hand dissolving from image to image on the screen. Do this in rhythm to some music and you'll have an unforgettable lecture demonstration! (My students report that

this is the best part of my course — to which, of course, I have mixed feelings. I would prefer that some of my explanations were the highlight of my course!)

[**Next-Time Question 31-1** on interference colors in a soap bubble]

Laser Light: Defuse the misconception that a laser is a powerful emitter of something other than light. Also defuse the notion that a laser is an efficient light source. It is extremely poor — your classroom laser is typically less than 1% efficient! If you showed the spectrum of neon in Chapter 28, state that the frequency of light emitted from a helium-neon laser is just one of those many neon spectral lines.
Helium-neon laser information: The low pressure mixture of 85% helium and 15% neon is subjected to a high voltage. This energizes (excites) the helium to a prolonged state. Before the helium radiates light it collides with neon atoms in the ground state, and transfers its energy to them. The amount of energy is just sufficient to excite neon to an otherwise difficult-to-come-by metastable state very close to the energy of the excited helium. The process continues and the population of excited neon atoms outnumbers neon in the ground state. This inverted population in effect is waiting to radiate its energy. When some neon atoms emit light, the radiation passes other excited neon atoms and triggers their de-excitation, exactly in phase with the stimulating radiation. Light parallel to the tube bounces from specially coated mirrors and the process cascades to produce a beam of coherent light. (To reduce information overload, note that the excitation model of light emission is not treated in the text, and is only briefly mentioned in the footnote on page 438 back in Chapter 28.)

DEMONSTRATION [31-5]: Give a laser show. Sprinkle chalk dust or smoke in the beam, show diffraction through a thin slit and so on. An unforgettable presentation is directing a laser beam on a mirror fastened to a rubber membrane stretched over a radio loudspeaker (order a ready-made apparatus from Edmund Scientific Co.). Do this to music and cover the darkened walls with a display of dancing lissajous patterns.

[**Transparency 75**, Figures 31.30 and 31.31, holograms]

Holograms: An effective sequence for explaining holograms is the following: With the aid of Figure 31.16, develop the idea further for multiple slits, the diffraction grating. With a large diffraction grating (I use one that is the size of a full sheet of typing paper, Edmund Scientific Co.) show the spectral lines of a gas discharge tube. Emphasize that there are really no physical lines where they appear to be, and that the lines are virtual images of the glowing tube (just as they would be images of slits if a slit were being used). With a fairly good idea of how these images are produced by the diffraction grating, show the class a really sophisticated diffraction grating, not of vertical parallel lines in one dimension, but of microscopic swirls of lines in two dimensions — a hologram illuminated with a laser.

More Think-and-Explain Questions

1. Monochromatic light illuminates two closely-spaced thin slits and produces an interference pattern on the wall. How will the distance between the fringes in the pattern differ for even closer-spaced slits?

   Answer: The fringes will be spaced farther apart. To see this, investigate Figure 31.16. Note that closer slits would mean greater distances from the central fringe before interference would produce regions of reinforcement and cancellation. Diffraction gratings with fine rulings produce more dispersion.

2. The white light undergoes interference when dispersion through a thin slit, what is the ordering of the various colors, starting from the middle?

   Answer: The first fringes are blue, and commense to red (just the opposite as through a prism).

3. Why do the iridescent colors seen in some sea-shells (such as the inside of abalone shells) change as the shells are viewed from different positions?

   Answer: The optical path of light from upper and lower reflecting surfaces changes as the shells are viewed from different positions. Thus different colors are seen when holding the shell at varying angles.

4. What differences is seen by an astronomer of the emission spectrum of an element in a receding star compared to a spectrum of the same element in the lab?

   Answer: The moving star will show a Doppler shift.

5. If you are viewing a hologram and you close one eye, will you still perceive depth? Explain.

   Answer: Two eyes are required to perceive depth by parallax, whether in a hologram or otherwise. If depth is perceived by other cues, such as relative sizes and relative brightnesses of objects, then one eye is sufficient.

32 Electrostatics

Objectives

- Describe electrical forces between objects.
- Explain, from the point of view of electron transfer, how an object becomes a) positively charged or b) negatively charged and relate this to the net charge.
- Describe the relation between the electrical force between two charged objects, their charge, and the distance between them.
- Compare the strengths of electrical forces and gravitational forces between charged objects.
- Distinguish between a conductor and an insulator.
- Describe how an insulator can be charged by friction.
- Describe how a conductor can be charged by contact.
- Describe how a conductor can be charged without contact.
- Describe how an insulator can be charged by charge polarization.

Possible Misconceptions to Correct

- The study of electricity is incomprehensible.
- Electric charges occur in some materials and not in others.
- Friction is a necessary factor in charging an object.
- Lighting rods are designed to attract lightning.

Demonstration Equipment

- [32-1] Fur, silk, rubber rod, glass or plastic rod, suspended pith ball
- [32-2] Electrophorus; metal plate with insulating handle, piece of acrylic plastic, regural plastic, or equivalent nonconductor
- [32-3] Whimshurst machine (electrostatic generator), a sharp metal point, an alligator clip
- [32-4] Vane of metal points that rotate on a needle pivot when charged
- [32-5] Van de Graaff generator, aluminum pie pans, puffed rise or puffed wheat, lamp tube
- [35-6] Rubber balloon
- [35-7] Piece of wooden 2 x 4, about a meter long, balanced upon a watch glass or metal spoon so it will rotate
- [32-8] Charged rubber rod and stream of water

Introduction

If you're into puns in your lectures on rainy days, Marshall Ellenstein has a few pictorial puns on the symbol for resistance that he and coworkers Connie Bownell and Nancy McClure came up with ("Ohmwork" or ΩF x D, *Physics Teacher* magazine, Sept 91, page 347). A few are shown to the right: Answers in order are: Mobile Ohm; Ohm Run; Ohm Stretch; Ohm Sick; Ohmwork; Ohmless; Ohm on the Range; Broken Ohm.

Much of electricity is generally misunderstood not only by the general public, but also by people involved in technology. The study of electricity begins with electrostatics, which is best introduced as a series of coordinated demonstrations. After showing charging via cat's fur, rubber rods and the like, and electrostatic attraction and repulsion (Coulomb's law), show (1) the electrophorus (a metal plate charged by induction by a sheet of plexiglass which has been charged with cat's fur, or equivalently, a pizza pan and a phonograph record), (2) the Whimshurst machine (electrostatic generator), and (3) the Van de Graaff generator. The demonstration sequence, 1, 2, and 3, with explanations should find this one of your better lectures.

This sequence is featured in the videotape *Electrostatics* from the *Conceptual Physics Alive!* video series.

The lab activity, *Static Cling*, can follow your introductory lecture, and it can replace lectures on Sections 32.6 *Charging by Induction* and 32.7 *Charge Polarization*. There are no follow-up experiments for this chapter, nor is there any for the next chapter. For practical purposes, this and the following chapter are theoretical background for the study of electric current in Chapter 34, and circuits in Chapter 35. Lab experiments are featured in those chapters.

So this chapter is prerequisite to the following chapters in Unit 5.

Suggested Lecture

Electrical forces Begin by comparing the strength of the electric force to gravitational force — billions of billions of times stronger. Acknowledge the fundamental rule of electricity: That *like charges repel and unlike charges attract*. Why? Nobody knows. Hence we say it is fundamental.

Electric Charges Electrical effects have to do with electric charges, minus for the electron and plus for the proton. Discuss the near balance that exists in common materials, and the slight imbalance when electrons transfer from one material to another. Different materials have different affinities for electrons, which explains why charge transfers from fur to rubber when rubbed. It also explains

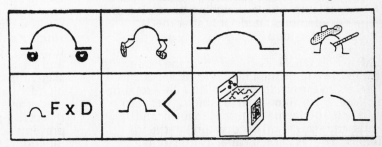

why its painful for people with silver fillings in their teeth to chew aluminum spitballs. Silver has more affinity for acquiring electrons than aluminum. The mildly acidic saliva in your mouth facilitates a flow of electrons, which when transmitted to the nerves of your teeth produce that familiar unpleasant sensation. Discuss **charging**.

DEMONSTRATION [32-1]: Bring out the cat's fur, rubber and glass rods, and suspended pith balls (or their alternatives). Explain the transfer of electrons when you rub fur against rubber rod (and silk against glass). Explain what it means to say an object is electrically charged, and discuss the **conservation of charge**.

[**Transparencies 76 and 77**, Figures 32.8 and 32.9 on charging by induction]

[**Practice Book 32-1** and **32-2**; Coulomb's law and charging]

Charging something can be compared to removing bricks from a road and putting them on a sidewalk. There are exactly as many "holes" in the road as there are bricks on the sidewalk.

Rubbing a rubber rod on cat's fur or a glass rod on silk illustrates charging by friction, but charge separation can occur without friction, by the simple contact between dissimilar insulating materials. In this case charge simply peels from one material to another, like dust is peeled from a surface when a piece of sticky tape is peeled from it.

DEMONSTRATION [32-2]: Charge the electrophorus, place the insulated metal disk on top of it, and show that the disk is not charged when removed and brought near a charged pith ball. Why should it be, for the insulating surface of the electrophorus has more grab on the electrons than the metal plate. But rest the plate on the electrophorus again and touch the top of the plate. You're grounding it (producing a conducting path to ground for the repelling electrons).

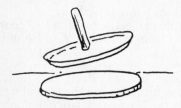

Bring the plate near the pith ball and show that it is charged. Then show this by the flash of light produced when the charged metal plate is touched to the end of a gas discharge tube — or a fluorescent lamp. Engage neighbor discussion of the process demonstrated. Only after this is generally understood, proceed to the next demo.

DEMONSTRATION [32-3]: Move up the lecture table to the Whimshurst machine, explaining its similarity to the electrophorus (actually a rotating electrophorus!). Show sparks jumping between the spheres of the machine and so forth, and discuss the sizes (radii of curvature) of the spheres in terms of their capacity for storing

charge. [The amount of charge that can be stored before discharge into the air is directly proportional to the radius of the sphere.]

DEMONSTRATION [32-4]: Fasten a metal point, which has a tiny radius of curvature and hence a tiny charge storing capacity, to one of the Whimshurst spheres and demonstrate the leakage of charge. You're showing ion propulsion, a means whereby science fiction spaceships are propelled. Science fiction today, but tomorrow?

If you wish to expand upon charge leakage from a point, you might simplify it this way: On the surface of an electrically charged flat metal plate, every charge is mutually repelled by every other charge. If the surface is curved, charges on one part of the plate will not interact with charges on some distant part of the plate because of the **shielding** effect of the metal — they are "out of the line of sight" of each other. Hence for the same amount of work or potential, a greater number of charges may be placed on a curved surface than on a flat surface. The more pronounced the curvature, the more shielding and the more charge may be stored there. To carry this idea further, consider a charged needle. Under mutual repulsion, charges gather to the region of greatest curvature, the point. Although all parts of the needle are charged to the same electric potential, the charge density is greatest at the point. The **electric field** intensity about the needle (in detail in the next chapter), on the other hand, is greatest about the point, usually great enough to ionize the surrounding air and provide a conducting path from the charge concentration. Hence charge readily gathers at points and readily leaks from points. DEMONSTRATE this leakage and the reaction force (ion propulsion) with a set of metal points arranged to rotate when charged. This is the "ion propulsion" that science fiction buffs talk about in space travel. Interestingly enough, this leaking of charge from points causes static with radio antennas; hence the small metal ball atop automobile antennas.

Discuss **lightning rods** and show how the bottoms of negatively charged clouds and the resulting induced positive charge on the surface of the earth below are similar to the electrophorus held upside down; where the charged Plexiglas plate is analogous to the clouds and the metal plate is analogous to the earth. After sketching the charged clouds and earth on the chalkboard, be sure to hold the inverted electrophorus pieces against your drawing on the board in their respective places. Discuss the lightning rod as a preventer of lighting while showing the similar function of the metal point attached to the metal

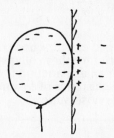

point attached to the Whimshurst machine. [Notice that one idea is related to the next in this sequence — very important, as the ideas of electricity are usually difficult to grasp the first time through. So be sure to take care in moving through this sequence of demonstrations and their explanations.]

Benjamin Franklin's kite, by the way, was not struck by lightning. If it had, he would likely have not been around to report his experience. Franklin showed that the kite collected charges from the air during a thunderstorm. Hairs on the kite string stood apart, implying that lightning was a huge electric spark.

[**Next-Time Question 32-2** on lightning]

After establishing the idea that charge capacity depends on the size and curvature of the conductor being charged, advance to what your students have been waiting for: **The Van de Graaff generator** (for humor, invented by Robert Generator).

DEMONSTRATION [32-5]: When showing the long sparks that jump from the dome of the generator to the smaller grounded sphere, do as Bruce Bernard suggests and hold a lightning rod (any sharp pointed conductor) in the vicinity of the dome and the sparking will stop. Bring the lightning rod farther away and the frequency of sparking will resume. Set a cup of puffed rice or puffed wheat on top of the Van de Graaff generator. Your students will like the fountain that follows when you charge it. Or do as Marshall Ellenstein does and place a stack of aluminum pie plates on the dome and watch them one by one levitate and fly away.

Charge Polarization: Define polarization by explaining Figures 32.11 through 32.14 in the text. When you rub a rubber balloon on a cat's fur, which will stick to the wall — the balloon or the cat!?

DEMONSTRATION [32-6]: Rub a balloon on your hair and show how it sticks to the wall. Draw a sketch on the board and show in induction how the attracting charges are slightly closer than the repelling charges. Closeness wins and it sticks!

DEMONSTRATION [32-7]: Show the effects of electrical force and charge by induction by holding a charged rod near the ends of a more-than-a-meter-long wooden 2 x 4, that balances and easily rotates sideways at its midpoint on a protrusion such as the bottom of a metal spoon. You can easily set the massive piece of wood in motion. This is quite impressive!

The demo with the 2 x 4 piece of wood is an example of charge polarization. When the charges are free to move we have induction; when they're only free to reposition in fixed atoms, we have charge polarization.

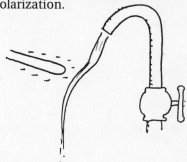

DEMONSTRATION [32-8] Place a charged rod near a thin stream of falling water. Whatever the sign of charge, the stream will be attracted to the rod. The explanation is in detail in the answer to Next-Time Question 32-3.

[**Next-Time Question 32-3** is on the polarization of a stream of water]

Conclude the chapter by going back to the Van de Graaff generator. Introduce the idea of electric field — that space near the generator dome is altered, as you can demonstrate by snuffing out a match held near the charged dome. This will be the focus of the next chapter.

More Think and Explain Questions

1. The two leaves of an electroscope repel each other and stand out at an angle. What balances the electrical force so the leaves don't stand out farther?
Answer: Their weight; gravity.

2. The leaves of a charged electroscope collapse after a while. At higher altitudes they collapse more readily. Speculate on an explanation for this behavior. (*Hint*: The existence of cosmic rays was first indicated by this observation.)

Answer: Cosmic rays produce ions in the air that discharge charged objects.

3. Exactly what is a positively charged hydrogen atom?
Answer: A proton.

4. How can a strong charge attract a metal coin that has no net charge?
Answer: By induction!

5. If a positive test charge is placed between a pair of oppositely charged plates, which way will the test charge move?
Answer: It will be attracted to and move toward the negative plate, or equivalently, it will be repelled by the positive plate and move toward the negative plate. [In the next chapter we will see that it will move in the direction of the electric field, from positive to negative.]

6. Imagine a proton at rest a certain distance from a negatively charged plate. It is released and collides with the plate. Then imagine the similar case of an electron at rest, the same distance away, from a plate of equal and opposite charge. In which case would the moving particle have the greater speed when the collision occurs? Why?

Answer: Electron. The force on both will be the same, but more acceleration and therefore more speed of the electron because of its smaller mass.

33 Electric Fields and Potential

Objectives

- Describe how the strength of an electric field at two different points can be compared.
- Decribe how the direction of an electric field at a point is determined.
- Relate the spacing of electric field lines to the strength of the field.
- Describe the conditions under which something can be completely shielded from an electric field.
- Explain why a charged object in a electric field is considered to have electric potential energy.
- Distinguish between electric potential energy and electric potential.
- Describe the purpose of a Van de Graaff generator.

Possible Misconceptions to Correct

- Electric potential energy and electric potential are the same thing.
- A capacitor is a source of electric energy.
- High voltage is dangerous under any conditions.
- The voltage produced by rubbing a balloon on one's hair is low compared to the voltage of electric circuits in the household.

Demonstration Equipment

- [33-1] Van de Graaff Generator and fluorescent lamp

No Lab for this Chapter

Introduction

This is a theoretical chapter, and will demand the most of your students ability to master it. I recommend that such effort be instead spent in the following chapters that are supported with hands-on activities, and that you move through this chapter quickly. Treat it as an overview rather than material to be mastered.

The vector nature of fields is enhanced with the Work Book sheet for this chapter, which depends on prior treatment of vectors (Chapter 6).

Suggested Lecture

Refer to the Van de Graaff generator, and the altered space around it when charged — the electric field. Compare gravitational and electric fields — both altered regions because of the presence of mass for the gravitational field, and charge for the electric field. The easiest to visualize are magnetic fields, because of the familiar iron filing patterns (ahead in Figures 36.4 and 36.6). Fields are called "force fields" because forces are exerted on bodies in their vicinity, but a better term would be "energy field," because energy is stored in a field. In the case of an electric field, any charges in the vicinity are ener-

gized. We speak about the potential energy that electrically charged bodies have in a field — or more often, the potential energy compared to the amount of charge — **electric potential**. Explain that the field energy, and correspondingly the electric potential, is greatest nearest the charged dome and weaker with increased distance (**inverse-square law**).

DEMONSTRATION [33-1]: Hold a fluorescent lamp tube in the field of a charged van de Graaff generator to show that it lights up when one end of the tube is closer to the dome than the other end. Relate this to the stronger electric field near the dome, and weaker farther away. Charges in the field experience more force in stronger parts, which means more work is done when they are moved in the stronger parts — more energy. The energy per charge is what we call potential. Show that when both ends of the fluorescent tube are equidistant from the charged dome, light emission ceases. (This can be effected when your hand is a bit closer to the dome than the far end of the tube, so current does not flow through the tube when the dome discharges through you to the ground. There is no potential difference across the tube and therefore no illuminating current, which sets the groundwork for your next lecture on electric current.)

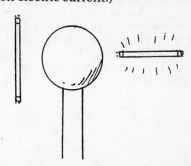

The Van de Graaff generator nicely illustrates the difference between **electric potential energy** and **electric potential**: Although it is normally charged to thousands of volts, the amount of charge is relatively small so the electric potential energy is relatively small. That's why you're normally not harmed when it discharges through your body. Very little energy flows through you. In contrast, you wouldn't intentionally become the short-circuit for household 110 volts because although the voltage is much lower, the transfer of energy is appreciable. Less energy per charge, but many many more charges! [All this is analogous to thermal energy — high temperature may or may not be associated with high or low thermal energy. Recall the white hot sparks of the fireworks sparkler — similarly, high energy per molecule, but not many molecules. Both the high-temperature sparkler and the high-voltage generator are relatively harmless.]

Electric Field Lines: Cite the vector nature of a force field and describe the lines of force as shown in the photos of Figure 33.5 in the text.

[**Practice Book 33-1**)emphasizes vector resolution to understand that the curved field lines of a pair of charges (or more!) are the resulting superposition of straight fiel lines]

[**Transparencies 78 and 79**, Figures 33.3 and 33.4 — Electric field lines]

CHECK QUESTION: If a tiny test charge were dropped in the oil bath shown in Figure 33.5, in what direction would it move? [Along the same directions as the bits of thread — away from the conductor of opposite sign of charge and toward the conductor of same sign of charge.

Shielding: Call attention to photo *d* of text Figure 33.5 that shows that the threads have no directional properties inside the charged cylinder. This shows that the electric field is shielded by the metal. The dramatic photo of the car being struck by lightning in text Figure 33.6 also illustrates that the electric field inside a conductor is normally zero, no matter what is happening outside. The explanation is only hinted at in the text in Figure 33.7. You can leave the discussion at that and move on to new material.

Should some of your students wish more information you can go a step beyond the test charge in the middle of the sphere (Figure 33.7). Consider the test charge off center, twice as far from region A as region B, as shown. The dotted lines represent a sample cone of action, subtending both A and B. Region A has twice the diameter, four times the area, and four times the charge as region B. Four times the charge at twice the distance in accord with the inverse-square law will have one-fourth the effect. So the greater charge is balanced out by the correpondingly greater distance. This will be the case for all points inside the conductor. And the conductor need not be a sphere, as is shown by the shapes in Figure 33.8.

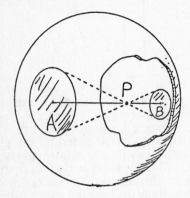

Another viewpoint: if the field inside a conductor were not zero, then free charges inside would move. Would the movement continue forever? No. The charges would finally move to positions of equilibrium. In these positions their effects on each other would be mutually balanced. There would be complete cancellation of fields everywhere inside the conductor. This is what happens — not gradually, but suddenly!

Go lightly on units of measurement. Your more able students will learn that N/C = V/m, and that J/C = V, without you making a big deal of it for the whole class. The art of teaching introductory physics is using broad strokes that give an overview. Detail is something that will come later to those needing it. If you do have a student or two who want it now let them try on a one-to-one basis. (Do you remember in your own student days how one or two annoying whiz types were able to misdirect the teacher's energies to picky pickyness much of the time?) Be strong and skip over detail when it's counterproductive!

Capacitors: A charged capacitor is a useful device not only for storing electric energy, but also for studying electrical properties. Although primarily used in ac circuits, capacitors can be a quasi-source of electric energy and serve as a substitute for a battery in a hands-on-circuit experience. This is hands-on-time if you are doing the experiment Brown Out described in the lab manual. Capacitors are treated again in Chapter 34.

Your lecture on this chapter should end with a return to the Van de Graaff demo and discussion of the lack of current in the lamp when there was no potential difference across its ends. This is the lead to the next chapter. [The simplified answer you're looking for at this point is that the close end is in a stronger part of the field than the far end. More energy per charge means more voltage at the near end. With a voltage difference across the tube, you get a current. When both ends are equidistant, there is no voltage difference across the tube, and no current. This leads into electric current. Strictly speaking, the current path is more than simply between the ends of the tube; it goes through you also and to ground where it returns to the generator.]

[**Next-Time Question** 34-1 picks up on the above]

More Think and Explain Questions

1. Measurements show that there is an electric field surrounding the earth. Its magnitude is about 100 N/C at the earth's surface and points inward toward the earth's center. From this information, can you state whether the earth is negative or positive?
   Answer: It is negatively charged. It it were positive, the field would point outward.

2. Would you feel any electric effects if you were inside the charged sphere of a Van de Graaff generator? Why or why not?
   Answer: You would feel no electrical effects inside any charged conducting body. Because of mutual repulsion, all charge resides on the outside surface of the conductor. The distribution of charge is such that complete cancellation of the interior electric field occurs. The electric field inside any conductor under static conditions is zero, whether the conductor is charged or not. (If the electric field were not zero, then conduction electrons would move in response to the field until electrical equilibrium was established — a zero electric field.)

Objectives

- Describe the conditions for flow of electric charge.
- Describe what is happening inside a current-carrying wire, and explain why there is no net charge in the wire.
- Give examples of voltage sources that can maintain a potential difference in an electric circuit.
- Describe the factors that determine the resistance of a wire.
- Relate the amount of current in a circuit to the voltage impressed across the circuit and the resistance of the circuit.
- Explain why wet skin increases the likelihood of receiving a damaging electric shock when a faulty electrical device is touched.
- Distinguish between direct current and alternating current.
- Compare the drift speed of conduction electrons in a current-carrying wire to the signal speed of changes in current.
- Compare the motion of electrons in a wire carrying alternating current to the flow of energy through the wire.
- Relate the electric power used by a device to current and voltage.

Possible Misconceptions to Correct

- A current-carrying wire is electrically charged.
- Electric current is a fluid of some kind.
- Electric current flows out of and into a battery, rather than flowing through a battery.
- Voltage flows through a circuit, instead of being impressed across a circuit.
- Power companies deliver electrons, rather than energy, from a power plant to consumers.
- Electrons travel at about the speed of light in a dc circuit.
- A voltage or power source supplies electrons to a circuit to which it is connected.

Demonstration Equipment

- [34-1] A 12-volt automobile battery, or other large battery, with self constructed brass or copper rods extended from the terminals. Alligator clips are used to fasten lamps between them. (See the sketch on this page and the comic strip, "Parallel Circuit" on page 553 in the text.)

Introduction

The intent of this chapter is to build a good understanding of current electricity and to dispel some of the popular misconceptions about electricity. If you are teaching only one chapter on electricity, this should be it.

Be sure to make up a battery-with-extended-terminals demonstration as shown above and also

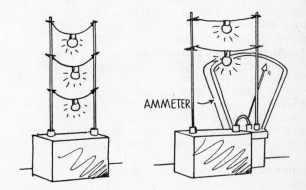

AMMETER

in the comic strip, "Parallel Circuit" on textbook page 553. One way to do this is to fasten binding posts to the terminals of the automobile storage battery, and set into them a pair of rigid vertical brass or copper rods. It is easily accepted that the 12-volt potential difference between the terminals is also across the rods. The rods behave as the lead wires in common circuits — they simply extend the difference in potential to distant locations. Then attach via alligator clips, lamps of equal resistance and show how the brightness of each lamp (and hence the current through each lamp) varies for different configurations. This demo has greatly improved the way I teach electric current and circuits, and is well worth the effort of putting together. It serves well in the following chapter also.

Ohm's law is the core of the chapter. No distinction is made between resistors that change their value and those that don't when voltage changes. We simply say that whatever the conductor, the amount of current produced by an impressed voltage is equal to that voltage divided by the particular resistance. Ohm's law is conceptually useful.

As a practical matter, Ohm's law is useful for predicting values only if the resitance of the deviced does not change with changes in vboltage or current, and usually where heating does not appreciably affect resistance. Devices that keep the same resistance for a wide range of voltages are said to b ohmic. Ohm's law is useful for predicting values of omic materials.

In the lab manual, the exploratory activity *Sparky, the Electrician* and the experiment, *Ohm, Ohm on the Range — Part I* should precede your lecture material. Strive to have all students complete Part A of each of the three *Ohm, Ohm on the Range* series. Do not require all students to get through all parts of all three of this series. (Parts II and III continue in the following chapter.) *Brown Out* will provide experience with the charging and discharging of capacitors.

Suggested Lecture

Begin by reviewing the lighting of a fluorescent lamp or neon discharge tube by the Van de Graaff Generator from your previous lecture Explain this in terms of current being directly proportional to a difference in voltage. That is, one end of the lamp was in a stronger part of the energy field than the other — more energy per charge on one end than the other — more voltage at one end than the other. Write on the board *Current ~ voltage difference*. (You're on your way to Ohm's law. Strictly speaking, the voltage term in Ohm's law implies the difference in potential, so voltage difference is redundant. But it underscores a point that may be missed, so go for it.) [A high moment in my life was a conversation with Richard Feynman about teaching physics conceptually, and the topic of redundancies in teaching electricity came up. Feynman advised me to put concepts above grammar, and go for redundancies when they underscore a point — so current flows in a circuit!]

[**Transparency 80**, Figure 34.5; analogy with hydraulic circuit]

[**Next-Time Question** 34-1 on current in the lamp by the Van de Graaff generator]

Voltage Sources Relate voltage to the idea of electrical pressure. Emphasize that a *difference* in electric potential must exist — or as above, a voltage difference. Cite how a battery provides this difference in a sustained way compared to suddenly discharging a Van de Graaff generator. Generators at power plants also provide a voltage difference across wires that carry this difference to consumers. Cite examples of voltage differences in cases of birds sitting on bare high-voltage wires, walking unharmed on the third rail of electric-powered train tracks, and the inadvisability of using electric appliances in the bathtub.

Discuss the function of the **third prong on electric plugs** (that it provides a ground wire between the appliance and the ground). The ground prong is longer than
the pair of flat prongs. Why? (So it will be first to be connected when plugging it into a socket, establishing a ground connection slightly before the appliance is electrically connected. This path to ground prevents harm to the user if there is a short circuit in the appliance that would otherwise include the user as a path to ground.)

Discuss **electric shock** and why electricians put one hand behind their back when probing questionable circuits [to prevent a difference in potential across the heart of the body]. Discuss how being electrified produces muscle contractions that account for such instances as "not being able to let go" of hot wires, and "being thrown" by electric shock.

Electrical Resistance Introduce the idea of electrical resistance, and complete Ohm's law. Compare the resistances of various materials, and the resistances of various thickness of wires of the same metal. Call attention to the glass supports on the wires that make up high-voltage power lines;

the rubber insulation that separates the pair of wires in a common lamp cord.

Ohm's Law Complete your chalkboard equation by introducing resistance and you have Ohm's law.

DEMONSTRATION [34-1]: Connect two or three lamps to a battery and relate the current, as viewed by the emitted light, to the voltage of the battery and the resistance of the lamps. (Be sure the lamps are not bright enough to make viewing uncomfortable). Interchange lamps of low and high resistance, relating this to the brightness of the lamps.

[**Practice Book 34-1** is on Ohm's law]

DC and AC Discuss the differences between DC and AC. Compare the DC current that flows in a circuit powered with a battery to the AC current that flows in a household circuit (powered by a generator). A hydrodynamic analogy for AC is useful: Imagine powering a washing-machine agitator with water power. Verbally describe with gestures a pair of clear plastic pipes connected to a paddle wheel at the bottom of the agitator, fashioned so water that sloshes to and fro in the pipes causes the agitator to rotate to and fro. Suppose the free ends of the plastic pipe are connected to a special socket in the wall. The socket is powered by the power utility. It supplies no water, but consists of a couple of pistons that exert a pumping action, one out and the other in, then vice versa, in rapid alternation. When the ends of the pipe containing water are connected to the pistons, the water in the pipes is made to slosh back and forth: power is delivered to the washing machine. There is an important point to note here: The **source** of flowing substance, water or electrons, is supplied by you. The power company supplies no water, just as the power utilities supply no electrons! The greater the load on the agitator, the more energy the power company must deliver to the action of the alternating pistons, affording a visual model for household current — especially with the transparent plastic pipes where your students can "see" the sloshing water!

Speed of Electrons in a Circuit To impart the idea of how DC current travels in a circuit, use the following analogy. Ask the class to suppose that there is a long column of marchers at the front of the room, all standing at rest close together. Walk to the end of this imaginary column and give a shove to the "last person." Ask the class to imagine the resulting impulse traveling along the line until the first marcher is jostled against the wall. (Or use the analogy of loosely coupled railroad cars.) Then ask if this is a good analogy for how electricity travels in a wire. The answer is no. Such is a good analogy for how sound travels, but not electricity. Cite how slowly the disturbance traveled, and how slowly sound travels compared to light or electricity. Again call attention to the column of marchers and walk to the far end and call out, "Forward march!" As soon as the command reaches each individual, each steps forward. The marcher at the beginning of the column, except for the slight time required for the sound to get to her, steps immediately. State that this is an analogy for electricity. Except for the brief time it takes for the electric *field* set up at the power source to travel through the wire, nearly the speed of light, electrons at the far end of the circuit respond immediately. State that the speed at which the command "forward march" traveled is altogether different from how fast each marcher moved upon receiving that command — and that the velocity of the electric signal (nearly the speed of light) is quite a bit different than the drift velocity of electrons (typically 0.01 cm/s) in a circuit.

CHECK QUESTION: When turning the key to start a car, electrons migrate from the negative battery terminal through the electric network to the starter motor and back to the positive battery terminal. Estimate the time required for electrons to leave the negative terminal, go through the circuit, and return to the battery? Less than a millisecond? Less than a second? About a second or two? Or about a day? (Class interest should be high when you announce the latter answer!)

Ask for an estimate of the number of electrons pumped by the local power plant into the homes and industries locally in the past year. [zero] Stress the idea that power plants sell not electrons, but energy. Discuss the origin of electrons in electric circuits.

Electric Power Distinguish between energy and power. Electric power is usually expressed in kilowatts, and electric energy in kilowatt-hours. It is effective if you use an actual electric bill to make your point. Note that a kilowatt-hour is 1000 joules per second times 3600 seconds, or 3600 kJ.

[**Practice Book 34-2** is on power]

More Think and Explain Questions

1. The text stresses that electrons travel very slowly in an electric circuit. Why, then, do the lights go off immediately when you turn off the light switch?
   Answer: The electric field goes through the circuit at the speed of light (somewhat less than the speed of light in a vacuum). When the field is cut off, the flow of electrons ceace.

2. If a current of one-tenth to two-tenths of an ampere flows into one hand and out the other, you will probably be electrocuted. But if the same current passes between your hand and your elbow of the same arm, you will survive. Explain.
   Answer: In the first case, the current probably passes through your heart. In the second case, it passes only through your forearm.

3. Energy is put *into* electricity by pumping electrons from a low voltage to a high voltage. How do we get energy *out of* electricity?
   Answer: Energy is obtained using electricity by transforming to other forms, and transferring to other places. The energy put into a system (battery, generator, etc.) goes to electrical devices (toasters, electrical toothbrushes, radios, etc.) and is transformed and transferred into other forms and places (heat in the toaster, mechanical motion in the toothbrush, sound in the radio, etc.).

4. Why will the resistance of a wire by slightly different immediately after you have held it in your hand?
   Answer: You have warmed it, and increased its resistance slightly.

5. Why is the current in an incandescant bulb greater immediately after it is turned on, than a few moments later?
   Answer: Before it heats up, the filament is cooler and more conducting.

6. Which will do more damgage: plugging a 120-volt appliance into a 240-volt circuit or plugging a 220-volt appliance into a 120-volt circuit? Explain.
   Answer: Damage generally occurs from excess heating caused by too much current through an appliance. For an appliance that converts electrical energy directly to heat this happens when excess voltage is applied. So don't connect a 120-volt iron, toaster, or electric stove to a 240-volt circuit. Interestingly enough, if the appliance is an electric motor, then applying too <u>little</u> voltage can result in overheating and burn up the motor windings. (This is because the motor

7. Is a current-carrying wire electrically charged?
   Answer: The net charge ia a wire, current or not, is normally zero. The number of electrons is ordinarily offset by an equal number of protons in the atomic lattice. Thus current and charge are not the same thing: Many people think that saying a wire carries current is the same thing as saying a wire is charged. But a wire that is charged carries no current at all unless the charge moves in some uniform direction. And a wire that carries a current is typically not electrically charged and won't affect an electroscope. (If the current consists of a beam of electrons in a vacuum, then the beam would be charged. Current is not charge itself: current is the <u>flow</u> of charge.)

8. Which has the thicker lamp filament, a 60-watt bulb or a 100-watt bulb?
   Answer: The 100-watt bulb. This follows from the fact that more current flows in the 100-watt bulb, consistent with the relationship <u>power = current x voltage</u>. More current for the same voltage means less resistance. So a 100-watt bulb has less resistance than a 60-watt bulb. Less resistance of the same material means a thicker filament. The filaments of high-wattage bulbs are thicker than those of low-wattage bulbs. (It is important to note that both watts and volts are printed on a light bulb. A bulb that is labled 100W, 120V, is 100W <u>only</u> if there are 120 volts across it. If there are only 110 volts across it, then the power output is only 84 watts!)

9. Will the current in a light bulb connected to 220 V be more or less than when the same bulb is connected to 110 V? By how much?
   Answer: There will be twice the current in the bulb when twice the voltage is applied (assuming its resistance remains constant).

10. What is the effect on current if both the voltage and the resistance are doubled? If both are halved?
Answer: If both voltage and resistance are doubled, current remains unchanged.

11. A car's headlights consume 40 W on low beam, and 50 W on high beam. Is there more or less resistance in the high beam filament?
Answer: There is less resistance in the higher wattage lamp. Power = V^2/R.

*12. If a 60-watt bulb and a 100-watt bulb are connected in series in a circuit, through which bulb will the greater current flow? How about if they are connected in parallel?
Answer: In a series circuit, each part of the circuit passes the same current. How much the current is depends on the sum of the resistances, and is nevertheless the same through each bulb. When connected in parallel, the voltage across each bulb is the same and

*13. If a 60-watt bulb and a 100-watt bulb are connected in series, which bulb will have the greater voltage drop? How about in parallel?
Answer: The 100-watt bulb has the thicker filament and lower resistance (as discussed in the answer to Question 6) so in series where the current is the same in each bulb, less energy goes to heat in going through the lower resistance. This corresponds to lower voltage across the resistance — a lower voltage drop. So the greater voltage drop is across the 60-watt bulb in series. So interestingly enough, in series the 60-watt bulb is brighter than the 100-watt bulb! When connected in parallel, the voltage across each bulb is the same, and the current is greater in the lower resistance 100-watt bulb, and it glows brighter than the 60-watt bulb.
*These are difficult questions.

More Think and Solves

1. How much current in amperes is in a lightning stroke that lasts 0.05 second and transfers 100 coulombs?
Answer: Current = 100 C/0.05 s = 2000 amps.

2. How much charge flows in a pocket calculator each minute when the current is 0.0001 ampere?
Answer: Charge = current x time = 0.0001 A x 60 s = 0.006 A.

3. How much current passes through a person whose resistance across 120 volts is 100 000 ohms? If resistance is lowered to 1000 ohms?
Answers: I = V/R = 120V/100 000 ohms = 0.0012 A, or 1.2 mA. For 1000 ohms, I = 120V/1000 ohms = 0.12 A, or 120 mA.

4. The resistance of a certain wire is 10 ohms. What would the resistance of the same wire be if it were twice as long? What would be its resistance if it were twice as thick?
Answers: 20 ohms; 2.5 ohms [because twice the diameter gives four times the cross-sectional area, and one-fourth the resistance].

5. A current of 4 A flows when a resistor is connected across a 12-volt battery. What is the resistance of this resistor?
Answer: R = V/I = 12V/4A = 3 ohms.

6. What is the resistance of a clothes iron that draws 8 amperes when connected to 120 volts?
Answer: R = V/I = 120V/8A = 15 ohms.

7. How much energy is expended in lighting a 100-Watt bulb for 30 minutes?
Answer: 50 kW-h.

8. A motor connected to 120 volts draws 10 amps. What power is being consumed? How much energy does it use in 8 hous of operation?
Answer: Power = current x voltage = 10 A x 120 V = 1200 W. In 8 hours, E = Pt = 1200 W x (8 x 3600) s = 4.32 MJ.

9. What current flows in a 60-W bulb in a 120-volt circuit? What is the resistance of the filament?
Answer: Current = power/voltage = 60 W/120 V = 0.5 A. By ohm's law, R = V/I = 120 V/0.5 A = 240 ohms.

Electric Circuits

Objectives

- Given a diagram of a battery and a bulb connected by wire, determine whether current will pass through the bulb.
- Distinguish between series and parallel circuits.
- Predict what will happen in a series circuit if there is a break at any point.
- Relate the current at any point in a series circuit to the current at any other point.
- Predict what will happen to the current at any point in a series circuit if an additional device is connected in series.
- Predict what will happen in a parallel circuit if there is a break in any branch.
- Relate the current in the lead to a parallel circuit to the current in each branch.
- Predict what will happen to the current at any point in a parallel circuit if an additional device is connected in parallel.
- Interpret a simple schematic diagram of an electric circuit.
- Given a circuit with two or more devices of equal resistance connected some in series and some in parallel, determine the equivalent single resistance for the circuit.
- Explain the cause of overloading household circuits and how this is prevented.

Possible Misconceptions to Correct

- In a parallel circuit, the equivalent resisance of the circuit increases with the addtion of more resistors.
- Voltage (rather than only current) flows through a circuit.

Demonstration Equipment

[35-1] Batteries, bulbs, and connecting wires for all students.
[35-2,3] Automobile 12-volt battery with brass or copper rods extended from the terminals, as described on page 152 (and the comic strip "Parallel Circuit" on page 553 in the text).

Introduction

This chapter extends the treatment of the previous chapter to simple series and parallel dc circuits. Complications such as the internal resistance of voltage sources, multiple sources of voltage in series and parallel are avoided. Only simple circuits are treated in this chapter. In this way the goal of many students understanding simple circuits can better be met. More information may benefit a few students, but leave too many with a counter-productive information overload. Since circuits are not the background for any other chapters in the text, this chapter may be omitted from your course. The material is suitable for home study if you do choose to omit it. Students can work in pairs and check each other, possibly with some simple credit plan.

This chapter is best discussed with circuit elements in hand, rather than lectured about. So the suggested lecture is different from previous ones, and merely guides student activity.

Very useful here is the battery with extended terminals, as shown in the comic strip, "Parallel Circuit" on page 553. Show the different brightnesses for series and parallel circuit configurations. An ammeter between one of the rods and the terminal shows line current, which is seen to increase as lamps are added. This is the simplest and most visually comprehensible demo of parallel circuits I have to offer. You can also show the features of a series circuit by stringing the lamps together and attaching the ends to the extended terminals. Neat!

What does it mean to say that a battery is dead? A battery, like anything else, has resistance. If the electrodes in a battery become corroded, the internal resistance prevents the flow of charge — we say the battery is dead. Interestingly enough, the dead battery may register full voltage on a voltmeter. This is because the voltmeter draws only a tiny current, which the battery can easily supply. Drawing a greater current is another story. This is similar to what happens in a rusty water pipe. As long as water does not flow in the pipe, a check at a faucet will show full water pressure. But when the faucet is opened and water flows in the pipe, pressure is reduced by the rusty obstruction to flow. In both cases the resistance only reduces the pressure or voltage when current flows. Putting a load on the battery produces an appreciable voltage drop because too much energy is required to force charge though its internal resistance.

If just as much current flows in a wire as in the lamp filament it connects, why does only the lamp filament glow? The lamp filament glows because of the energy delivered to it. Because of its high resistance, there is a voltage drop across it — appreciable energy per charge is given to the filament. This energy heats the filament to incandescence. Although just as many electrons flow in the connecting wires, the low wire resistance means the electrons carry their energy through the wires rather than delivering their energy to them. That's what it means to say there is no voltage drop along the connecting wires — energy is not dropped or deposited to them.

In lab, *Getting Wired* is intended to help students visualize what is going on inside wires when electricity flows. The lab *Cranking Up* allows your students to compare parallel and series circuits. In *3-Way Switch* students will see how simple but tricky such a common circuit can be!

Bring out the batteries and bulbs and go to it! Play around with successful and unsuccessful ways to light a bulb (Figure 35.2).

DEMONSTRATION [35-1]: This is not done by you, but by your students tinkering around with different ways to light a bulb.

[**Transparency 81**, Figure 35.4; series circuit]

[**Next-Time Questions 35-1** and **35-2**; series circuit]

Series Circuit: Make a simple series circuit, as shown in Figure 35.4, and apply the 5 characteristics listed on pages 550 and 551 to it. Show that the circuit is broken when any bulb is loosened.

DEMONSTRATION [35-2]: Show a series connection between the extended battery terminals.

[**Transparency 82**, Figure 35.5; parallel circuit]

[**Practice Book 35-1** on series and parallel circuits]

Parallel Circuit: Make a simple parallel circuit, as shown in Figure 35.5, and apply the 4 characteristics that start at the bottom of page 552 to it.

DEMONSTRATION [35-3] Show a parallel connection between the extended battery terminals. Show that the circuit remains in operation when any bulb is loosened. If you attach an ammeter between the battery terminal and the extention rod, you can show how the circuit draws more current as more lamps are added.

[**Transparency 83**, Figure 35.7; circuit diagrams]

[**Practice Book 35-2** on compound circuits]

Circuit Diagrams: Have your students make up simple circuits with lamps, wire, and a battery, and then represent their own circuits with circuit diagrams. The practice book page for this chapter will be helpful.

[**Transparency 84**, Figures 35.8 and 35.11]

Combining Resistors: Note that the numerical values of resistors in the text lend themselves to simple computations. This is because the important goal is teaching concepts, not handling calculations. Give some forethought in the resistance values you select for sample circuits (rule given in the discussion above) and also avoid arithmetic complications that will detract from the concepts. A pocket calculator helps.

Home Lighting Circuits: Draw a simple parallel circuit of lamps and appliances on the board, such as in Figure 35.12. Estimate the current flowing through each device, and point out that the current in any branch is not affected when other devices are turned on. Show on your diagram the currents in the branches and in the lead wires. Show where the fuse goes and describe its function. Then short your circuit and blow the fuse.

Discuss the consequences of too many appliances operating on the same line, and why different sets of lines are directed to various parts of the home. Most home wiring is rated at 30 amperes maximum. A common air conditioner uses about 2400 watts, so if operating on 120 volts the current would be 20 amps. To start, the current is more. (To explain why the starting current is larger would be premature to explain here — if it comes up you can explain that every motor is also a generator, and the input current is met with a generated output that reduces the net current.) If other devices are drawing current on the same line, the fuse will blow when the air conditioner is turned on, so a 220-volt line is usually used for such heavy appliances. Point out that most of the world operates normally at 220 - 240 volts.

More Think-and-Explain Questions

1. Which will draw more current — a lamp with a thin filament or a lamp with a thick filament (assuming the same filament length)?
Answer: The thick filament has less resistance and will draw (carry) more current than a thin wire connected across the same potential difference. (It is common to say that a certain resistor "draws" a certain current, but this may be misleading. A resistor doesn't "attract" or "draw" current, just as a pipe in a plumbing circuit doesn't "draw" water; it instead "allows" or "provides for" the passage of current when an electrical pressure is established across it.)

2. Which type of current would you expect powers the lamps in your home — ac or dc? What about lamps in an automobile?
Answer: Electric power in your home is probably supplied at 60 hertz via 110-volt to 120-volt electical outlets. This is ac (and delivered to your home from transformers between the power source and your home. We will see in Chapter 37 that transformers require ac power for operation.). Electric power in a car must be suppliable by the battery. Since the positive and negative terminals of the battery do not alternate, the current they produce does not alternate either. Hence current flows in one direction and is dc.

More Think and Solves

1. How much does it cost to operate a 100-watt lamp continuously for 1 week if the power utility rate is 10 cents per kilowatt-hour?
Answer: $1.68. First, 100 watts = 0.1 kilowatt. Secondly, there are 720 hours in one month (7 days x 24 hours/day = 168 hours). So 168 hours x 0.1 kilowatt = 16.8 kilowatt-hours, which at 10 cents per kwhr comes to $1.68.

2. A 4-watt night light is plugged into a 120-volt circuit and operates continuously for 1 month. Find the following: (a) the current it draws, (b) the resistance of its filament, (c) the energy consumed in a month, and (d) the cost of its operation for a month at the utility rate of 10 cents per kilowatt-hour.
Answers: (a) From power = current x voltage, current = power/voltage = (4W)/(120 V) = 1/30 amp. (b) From current = voltage/resistance (Ohm's law), resistance = voltage/current = (120 V)/(1/30 A) = 3600 ohms. (c) First, 4 watts = 0.004 kilowatt. Second, there are 720 hours in a month (24 hours/day x 30 days = 720 hours). So 720 hours x 0.004 kilowatt = 2.88 kilowatt-hours. (d) At the rate of 10 cents per kilowatt-hour, the monthly cost is 2.88 kilowatt-hours x 10 cents/kilowatt-hour = 29 cents.

36 Magnetism

Objectives

- Describe the differences and similarities between magnetic poles and electric charges.
- Interpret the strength of a magnetic field at different points near a magnet from the pattern formed by iron filings.
- Relate the motion of electrons within a material to the ability of the material to become a magnet.
- Describe what happens to the magnetic domains of iron in the presence of a strong magnet.
- Explain why magnets lose their magnetism when dropped or heated.
- Describe the magnetic field produced by a current-carrying wire, and give examples of how the field can be made stronger.
- Describe the conditions for a magnetic field exerting a force on a charged particle in the field.
- Describe some practical applications of a magnetic field exerting a force on a current-carrying wire.
- Suggest possible causes for the earth's magnetic field.

Possible Misconceptions to Correct

- Magnetic poles are to magnets what electric charge is to electricity.
- Magnetic poles move in iron like electrons move in electrical conductors.
- The magnetic force on charged particles, like the electric force on charged particles, is in the direction of the magnetic field (rather than at right angles to both the field and the velocity of the charge).
- Like an electric field, a magnetic field can increase the speed of charged particles.

Demonstration Equipment

- [36-1] Overhead projector, iron filings, one or two magnets, and a sheet of transparent plastic.
- [36-2] Compass and dc-current-carrying wire.
- [36-3] Electromagnet construction items: iron bar, wire, and battery.
- [36-4] Oscilloscope or television monitor and magnet to distort image.
- [36-5] DC current-carrying wire and horseshoe-shaped magnet.
- [36-6] Large meter (galvanometer, ammeter, voltmeter) in which the coil that rotates in the magnetic field is visible.
- [36-7] DC demonstration motor (Genecon) with power source.

Introduction

This chapter, like so many others, links the subject matter to the environment. The material in this chapter is a prerequisite for the next chapter.

Note that the text avoids the confusion of the north geographic pole of the earth being a south magnetic pole (to attract the opposite north poles of magnets), and the south geographic pole being a north magnetic pole. It is annoying when this exercise in reverse language is featured on exams. Please stick to physics!

The galvanometer is named after Luigi Galvani (1737-1798), who while dissecting a frog's leg discovered that electric charge caused the leg to twitch. This chance discovery led to the invention of the chemical cell and the battery. The next time you pick up a galvanized pail, think of Luigi Galvani in his anatomy laboratory.

Microscopic views of magnetic domains are shown in the Ealing film loop (#A80-2033/1, Ferromagnetic Domain Wall Motion).

Details of a do-it-yourself paper clip electric motor are available. If you want a copy, I will be happy to send you one. (Address: Paul Hewitt, c/o City College of San Francisco, SF, CA 94112)

In lab, *3-D Magnetic Field* enables your students to explore the shape of a magnetic field whereas *You're Repulsive* allows them to observe the effect of an electric charge moving in a magnetic field.

Suggested Lecture

Begin by holding a magnet above some nails or paper clips on your lecture table. State that the nails or clips are flat on the table because every particle of matter in the whole world is gravitationally pulling them to the table. Then show that your magnet will outpull the whole world and lift the nails or clips off the table.

Magnetic Field: Introduce the concept of magnetic field with the following:

DEMONSTRATION [36-1]: Show field patterns about bar magnets with the use of an overhead projector and iron filings. Simply place a magnet on the glass surface of the projector and cover it with a sheet of plastic. Then sprinkle iron filings on the plastic. (This is shown for a bar magnet in Figure 36.4, and for pairs of magnets in Figure 36.6.)

CHECK QUESTION: How do the field lines of magnetic, electric, and gravity fields differ? [Magnetic field lines form closed loops, and conventionally circle from north to south poles outside a magnet, and from south to north poles inside the magnet. Electric field lines emanate from positive charges, and toward negative charges. Gravity field lines emanate only from mass.]

[**Transparencies 85** and **86**, Figures 36.4 and 36.5, magnetic field lines]

[**Practice Book 36-1** on magnetic forces and fields]

[Next-Time Question 36-1; Newton's third law via magnetic forces]

Magnetic Domains: Discuss the source of magnetism — the motion of charges. All magnetism starts with a moving electric charge: in the spin of the electron about its own axis, revolution about the nuclear axis, and as it drifts as part of an electric current. It should be enough to simply acknowledge that the magnetic field is a relativistic "side effect" or "distortion" in the electric field of a moving charge. (Unless you've already treated special relativity in great detail, the relativistic explanation may be too involved to be effective.)

Describe magnetic induction, and show how bringing an unmagnetized nail near a magnet induces it to become a magnet and be attracted. Then contrast this with a piece of aluminum. Discuss unpaired electron spins and magnetic domains. Compare Figures 32.12 and 32.13, where bits of paper were attracted to a charged object, and charged balloons stuck to walls by electrostatic induction, with the similar case of the magnet and nails in Figure 36.10. Stress the similarities of electrically inducing charge polarization and magnetically inducing the alignment of magnetic domains.

CHECK QUESTION: Just as charges are either positive or negative, are magnets either north or south? [No, every magnet has both a north and south pole just as every coin has two sides. Every pole is either a north or south, and every single charge is either a positive or a negative. But a single magnet is a pole pair, north and south. Be sure that your students don't confuse the positive and negative charges of electricity with magnetism. (Some theoretical physicists believe there are "monopoles," elemental magnetic particles, north or south. At this writing, no evidence supports this theory.)]

[Next-Time Question 36-2 on trick magnets - fun]

Electric Currents and Magnetic Fields: Show the interaction of a current-carrying wire and a magnet.

DEMONSTRATION [36-2]: Place a wire without current near a compass needle. Show that with current in the wire, the compass needle deflects. (This was Orested's classroom discovery.)

Interesting sidelight: When the magnetic field around a current carrying conductor is undesirable, double wires are used, with the return wire right next to the wire. Then the net current for the double wire is zero, and no magnetic field surrounds it. Wires are often braided to combat slight magnetic fields where the cancellation nearby is not perfect.
Explain the bunching up of magnetic field lines in a loop (Figure 36.12), and then multiple loops (Figure 36.13c). Now you have an electromagnet.

DEMONSTRATION [36-3]: Make a simple electromagnet in front of your class, like winding wire around a nail and picking up paper clips. Relate this to the junk yard magnet shown in Figure 36.1. Then show other types of magnets. Discuss solenoids.

Acknowledge that magnets can repel as well as attract and discuss the application of magnetic repulsion to high-speed passenger trains, page 569. Japan, Germany, and the United States are strong players in developing magnetically levitated, or "maglev" transportation. A vehicle being developed in the United States, called a magplane, carries superconducting coils on its underside. Moving along an aluminum trough, these coils generate currents in the aluminum that act as mirror-image magnets and repel the magplane. It floats six inches above the guideway, and its speed is limited only by air friction and passenger comfort. Someday we may ride swiftly and smoothly from one city to another in a magplane.

Magnetic Forces on Moving Charges: Perform the following demonstrations in the order indicated. This way both phenomena are seen to be applications of the fact that a force acts on electric charges that move through a magnetic field.

DEMONSTRATION [36-4]: Show how a magnet distorts the beam of an oscilloscope or TV picture. Stress the role of motion.

Discuss the motion of a charged particle injected into a magnetic field perpendicular to the field lines, and explain how the beam moves in a circular path. The perpendicular push is a centripetal force that acts along the radius of its path. Briefly discuss cyclotrons and bevatrons, with radii ranging from less than a meter to more than a kilometer. Note that since the magnetic force on moving charges is always perpendicular to velocity, there is never a component of force in the direction of motion. This means a magnetic field cannot do work on a moving charge. A magnetic field can only change the direction of the charge. So in cyclotrons and bevatrons, electric fields accelerate the charges and increase their kinetic energies; magnetic fields simply guide their paths.

Forces on Current-Carrying Wires: It is a simple step from the deflection of charges to the deflection of wires that enclose these deflected charges.

DEMONSTRATION [36-5]: Show how a wire jumps out of (on into) a magnet when current is passed through it (Figure 36.16). Reverse current (or turn the wire around) to show both cases.

Electric Meters and Electric Motors: Extrapolate the previous demonstation to the same deflection occuring in galvanometers, ammeters, and voltmeters.

DEMONSTRATION [36-6]: With your largest meter (galvanometer, ammeter, voltmeter), point out to your class the coil of wire that is suspended in the magnetic field of the permanent magnet (Figure 36.18).

Now you are ready to extend this idea to the electric motor.

DEMONSTRATION [36-7]: Show the operation of a dc demonstration motor.

Earth's Magnetic Field: Discuss the field pattern about the earth and how cosmic rays are deflected by the magnetic field. In discussing pole reversals, add that the magnetic field of the sun undergoes reversals about every eleven years.

Magnetic Sidelights Not Treated in the Text: Not mentioned in the text are the Van Allen radiation belts (Named after James Belts?). These belts are composed of charged particles trapped in the earth's magnetic field, 3000 to 15000 kilometers above the earth's surface. Protons and electrons are in the outer part, and principly electrons in the inner part. They used to consist of two donut-shaped rings, but have since been combined by high-altitude nuclear explosions detonanted in 1962. At the magnetic poles, ions dip into the atmosphere and cause it to glow like a fluorescent lamp. This is the beautiful aurora borealis (northern lights).

The magnetic field of the earth protects us from much of the cosmic rays we would otherwise receive. Cosmic ray bombardment is maximum at the poles, because incoming particles do not criss-cross the earth's field (they would be deflected), but follow the field lines and are not deflected. At sea level at the equator, incidence of cosmic rays averages from one to three particles per square centimeter per minute; this number increases rapidly with altitude. This is a primary reason for the relatively short working hours of flight personnel in high-flying aircraft. Two cross-country round trips expose us to a radiation dosage equivalent to a chest X-ray (more about this in the Chapter 39 material in this Teaching Guide).

Not treated in the chapter material, but in Think and Explain Question 11, is the probable role of the earth's magnetic field in evolution. One theory is that when life was passing through its earliest phases, the magnetic field of the earth was strong enough to hold off cosmic and solar radiations violent enough to destroy life. During pole reversals, cosmic radiation on the earth's surface was increased, aided by the spilling of the particles in the Van Allen belts, which increased mutations of the primitive life forms then existing. Sudden bursts of radiation may have been as effective in changing life forms as X rays have been in the famous heredity studies of fruit flies. The coincidences of the dates of increased life changes and the dates of the magnetic pole reversals lend support to this theory.

Not in the chapter material, but referred to in Think and Explain Question 10, is the multiple-domain magnetite magnets within the skulls of pigeons. These are connected with a large number of nerves to the pigeon brain. It has for several years been known that single-domain magnetite grains strung together to form internal compasses exist in certain bacteria. Bacteria south of the equator build the same single-domain magnets as their counterparts north of the equator, but aligned in the opposite direction to coincide with the oppositely directed magnetic field in the southern hemisphere. Magnetic material has also been found in the abdomens of bees. Searches of human beings to date show no such magnetic materials.

Not in the text is MRI — magnetic resonance imaging — formerly called NMR, nuclear magnetic resonance, which avoids the phobic word nuclear for public acceptance. This is a relatively new and widely used application in medicine; particularly as a method of cancer detection. An external alternating magnetic field is applied to a part of the body of a patient. Slight differences in the natural frequencies of magnetic quadrupole moments of atomic nuclei, commonly protons, due to the environment of neighboring atoms are detected by a "magnetic echo". The resonant signals from the nuclei of atoms in living cells differs slighty for cancerous tissue and is picked up by a sensitive magnetometer.

More Think-and-Explain Questions

1. The core of the earth is probably composed of iron and nickle, excellent metals for making permanent magnets. Why is it unlikely that the earth's core is a permanent magnet?
Answer: The earth's interor is simply too hot for permanent alignment of domains. Elcectric currents are the likely source.

2. One way to make a compass is to stick a magnetized needle into a piece of cork and float it in a wooden bucket of water. The needle will align itself with the earth's magnetic field. Since the north pole of this compass is attracted northward, will the needle float toward the northward side of the bucket? Defend your answer.
Answer: The needle is not pulled toward the north side of the bucket because the south pole of the magnet is equally attracted southward. The net force on the needle is zero.

3. In what way, if at all, does your answer to the preceding question differ if the bucket is iron instead of wood?
Answer: If the bucket is iron, then the side of the needle nearest to the bucket would be drawn to it. This is because the bucket would become magnetized oppositely by magnetic induction. In this case the attractive force of the pole closest to the bucket would be appreciably greater than the repulsion for the farthest pole, and net attraction would occur.

4. What is the net magnetic force on a compass needle? By what mechanism does a compass needle line up with a magnetic field?
Answer: The net force on a compass needle is zero because its north and south poles are pulled with equal and opposite forces. When the needle is not aligned with the magnetic field of the earth, then a pair of torques is produced — called a *couple*, which rotates the needle into alignment with the earth's magnetic field.

5. Can an electron be set into motion with a magnetic field? An electric field?
Answer: Magnetic field, no. Electric field, yes.

6. Will a pair of parallel current-carrying wires exert forces on each other?
Answer: Yes, each is in the magnetic field of the other. They will repel when currents are in opposite directions, and attract when in the same direction. This is a method of determining the magnetic fields of the wires, or the currents.

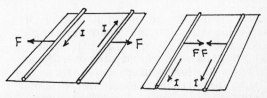

OPPOSITE CURRENTS: REPULSION   SAME DIRECTIONS: ATTRACTION

Electromagnetic Induction

Objectives

- Describe how voltage is induced in a coil of wire.
- Relate the induced voltage in a coil to the number of loops in the coil and the rate of change of an external magnetic field intensity through the loops.
- Describe a generator and how it works.
- Compare and contrast motor effect and generator effect.
- Describe a transformer and how it works.
- Explain why transformers are used for transmission of electric power.
- Relate the magnitude and direction of an induced electric field to the inducing magnetic field.
- Relate the magnitude and direction of an induced magnetic field to the inducing electric field.
- Explain how the electric and magnetic fields of an electromagnetic wave regenerate each other so that the wave pattern moves outward.

Possible Misconceptions to Correct

- Voltage is produced by a magnet (rather than by the work done when a magnet and closed loop(s) of wire are moved relative to each other).
- A generator and a motor are fundamentally different from each other.
- A transformer can step up energy, or step up power.

Demonstration Equipment

- [37-1] Galvanometer, loop of wire, horseshoe magnet.
- [37-2] Same as above with wire that can be bent into a coil, or attached to already-wound coils.
- [37-3] Demonstration motor that can be shown as a generator, with galvanometer (Genecon will do).
- [37-4] Hand-cranked generator (Genecon) and lamp to light it with.
- [37-5] Step-down transformer with nail to weld when connected to ac source.[37-6]
- [37-6] Elihu Tompson electromagnetic apparatus (facing page), with lamp on waterproof coil that you immerse in a glass of water.
- [37-7] Elihu Tompson electromagnetic apparatus and aluminum ring that levitates or jumps when power is applied.

Introduction

This chapter focuses on the important features of electromagnetic induction, and avoids such complications as reactance, back emf, Lenz's law, and the left and right hand rules that often overwhelm students. The important concept here is transmitting of energy from one place to another without physical contact. The chapter should be supported by various lecture demonstrations of electromagnetic induction, such as those in the figures.

If you have a Tesla coil, demonstrate induction by lighting up a non-connected fluorescent lamp a meter or more away. This is impressive.

Two computer programs (*Radiating Dipole* and *Moving Charge*) from the computer disk *Good Stuff!* nicely compliment material in this chapter. The first shows the emanation of electric field lines from an antenna. Press the "s" key repeatedly and show how the lines break away from the antenna and form closed loops which then proceed "on their own." *Moving Charge* shows how all kinds of electromagnetic radiation are produced by accelerating charges. With this program you can move an electric charge up and down and see how the electric field lines bend. The transverse kinks represent radiation.

A sensitive galvanometer is required to observe a deflection in the lab activity *Jump Rope Generator*. Quite impressive!

Suggested Lecture

In the previous chapter we discussed beginning with electricity and producing magnetism. The question was raised in the first half of the 1800s, "Can it be the other way around?" Can we start with magnetism and produce electricity? Indeed we can — enough to light entire cities! Now produce a galvanometer, magnet, and wire loop — well away from the electric power sources of your previous lecture.

Faraday's Law: This lecture is a series of demonstrations.

DEMONSTRATION [37-1]: Produce motion between a wire loop and a magnet as shown in Figure 37.2, preferably with a big classroom demonstration galvanometer.

Follow this up with a bar magnet and coil.

DEMONSTRATION [37-2]: Plunge a bar magent in a coil as per Figure 37.3. Show the twice-as-much deflection for a coil with twice the turns, and so on. Establish the directly proportional relationship between induced voltage and number of turns in the coil.

[**Transparencies** 87 and 88, Figures 37.2 and 37.3; inducing voltage]

Summarize the foregoing and cite Faraday's law of electromagnetic induction. Emphasize the importance of this discovery by Faraday and Henry, and how its application transformed the world. Isn't it difficult to imagine having no electric lights — to live in a time when illumination after the sun goes down is by candles and whale-oil lamps? And no electric motors! Not so long ago, really. In our older cities many buildings still have pre-electric light fixtures: gas and oil lamps.

Point out that the magnet is not a source of voltage, but rather the voltage is induced when work is done to push the magnet into the coil. It may seem that one obtains voltage by simply increasing the number of loops in a coil. Yes, but at the expense of added difficulty in pushing the magnet into more loops (Figure 37.4). It turns out that the current induced is surrounded by its own magnetic field, which resists the magnet you are pushing or pulling. So the greater the current you induce by your action, the more resistance you also meet. This is evident when cranking a generator when additional electrical load is suddenly introduced. All this has an interesting consequence: Driving a car with the lights on burns more fuel. In the interest of lowering fuel concumption, should drivers drive with no lights at nighttime?

Discuss the operation of traffic control signals that are activated by the passing of a metal vehicles over wire loops imbedded in the road surface (Think and Explain Question 7). Also the metal detectors used in airports. The passage of ferromagnetic material through or over these loops alters (changes) the magnetic field and induces voltage in the loops.

[**Transparency 89**, Figure 37.9; motor and generator effect]

Generators:

DEMONSTRATION [37-3]: Return to the motor you previously demonstrated, and show that when you apply mechanical energy, it becomes a generator (a Genecon will do).

Compare motor and generator — in principle the same. When electric energy is put in it converts it to mechanical — motor. When mechanical energy is put in it converts it to electrical energy — generator. In fact, a motor acts also as a generator creates a "back voltage" (back emf) and an opposing current. The net current in a motor is the input current minus the generated back current. The net current in a power saw will not cause its overheating and damage to its motor windings — so long as it is running and generating a back current that keeps the net current low. But if you should jam the saw so that it can't spin, without the back current generated by the spinning armature, the net current is dangerously high and can burn out the motor.

Interestingly enough, electric motors are used in diesel-powered railroad engines. The combustion engine cannot bring a heavy load from rest, but an electric motor can. Why? Because when the armature is not turning, the current in the windings is huge, with a corresponding huge force. As both the train and the motor gain speed, the back current generated by the motor brings the net current in the motor down to non-overheating levels.

DEMONSTRATION [37-4]: Light a bulb with a hand-cranked generator (Genecon) and show how the turning is easier when the bulb is loosened and the load removed. Allow students to try this themselves during or at the end of class.

Stress again the fact that we don't get something for nothing with electromagnetic induction, and acknowlede Figure 37.4. This can be readily felt when lamps powered with a hand-cranked or a bicycle generator are switched on. Each student should experience this. The conservation of energy reigns!

In discussing the operation of a generator via Figures 37.5, 37.6 and 37.7, point out that maximum voltage is induced not when the loop contains the most magnetic field lines, but when the greatest number of field lines are "clipped" (changed) as the loop is turned. Hence in Figure 37.7 the voltage is maximum when the loop passes through the zero-number-of-lines point. It's rate of change of magnetic field lines is greatest at this point.

Continue with a historical theme: With the advent of the generator the task was to design methods of moving coils of wire past magnetic fields, or moving magnetic fields past coils of wire. Putting turbines beneath waterfalls, and boiling water to make steam to squirt against turbine blades and keep them turning — enter the industrial revolution.

[**Practice Book 37-1** on induction of voltage, and transformers]

Transformers: Explain a transformer. (I remember as a student being very confused about the seeming contradiction with Ohm's law — the idea that when voltage in the secondary was increased, current in the secondary was decreased.) Make clear that when the voltage in the coil of the secondary and the circuit it connects is increased, the current in *that* circuit also increases. The decrease is with respect to the current that powers the *primary*. So P = IV does not contradict Ohm's law!

DEMONSTRATION [37-5]: With a step-down transformer, weld a pair of nails together. This is a spectacular demontration when you casually place your fingers between the nail ends before they make contact. Then after removing your fingers bring the points together allowing the sparks to fly while the nails quickly become red and then white hot.

Cite the role of the transformer in stepping down voltages in toy electric trains, power calculators, and portable radios, and the role of stepping up voltages in TV sets and various electrical devices, and both stepping up and stepping down voltages in power transmission. Stress that in no way is energy or power stepped up or down — a conservation of energy no no! Carefully go over the comic strip "Power Lines," on page 588. The physics here is deeper than in the other comic strips, and may need elaboration.

Induction of Fields: Continue with the switch to ac and bring out the classical Elihu Thompson Electromagnetic Demonstration Apparatus (as shown in the sketch, next page).

DEMONSTRATION [37-6]: Show the classic lighting of the lamp in a jar of water. Impressive! (The lamp is mounted on a waxed waterproof coil that intercepts the changing magnetic flux of the device, induces current, and illuminates the lamp. The water serves no purpose other than making the demonstration more interesting.)

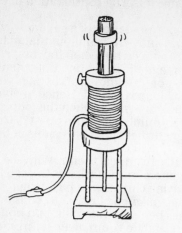

DEMONSTRATION [37-7]: With the power on, levitate an aluminum ring over the extended pole of the Elihu Tompson device.

CHECK QUESTION: Do you know enough physics to state how much electromagnetic force supports this 1-Newton aluminum ring (assuming the ring weighs 1 N)? [1 N, not particularly from a knowledge of electromagnetic forces, but from knowledges about forces in general that go back to Newton's laws. Since the ring is at rest and not accelerating, the upward electromagnetic force (in newtons!) must be equal to the downward force of gravity.]

With the power off, place the ring at the base of the extended pole. When you switch on the power the current induced in the ring via electromagnetic induction converts the ring into an ac electromagnet. (By Lenz's law, not covered in the text, the polarity of the induced magnet is always such to oppose the magnetic field imposed.)

CHECK QUESTION: Do you know enough physics to state whether or not the electromagnetic force that popped the ring was more, equal to, or less than the magnetic force that produced levitation earlier? [More, because it accelerated upward, evidence the upward force was more than the weight. This is also understandable because the ring was lower and intercepting more changing magnetic field lines.]

State that underlying all the things discussed and observed is something more basic than voltages and currents — the induction of fields, both electric and magnetic. And because this is true we can send signals without wires — radio and TV — and futhermore, energy reaches us from the sun, sunlight.

Point not stated in the text: The concept that a change in either field induces the other led Einstein to the development of his special theory of relativity. Einstein showed that a magnetic field results when an electric field is seen by a moving observer, and an electric field results when a magnetic field is seen by a moving observer. The fields are relative.

[**Next-Time Question 37-1** on induction]

Power Transmission: Not mentioned in the text is that cost is a main reason for high-voltage power lines. If higher currents were carried in the lines, the wires would have to be thicker and therefore costlier. They would also be heavier, which would require stronger towers.

[**Practice Book 37-2** on power transmission]

Electromagnetic Waves: Ask your class to recall your recent demonstration of charging a rubber rod with cat's fur. When you brought the rod near a charged pith ball, you produced action at a distance. When you moved the charged rod, the charged ball moved also. If you gently oscillated the rod, the ball in turn oscillated. State that one can think of this behavior as either action-at-a-distance or the interaction of the ball and rod with the surrounding space — the electric field. For low frequencies, the ball will swing in rhythm with the shaking rod. But the inertia of the ball and its pendulum configuration makes response poor for any vigorous shaking of the rod (that's why it's best not to actually show this, but to only describe it, and go through the motions as if the equipment were present — you avoid the "that's the way it should behave" situation). You can easily establish in your students' minds the resonableness of the ball shaking back and forth in response to the shaking (changing) electric field around the shaking rod. Carry this further by considering the ball to be simply a point charge with negligible mass. Now it will respond in synchronous rhythm to the shaking rod. Increase the frequency of the shaking rod and state that not only is there a shaking electric field about the rod, but because of its changing, there is now a different kind of field.

CHECK QUESTIONS: What kind of field is induced by the shaking rod? What kind of field in turn, does this induced field induce? And futher in turn, what kind of field does this further induced field induce? And so on. [The shaking charge induces a magnetic field, which changing in turn induces an electric field, etc. The result is an electromagnetic wave.]

Cite the idea of the optimum speed of field disturbances from the shaking rod to the ball (consistent with energy conservation, page 590).
Review the family of electromagnetic waves back in Figure 27.4 on page 408.

[**Transparency 91**, Figure 37.18 on radiation and receiving of EM waves]

CHECK QUESTION: Why are sound waves not included in Figure 27.4? [Because sound is a mechanical wave, and not electric or magnetic, and not part of the electromagnetic spectrum!]

If misconceptions are still evident,

CHECK QUESTION: Multiple choice: The speed of radio signals from the antenna of the local radio-broadcasting station are, (1) usually less than 340 m/s (2) about 340 m/s, depending on atmospheric conditions (3) always greater than 340 m/s; or for humor, (4) none of the above! [Choice (3), because the speed of an electromagnetic signal is 3×10^8 m/s, considerably more than 340 m/s! (In this case, there is no exception to the "always" nature of this question.)]

Leave the class with the knowledge that the room they sit in is chock full of waves of many many frequencies. You might turn out the lights and state that the total amount of radiation in the room slightly decreased very slightly as a result — that the light waves make up a tiny part of the vibrations that engulf us at every moment.

Going further, discuss how up to the present century, reality was what people could see and touch. Since knowledge of the electromagnetic spectrum, people have learned that what they can see and touch is less than one-millionth of reality. And as Buckminster Fuller once stated, ninety-nine percent of all that is going to affect our tomorrows is being developed today by humans using instruments that work in ranges of reality that are not humanly sensible.

More Think-and-Explain Questions

1. What is the basic difference between an electric generator and an electric motor?
   Answer: There is no basic difference between an electric motor and electric generator. When mechanical energy is put into the device and electric energy comes out, we call it a generator. When electrical energy is put in and it mechanical energy comes out, we call it a motor. (There are, however, many practical differences in designs of motors and generators.)

2. With no magnets around, why will current flow in a coil of wire waved around in the air?
   Answer: Waving it changes the magnetic field intensity in the coil, which induces voltage and hence current.

3. Why is it important that the core of a transformer pass through both coils?
   Answer: High efficiency requires that the maximum number of magnetic field lines produced in the primary are intercepted by the secondary. The core guides the lines from the primary through the secondary. Transformed power would be needlessly lost otherwise.

4. Why can a hum often be heard when a transformer is operating?
   Answer: The hum heard when a transformer is operating on a 60 hertz AC line is a 60 hertz forced vibration of the iron slabs in the transformer core as their magnetic polarities alternate. The hum is greater if resonance puts other mechanical parts into vibration.

5. If a bar magnet is thrown into a coil of wire, it will slow down. Why?
   Answer: The moving magnet will induce a current in the loop. The field so produced tends to repel the magnet as it approaches and attract it as it leaves, slowing it in its flight. From an energy point of view, the energy of the current that is induced in the loop is equal to the loss of kinetic energy of the magnet.

6. What do we call the electomagnetic wave that has a frequency range between infrared and ultraviolet?
   Answer: Visible light.

7. What is the source of all electromagnetic waves?
   Answer: An accelerating electric charge.

38 The Atom and the Quantum

Objectives

- Give examples of models for the atom and for light.
- Explain why the energy of light can be considered to be a multiple of small units of energy.
- Relate the energy of a photon to its frequency.
- Explain why the photoelectric effect is evidence for the particle nature of light.
- Cite evidence for the wave nature of electrons.
- Describe De Broglie's model of matter waves in the atom and use it to explain the lines seen in atomic spectra.
- Explain why the diameters of heavier elements are not much larger than the diameters of lighter elements.
- Describe the limits of Newton's laws of motion.

Possible Misconceptions to Correct

- If something is a wave, it can't be a particle, and vice versa.
- The heavier the atom, the larger in size it is.
- Quantum physics applies only to the microscopic world.

Demonstration Equipment

- [38-1] A box about the size of a cigar box, a tennis ball, a styrofoam ball about the same size painted red, and a massive ball like a superball painted blue.
- [38-2] Photoelectric effect apparatus: Electroscope, freshly polished piece of zinc, open carbon-arc lamp, quartz lens to focus light on the zinc, cat's fur and silk.

Introduction

Although this chapter begins Unit VI, it is somewhat a continuation of Chapters 27 and 28. It could well follow the last part of Chapter 28, Section 28.11, "The Atomic Color Code — Atomic Spectra." This chapter can, with some discussion of atomic spectra, stand on its own as a continuation and conclusion of Chapter 17, *The Atomic Nature of Matter*. For a short course, Chapter 9 followed by this chapter should work quite well. It is background for Chapters 39 and 40, but is not a prerequisite.

For more information about the physicists who took part in the developing of quantum mechanics, read Barbara Cline's book, *The Questioners: Physicists and the Quantum Theory*, (Crowell, NY, 1973). For more on modern physics, I recommend *The Cosmic Code: Quantum Physics as the Language of Nature*, by Heinz Pagels (Simon & Schuster, NY, 1982). *Sympathetic Vibrations: Reflections of Physicists as a Way of Life* by K.C. Cole (Morrow, NY, 1984) delightfully unravels some of the theories of Bohr, Einstein, and other developers of quantum

physics. K.C. (as she is called by her friends) was a dear friend of Frank Oppenheimer, her mentor at the Exploratorium, and much of her book is sprinkled with some of the insights of Frank and her other mentor, Victor Weisskopf. K.C. was in my first physics class at the Exploratorium in 1982, and was one of the most inquizative students a teacher could hope to have in class. Delightful!

The computer program *Free Particle* from the computer disk *Good Stuff!* simulates the appearance of a small particle moving in terms of wave motion, and nicely complements this chapter.

In lab, *Particular Waves* clearly demonstrates the photoelectric effect.

Practice Book 38-1 can go anywhere in this chapter.

Suggested Lecture

Recall the treatment of atomic spectra in Chapter 27. We learned that different colors of light have different frequencies — red lowest, and violet highest. Then below red is the infrared (IR) part of the electromagnetic spectrum, and above violet, the ultraviolet (UV). State that these different frequencies have different energies — red lowest and violet highest. (It is the high-energy UV components of sunlight that are responsible for sunburn.) Summarize this on the board by writing the proportion, $E \sim f$. The energy of a packet of light energy, a *photon*, is directly proportional to its frequency.

CHECK QUESTION: What color light is best for a safety light in a photographer's darkroom, where low-energy photons are desired that won't expose film? [Red.]

State that the ratio of the energy E of light to its frequency f, is always the same: 6.67 x 10^{-34} joule seconds, abbreviated h, Planck's constant. The proportion is expressed as an exact equation, $E = hf$. (You may compare this with Hooke's law, $F \sim x$, where k is the proportionality constant that makes $F = kx$ an exact equation.)

Photoelectric Effect: Einstein is best remembered for his theories of relativity, but his Nobel Prize in Physics was for the photoelectric effect.

DEMONSTRATION [38-1]: Do as Chelcie Liu of CCSF does and show a simulated photoelectric effect with a tennis ball in a small shallow box about the size of a cigar box. The tennis ball represents an electron. Toss a red styrofoam ball at the tennis ball to show it does not have enough energy to knock the tennis ball out of the box. Then toss a more-massive blue ball into the box and out the tennis ball pops. The red styrofoam ball represents a photon of red light — a small KE. The blue ball (Chelcie uses a superball) represents a photon of blue or violet light — a greater KE. You explain that high-energy photons knock electrons from the material whereas low-energy photons don't. You can simulate the work function of the material by adjusting the depth of the box with slabs of material that cover its bottom. A deep-set ball is more difficult to dislodge than one resting on a slab that is nearly as thick as the box is deep.

DEMONSTRATION [38-2]: Show the actual photoelectric effect by placing a freshly polished piece of zinc on a charged electroscope and illuminate it with an open carbon arc lamp (no glass lens). To focus the beam, use a quartz lens (to pass the UV). Show that a positively-charged electroscope will not lose its charge when the light shines on the zinc plate. But that a negatively-charged electroscope will quickly discharge in the same light. Electrons are ejected from the zinc surface. Block UV with a glass plate and the discharge ceases. Go further if you have a quartz prism and pass the light through a slit, then through the prism, and onto the zinc. Show that the negatively charged electroscope discharges only when the portion of the spectrum beyond the violet end strikes the zinc plate.

[**NEXT-TIME QUESTION 38-1** parallels the photo-electric effect]

Wave-Particles: There is a lot of confusion in the minds of many people about the wave-particle duality — more than is warranted. It so happens that light behaves like a wave when it travels in empty space, and like a particle when it interacts with solid matter. It is mistaken to insist it must be both a particle and a wave at the same time. What something *is* and what it *does* are not the same.

Planck's constant surfaces again in the de Broglie formula that relates the wavelength of a "matter wave" with its momentum. Like light, matter traveling through space has wave properties. When incident upon a target, its particle nature is evident. We don't ordinarily notice the wave nature of matter only because the wavelength is so extremely small. The footnote on page 600 illustrates this.

The matter-wave concept gives a clearer picture of the electrons that "circle" the atomic nucleus. Instead of picturing them as tiny BBs whirling like planets, the matter-wave concept suggests we see them as smeared standing waves of energy — existing where the waves reinforce, and nonexisting where the waves cancel (Figures 38.9 and 38.10). Explain that if the distance around the orbit (the circumference) equals an integral number of wavelengths, then this explains why the orbits have the discrete radii described by Bohr. The paper-clip analogy in the text illustrates this concept.

[**Transparency 92**, Figure 38.11, schematic of relative size atoms]

Atomic Sizes: Draw a model of the hydrogen atom on the board. Then place a second positive charge in the nucleus and ask what will happen to the force that holds the electron in orbit. The force on the electron will double. What will this doubled force do to the size of the orbit (wave or particle)? It will pull it in tighter. The double charge will also hold an extra electron and we have helium. So it is under-standable that helium is a smaller atom than hydrogen (no wonder it leaks so readily through balloons!). Similarly, uranium's innermost orbits (wave model or particle model) are close to the nucleus, and the uranium atom is only about three times the diameter of the hydrogen atom.

While on the sizes of atoms, you might mention that elements shrink in size as one goes from left to right in the periodic table. Fluorine, for example, is considerably smaller than the atoms in its row that precede it. Because of its smallness it is able to penetrate the enamel of teeth, and once inside, add strength to the teeth like steel girders strengthening a building. Interesting.

Quantum Physics: Distinguish between *classical physics* and *quantum physics*. State that classical physics is primarily physics before 1900 that involves the study of familiar things such as the forces, motions, momenta and energy of massive particles that behave in a predictable manner in accord with Newton's laws. For this reason classical physics is often called Newtonian physics. After 1900 it was found that Newtonian rules simply don't apply in the domain of the very small — the submi-croscopic. This is the domain of quantum physics, where everything is "grainy" and where values of energy, momentum, position, and perhaps even time, occur in lumps, or quanta, all of which are governed by probabilities rather than certainties. The physics in this domain does not lend itself to the words and visual pictures we ascribe to the everyday macroscopic domain. Many people have said that quantum physics is "weird." But any weirdness of quantum physics is not in the physics, but in the description of the physics. (I'm reminded that when we do a demo and it doesn't work, we sometimes think that something is wrong with the physics, only to find that the physics is fine — something is wrong with the apparatus or with our explanation of what is going on.)

Clarify what is meant by *quantum*, (plural, *quanta*)— a quantity that occurs or changes only in elemental "lumps." The total weight of a bag of pennies is quantized in the sense that its weight is a whole multiple the weight of a single penny. Electric charge is quantized, for the charge on any body is a whole number multiple of the charge of a single electron (quarks notwithstanding). A chunk of gold is quantized in that it is made of a whole number of gold atoms. This is old stuff. The new stuff is that energy, angular momentum, and perhaps even time, are composed of "lumps." It seems that everything is "grainy" if looked at close enough. Everything is made of "quanta."

Quantum physics is concerned with the ex-tremely small. Today's physicists, after all, are involved in exploring extremes: the outer limits of fast and slow, hot and cold, few and many, and big and small. In a lighter vein it can be said that everything in the middle is engineering.

The philosophical implications of quantum physics is left to your lecture. You may or may not have much to say about this. At minimum you might warn your class that there are many people who have much to say about quantum physics who don't understand it. Quantum physics is not all sewed up like other bodies of knowledge that are less complex or more easily studied. It has holes, and is still regarded by many physicists as an incomplete theory. It is a widely respected theory, however, and we should be wary of quasi-scientists who attempt to fit their own theories into these holes, and ride on the back of the hard-earned reputation of quantum theory.

More Think-and-Explain Questions

1. Distinguish between *classical physics* and *quantum physics.*
   Answer: Classical physics is primarily physics before 1900 that involves the study of familiar things such as the forces, motions, momenta and energy of massive particles that behave in a predictable manner in accord with Newton's laws; for this reason classical physics is often called Newtonian physics. After 1900 it was found that Newtonian rules simply don't apply in the domain of the very small — the submicroscopic. This is the domain of quantum physics, where everything is "grainy" and where values of energy, momentum, position, and perhaps even time, occur in lumps, or quanta, all of which are governed by probabilities rather than certainties. The physics in this domain does not lend itself to the words and visual pictures we ascribe to the everyday macroscopic domain (which accounts for much of the "weirdness" of quantum physics).

2. We don't notice the wavelength of moving matter in our ordinary experience. Is this because the wavelength is extraordinarily large or extraordinarily small?
   Answer: The momenta of moving things in our everyday environment are huge compared to the momenta of submicroscopic particles even at speeds near the speed of light. This is because the masses are so huge in comparison. The large momenta, in accord with de Broglie's formula, correspond to incredibly short wavelengths. See the footnote on page 600.

3. When a photon hits an electron and gives it energy, what happens to the frequency of the photon after bouncing from the electron? (This occurs, and is called the Compton Effect.)
   Answer: The photo loses energy, so its frequency decreases.

4. How might an atom get enough energy to become ionized?
   Answer: By absorbing energy of particle or photon impact.

5. What device utilizes the wave nature of electrons?
   Answer: Many. Electron microscopes, for starters.

6. What happens to the de Broglie wavelegth of an electron when its speed is increased?
   Answer: Greater momentum means smaller wavelength.

7. Which has the longer de Broglie wavelength, and electron or a proton moving at the same speed?
   Answer: The proton has the greater momentum, and therefore the smaller wavelength.

8. A friend says, "If an electron is not a particle, then it must be a wave." What is your response? (Do you hear "either-or" statements like this often?)
   Answer: We don't know if an electron *is* a particle or a wave; we know it *behaves* as a wave when it moves from one place to another and behaves as a particle when it is incident upon a detector. The unwarranted assumption is that an electron must *be* either a particle *or* a wave. It is common to hear some people say that something can only be either this or that, as if both were not possible (like those who say we must choose between biological evolution *or* in the existence of a supreme being).

39 The Atomic Nucleus and Radioactivity

Objectives

- Distinguish between the two kinds of nucleons in the nucleus and compare the numbers of each found in the nuclei of different elements.
- Compare the strong force to the electrical force.
- Distinguish among the three types of rays given off by radioactive nuclei and compare their penetrating powers.
- Interpret the symbols used to label isotopes of an element.
- Predict, given the half life of a radioactive isotope and the original amount of the isotope, how much will remain at the end of some multiple of the half life.
- Predict, given the symbol for a radioactive isotope and the particle it gives off, the product of the decay.
- Explain how transuranic elements are produced and why they are not found naturally.
- Give examples of different types of uses for radioactive isotopes.
- List the major sources of natural background radiation.
- Explain why additional exposure to radiation is harmful.

Possible Misconceptions to Correct

- Radioactivity is sinister (as is everything else we can't see and can't understand).
- Radioactivity is something that has been introduced by 20th-century technology.
- Most of the radiation that people receive stems from 20th-century technology.
- Atoms cannot be changed from one element to another.
- Atoms are the smallest particles of matter that exist.
- Atoms exposed to radiation differ from those that are not exposed to radiation.

No Demonstration Equipment

Introduction

This chapter begins with a description of the atomic nucleus and radioactive decay. Formulas for decay reactions are illustrated with supporting sketches for better comprehension. The background for this material goes back to Chapter 17. This chapter is a prerequisite to Chapter 40.

On page 624 of the text it is stated that a couple of round-trip flights across country exposes one to as much radiation one receives in a normal chest X ray. More specifically, a dose of 2 millirems is typically received in flying across the United States in a jet. This is the same dose received annually from those old luminous dial wristwatches. Cosmic radiation at sea level imparts 45 millirems annually, and radia-tion from the earth's crust imparts about 80 mil-lirems. Living in a concrete or brick house makes this figure slightly higher, for these materials contain more radioactive material than wood. The human body contains small amounts of carbon-14, potassium-40, and traces of uranium and thorium daughter products, which give an annual dose of 25 millirems. So the total natural background radiation annually is about 150 millirems. This makes up about 56% of the radiation the average person encounters, the rest being mainly medical and dental X rays.

The lab manual has one lab activity on half life. Likewise with the Practice Book.

Suggested Lecture

If you have discussed the excitation of light previously, consider beginning this lecture with a comparison of the emission of X rays with the emission of light, showing that X rays are emitted when the innermost electrons of heavy elements are excited. Not mentioned in the text, the discovery of X rays preceded the discovery of radioactivity in 1896 by two months. So the story of radioactivity begins with Wilhelm Roentgen's discovery of X rays. Cite the fact that the eye is the part of the body most prone to radiation damage — something that seems to be ignored by many dentists when making exposures of the teeth (and inadvertently, the eyes). (Why not eye masks as well as chest masks?)

The Atomic Nucleus: Review the model of the atom with its central nucleus composed of protons and neutrons. Acknowledge that these in turn are composed of still smaller particles, the quarks, which will not be central to the "plow setting" of this chapter. Understanding the role of protons and neutrons will be enough. Ask why electrostatic repulsion doesn't make a nucleus fly apart. After all, those protons are very close together! They don't fly apart because of a stronger force, the nuclear *strong force*. Explain, via Figure 39.3, why big nuclei are unstable.

Radioactive Decay: Distinguish between alpha, beta, and gamma rays. An alpha ray is simply a beam of alpha particles, and a beta ray is similarly a beam of beta particles (electrons). Identify alpha particles as chunks of matter ejected by heavy elements. These ejected chunks are nothing more than the nuclei of helium atoms. The energy they impart to a target is nothing more than their kinetic energy. Once stopped they are as harmless as cannonballs at rest. Call attention to the fact that helium, as is commonly used in childrens' balloons, is actually the non-radioactive debris of radioactive decay! It is also used as an inert gas to dilute the oxygen content in the tanks of scuba divers. Not all radioactive byproducts are toxic!

If you've covered electricity and magnetism, ask if the rays could be separated by an electric field, rather than the magnetic field depicted in Figure 39.5. [Either field will deflect opposite charges in opposite directions.] Compare the penetrating power of these via Figure 39.8.

[**Transparency 93**, Figure 39.5; ray deflection by a magnet]

[**Transparency 94**, Figure 39.8; penatrating power of alphas, betas, and gamma]

Radioactive Isotopes: Distinguish between isotopes and ions (commonly confused), and the symbolic way of representing elements (Figures 39.11, 39.12, and 39.13). Skip over the concept of half life for the time being and demonstrate the symbolic way of writing atomic equations. Write some transmutation formulas on the board while your students follow along with their books opened to the periodic table, page 254. A repetition and explanation of the reactions shown on page 619 is in order, if you follow up with one or two new ones as check questions. For example, have your class write the formula for the alpha decay of Pa-234 [which becomes Ac-230], and then for the beta decay of Ac-230 [which becomes Th-230].

[**Transparency 95**, Figure 39-10; atomic number and mass symbols]

[**Transparency 96**, Figure 39.11; helium isotopes]

Beta decay is trickier than alpha decay, so be sure to treat alpha decay thoroughly, so that your students are comfortable with it and can write their own alpha decay reactions, before you write reactions for beta decay.

Treat both natural transmutations and artificial transmutations, and put Rutherford's formula, page 620, on the board. Follow this up with the carbon cycle, page 621. Now you should treat half life.

[**Practice Book 39-1**; decay and half life]

Half Life: Talk of jumping half way to the wall, then half way again, then half way again and so on, and ask how many jumps will get you to the wall. Similarly with radiactivity. Of course, with a sample of radioactive material there is a time when all the atoms undergo decay. But measuring decay rate in terms of this occurrence is a poor idea if only because of the small smaple of atoms one deals with as the process nears the end of its course. Insurance companies can make accurate predictions of car accidents and the like with large numbers, but not so for small numbers. The concept of radioactive half life at least insures dealing with half the large number of atoms you begin with.

The concept of half life is established in the exploratory activity with the M and Ms (or coins). Pose some check questions:

CHECK QUESTIONS: If the radioactive half life of a certain isotope is one day, how much of the original isotope in a sample will remain at the end of two days? Three days? Four days? [1/4; 1/8; 1/16.]

Discuss and compare the various detectors of radiation. If you have the materials, show a cloud chamber demonstration.

Cite the role of radioactive isotopes in some kinds of home smoke detectors. These typically use minute amounts of radioactive material, americium 241 (a waste product of processes conducted at Oak Ridge), which is an alpha emitter that that transforms air inside its chamber into a conductor of electric current. When smoke particles enter the detector, they impede the flow of current through this ionized air and set off an alarm. Thousands of people's lives are saved each year by these devices — radioactive elements can save lives!

[**Practice Book 39-2**; nuclear transmutations and reactions]

Dating: Return to the measurements of radioactivity as a means of dating ancient objects by carbon dating. Discuss the questions posed on page 622. Cite the usefulness of uranium and other isotope dating in geology.

[**Transparency 97**, Figure 39.20 on relative radiation exposures]

Radiation and You: Radiation is not good for anybody, but we can't escape it. It is everywhere. But we can take steps to avoid unnecessary radiation. Radiation, like everything else that is both damaging and little understood, is usually seen to be worse than it is. You can alleviate a sense of hopelessness about the dangers of radiation by pointing out that radiation is nothing new. Many feel it is a product of new technology that people generations ago were spared. This is not true. As the boy on page 595 states, the warmth of the inner earth that gives us hot springs and geysers is a result of radioactive decay that has been going on since the earth formed — or more correctly, before and during the formation of the earth. It is a part of nature that must be lived with. Good sense simply dictates that we avoid unessessary concentrations of radiation.

[**Next-Time Questions 39-1, 39-2** on normal background radiation]

More Think-and-Explain Questions

1. Why are alpha and beta rays deflected in opposite directions in a magnetic field? Would they be deflected in opposite directions in an electric field? Why are gamma rays undeflected in either field?
Answer: Alpha and beta rays are deflected in opposite directions in both a magnetic field and an electric field because they are oppositely charged. Gamma rays have no electric charge and are therefore undeflected.

2. When an alpha particle leaves the nucleus, would you expect it to speed up? Defend your answer.
Answer: An alpha particle undergoes an acceleration due to mutual electric repulsion as soon as it is out of the nucleus and away from the attracting nuclear force. This is because it has the same charge sign as the nucleus. Like charges repel.

3. Why does an alpha particle traveling in a magnetic field normally undergo less deflection than a beta particle?
Answer: Because of inertia. Alpha particles have twice the charge but thousands of times the mass as electrons. They also travel slower.

4. Exactly what is a positively charged hydrogen atom?
Answer: A proton.

5. Why do different isotopes of the same element have the same chemical properties?
Answer: Chemical properties have to do with electron structure, which is with rare exceptions unaffected by the number of neutrons in the nucleus.

6. If a sample of radioactive material has a half life of 1 week, how much of the original sample will be left at the end of the second week? Third week? Fourth week?
Answer: At the end of the second week 1/4 of the original sample will be left; third week, 1/8 will be left; and at the end of the fourth week, 1/16 will be left.

7. A radioisotope is placed near a radiation detector which registers 80 counts per second. Eight hours later the detector registers 5 counts per second. What is its half life?
Answer: The half life of the material will be two hours. A little thought will show that 80 halved 4 times is 5. So there have been four half life periods in the 8 hours. And 8 hours/4 = 2 hours.

8. What element results when radium-226 decays by alpha emission? What is the atomic mass of this element?
Answer: When radium (atomic number 88) emits an alpha particle, its atomic number reduces by 2 and becomes the new element radon (atomic number 86). The resulting atomic mass is reduced by 4, which results in radon-226.

9. The age of the Dead Sea Scrolls was found by carbon dating. Would this technique have worked if they were carved in stone tablets? Explain.
Answer: Stone tablets cannot be dated by the carbon dating technique. Nonliving stone does not ingest carbon and transform that carbon by radioactive decay. Carbon dating works only for organic material.

40 Nuclear Fission and Fusion

Objectives

- Describe the role of neutrons in causing and sustaining nuclear fission.
- Explain how nuclear fission can be controlled in a reactor.
- Distinguish between a breeder reactor and a uranium-based fission reactor.
- Predict, from a graph of mass per nucleon vs. atomic number, whether energy would be released if a given nucleus split via fission into fragments.
- Distinguish between nuclear fission and nuclear fusion.
- Describe the advantages of fusion over fission as a source of power.
- Describe the current problems associated with using fusion as a source of power.

Possible Misconceptions to Correct

- Nuclear power is sinister (as were electricity, steam power, and other technological advances when they were introduced).
- Nuclear fission and fusion are something new.
- Plutonium is the most dangerous substances in existence.
- Nuclear fusion can only occur at high temperatures.
- Nuclear power is ecologically more devastating than fossil-fuel power.

No Demonstrations for this Chapter

Introduction

This material has great technological and sociological significance. Nuclear bombs are not avoided in nuclear applications, but the emphasis is on the positive potential of nuclear power. Much of the public sentiment against anything "nuclear"has to do with a distrust of what is little or not understood, with the sentiments against centralized power, and with its association with nuclear weapons and nuclear war — rather than with the technological pros and cons. In this climate, our responsibility is to provide students with an understanding of the basics physics of nuclear power. In your physics class, an appropriate slogan is "KNOW NUKES."

Note that unlike other physics textbooks, the energy release of opposite processes of fission and fusion is approached from the viewpoint of decreased mass rather than the customary treatment of increased binding energy. Hence the usual binding-energy curve is turned upside down in Figures 40.13, 40.14, and 40.16, and shows the relationship of the mass per nucleon versus atomic number. I find this conceptually more understandable, for it shows that any reaction wherein mass decreases releases energy in accord with mass-energy equivalence.

Mass-energy can be measured in either joules or kilograms (or in ergs or grams). For example, the KE of a 2-gram beetle walking 1 cm/s = 1 erg, and the energy of the Hiroshima bomb = 1 gram. So we can express the same quantity using different units.

A videotape, now an "oldie but goodie," that is not part of the Addison-Wesley series may be of interest. It is *Fusion Torch and Ripe Tomatoes* (45 min),which has been my opening general lecture that makes sweeping generalizations about fusion power and an idealized description of a fusion torch and a follow-up device to the fusion torch — a replicator, similar to that described by Arthur C. Clark in his oldie-but-goodie 1963 book, *Profiles of the Future*. Information about this tape and two others is available from Media Solutions, 1128 Irving St., San Francisco, 94122. Phone 415-665-1077.

There is one lab activity for this chapter, *Chain Reaction*, which may challenge your students.

Suggested Lecture

Nuclear Fission: Continue the practice of writing nuclear reactions as in the previous chapter and write on the board the fission reaction on page 630. Discuss its historical significance (the accidental 1939 discovery in Germany by Otto Hahn and Fritz Strassmann, which was communicated to Lise Meitner and Otto Frisch, then refugees from Nazism in Sweden. Meitner and Frisch recognized its potential and passed the information on to American physicists who urged Einstein to write his famous letter urging President Roosevelt to consider its potential in warfare). The reaction was considered vitally important not only because the reaction products had a combined mass less than the mass before reaction, which released enormous energy, but the fact that the reaction released three or so neutrons to produce a chain reaction (exploratory activity, *Chain Reaction*.)

[**Transparencys 98** and **99**, Figure 40.9, nuclear fission, and Figure 40.7 of a nuclear power plant]

Fission Reactors: Explain that ordinary uranium metal doesn't undergo fission because it is mainly composed of the non-fissioning isotope U-238. It is the isotope 235, about 0.7 percent of natural uranium, that will spontaneously fission upon neutron capture. These isotopes are "lost" among the more prevalent U-238 or other isotopes. The uranium in reactors is enriched with fissionable isotopes.

Of interest is evidence that to a small degree fission has occurred in nature — millions of years ago when isotopic abundances were different and occurred in unusually rich concentrations under very unusual circumstances (Scientific American, July 1976).

Plutonium: Show how U-238 is converted to Pu-239 (Figure 40.8). You may wish to discuss the current state of development for fission reactors, particularly breeder reactors.

Mass-Energy Relationship: Depart from the chapter order and journey into fantasy to compare the masses of different atoms by pretending to grab their nuclei with bare hands and shaking them back and forth. Show with hand motion, holding an imaginary giant nucleus, how the difference might appear in shaking a hydrogen atom and a lead atom. State that if you were to plot the results of this investigation for all the elements, that the relationship between mass and atomic number would look like Figure 40.12, (which you draw on the board). This graph is no big deal. It is not surprising, for atoms of greater atomic number are expected to have greater masses.

Then distinguish between the mass of a nucleus and the mass of the nucleons that make up a nucleus. Ask what a curve of mass/nucleon versus atomic number would look like — that is, if you divided the mass of each nucleus by the number of nucleons composing it, and compared the value for different atoms. If all nucleons had the same mass in every atomic configuration, then of course the graph would be a horizontal line. But the masses of nucleons differ. The interrelationship between mass and energy is apparent here, for nucleons have mass-energy, which is manifest partly in the congealed part which is the material matter of the nucleons, and the other part that we call binding energy. The most energetically-bound nucleus has the least mass/nucleon (iron). Go into the nucleon shaking routine again and demonstrate how the nucleons (not the whole nucleus!) become easier to shake as you progress from hydrogen to iron, and how they become harder to shake as you progress beyond iron to uranium. Then draw the curve that represents your findings, and you have Figure 40.13 (the most important graph in your course) on the board.

From the curve you can show that any nuclear reaction that produces products with less mass than before reaction releases energy, and any reaction wherein mass of the products increases requires energy. Further discussion will show how the opposite processes of fission and fusion release energy.

CHECK QUESTIONS: Will the process of fission or fusion release energy from atoms of lead? [Fission.] Gold? [Fission.] Carbon? [Fusion.] Neon? [Fusion.] Iron? [Neither!] (Be careful in selecting atoms too near atomic number 26 in this exercise — for example, elements slightly beyond 26 when fissioned will have more massive products, that extend "up the hydrogen hill"; elements near 26 when fused will combine to elements "up the uranium hill." Acknowledging this point, however, may only serve to complicate the picture — unless, of course, a student brings it up in class.)

[**Transparency 100**, Figures 40.14 and 40.15; fission-fusion mass-energy curves]

[**Practice Book 40-1**; fusion and fission reactions]

[**Next-Time Questions 40-1, 40-2**; nuclear equations]

Nuclear Fusion: Expand upon the latest developments in *inertial confinement fusion*, including not only fusion induced by lasers, but also by particle beams. Explain how in each case a small fuel pellet is ignited to yield a thermonuclear micro-explosion, and how the greatest problem to overcome other than obtaining significant energies is the precise timing of laser firings.

Cold Nuclear Fusion: Nuclear fusion CAN occur at ordinary temperatures, but not via the fusion-in-a-jar experiments of 1989 that turned out to be a flop. Fusion can be initiated by subatomic particles called muons, which have the charge of electrons, but are much heavier. When muons take the place of electrons in a hydrogen atom the electrical barrier is effectively removed. For more on this refer to the Scientific American article in the July 1987 issue.

Prospects of Fusion Power: With all the input students get from the prophets of doom, it is well to balance some of this negativity with positive prospects. Abundant energy from controlled fusion is one that should concern not only physicists, but economists, political scientists, sociologists, ecologists, psychologists — everybody. Particularly exciting is the prospect of the fusion torch, which may provide a means of major materials recycling and a sink for wastes and pollutants. Ideally, all unwanted wastes could be dumped in the fusion torch and vaporized. Atoms could be separated into bins by being beamed through giant mass spectrographs. Such a fusion torch may not happen — but not because technology won't progress to such a point, but because it may progress further. If the past is any guide, something even better will make this 1970's idea obsolete. Whether or not the fusion torch is around the corner, the more important questions to consider are how this or comparable achievements will affect the life of people.

This is a time of transition — an exciting time to be — and stay — alive! Particularly for those who are participating in the transition. Ask how many of your students would prefer living in the past.

More Think-and-Explain Questions

1. Why does uranium ore not spontaneously explode?
   Answer: Because the uranium in it is primarily the isotope U-238, which doesn't fission. U-235 atoms in the ore are too far apart for a chain reaction.

2. Which produces more energy — the fissioning of one uranium atom or the fusing of a pair of deuterium atoms? The fissioning of one gram of uranium or the fusing of one gram of deuterium? (Why are your answers different?)
   Answer: Although more energy is released when a single uranium atom fissions, the much greater number of lighter deuterium atoms in a gram of matter results in more energy liberated per gram for the fusion of deuterium.

3. Why, unlike fission fuel, is there no limit to the amount of fusion fuel that can be safely stored in one locality?
   Answer: If enough fission fuel is localized, it can ignite spontaneously by the triggering of a single neutron. Fusion fuel, however, is not ignited by the triggering of a chain reaction, has no critical mass, and can be stored like wood, coal, or oil without undergoing spontaneous ignition.

4. Explain how radioactive decay has always warmed the earth from the inside, and nuclear fusion has always warmed the earth from the outside.
   Answer: Radioactivity in the earth's core warms its interiao, and sunshine from solar fusion warms its outside.

Appendix: Exponential Growth and Doubling Time

This material, adapted from papers written by Al Bartlett of the University of Colorado, is excellent for class discussion. It's not only important, but fascinating — and very wide in scope. It can be coupled to a discussion of radioactive half life as treated in Chapter 39. Or it can be treated in any break — following an exam, perhaps, or on any day that lends itself to a departure from chapter material.

We get the formula for doubling time of exponential growth from the equation

$N = N_o e^{kt}$

where k is the rate of increase of the quantity N_o. Then for doubling time, T, $N = 2N_o$, and

$2N_o = N_o e^{kT}$

Taking the natural logarithm of each side we get

$\ln 2 = kT$; so $T = \ln 2/k = 0.693/k$

With k as percent,

$T = 69.3/\%$ or $70/\%$

[The same is true for half life, where $N = 0.5N_o$ gives a halving time of $T = \ln 0.5/k = -0.693/k$.]

When percentage figures are given for things such as interest rates, population growth, or consumption of non-renewable resources, conversion to doubling time greatly enhances the meaning of these figures. For example, saying that the growth rate of a community is 7% annually has more impact when you say the growth rate will double the population in ten years. The following questions can be tackled after your students have read Appendix E.

Think, Solve, and Explain

1. In an economy that has a steady inflation rate of 7% per year, in how many years does a dollar lose half its value?
   Answer: A dollar loses half its value in one doubling time of the inflationary economy; this is 70/7% = 10 years.

2. If the population of a city with one overloaded sewage treatment plant grows steadily at 5% annually, how many overloaded sewage treatment plants will be necessary 42 years later?
   Answer: For a 5% growth rate, 42 years is three doubling times (70/5% = 14 years; 42/14 = 3). Three doubling times is an eightfold increase. So in 42 years the city would have to have 8 sewage treatment plants to remain as presently overloaded; more than 8 if overloading is to be reduced while servicing 8 times as many people.

3. In 1996 the birthrate for the United States was 1.5 percent, for Mexico 2.6 percent, and for Niger, the highest in the world, 5.4 percent. If these rates were steady, neglecting death and immigration rates, how long would it take for the population in each of these countries to double?

Answer: For the U.S., 70/1.5 = 47 years; for Mexico, 70/2.6 = 27 years; for Niger, 70/5.4 = 13 years. (The unusually high growth rates for Mexico and Niger are typical of underdeveloped countries — countries that are least economically capable of supporting growing populations.)

4. Suppose that the 5.4 percent birth rate for Niger has always been about the same, and will continue at the same rate for the coming decades. True or false: In the year 2009 there will be more children under the age of 13 in Niger than the total number of people who ever lived in Niger.
   Answer: That is true! This assumes the birthrate will continue at 5.4 percent, with no major changes in the rates of death, immigration, or emigration. In practice, such high birthrates are not matched by as high population growth rates, for major changes inevitably occur. Nevertheless, the world has added to its population in the last decade more than the equivalent of another India. Can you now better understand Professor Bartlett's statement in the footnote on page 656?

5. If world population doubles in 40 years and world food production also doubles in 40 years, how many people then will starve each year compared to now?
   Answer: All things being equal, doubling of food for twice the number of people simply means that twice as many people will be eating, and twice as many will be starving as are starving now.

6. Suppose you get a prospective employer to agree to hire your services for a wage of a single penny for the first day, 2 pennies the second day, and doubling each day thereafter providing the employer keep to the agreement for a month. What will be your total wages for the month?
   Answer: Doubling one penny for 30 days yields a total of $10,737,418.23.

7. In the last question, how will your wages for only the 30th day compare to your total wages for the previous 29 days?
   Answer: On the 30th day your wages will be $5,368,709.12, which is one penny more than the $5,368,709.11 total from all the preceding days.

8. Oil has been produced in the U.S. for about 120 years. If there remains undiscovered in the country as much oil as all that has been used, what is wrong with the argument that the remaining oil will be sufficient for another 120 years?
   Answer: The argument that half our oil reserves have served us for 120 years, and that the remaining half therefore ought to serve us for another 120 years, fails to take into account the growth in consumption. If consumption grows at a steady rate then the remaining oil is used in one doubling time, not 120 years.